Wilbert Marcellus Leonard II

Illinois State University

BASIC SOCIAL
STATISTICS

STIPES PUBLISHING L.L.C.
202-204 West University Avenue ● Champaign, Illinois 61820

ISBN 0-87563-580-6

Affectionately dedicated to

my wife, Patsy

and

my children,

Marcelle, Marc, Ryan, and Jason

for the enrichment they've brought to my life

PREFACE

My objective in writing this text was to convey to the beginning student how statistical techniques are part of the research process. The tendency in higher education to compartmentalize courses into theory, methods, and statistics often does an injustice to students in the sense that the "gestalt" of the research act is never fully appreciated. To circumvent this I have devoted a fairly lengthy chapter (2) to the significant interplays among social theory, methodology, and statistics. Perhaps, more than anything, the contents of this unit make the student cognizant of the active role of the investigator, that is, there are choices and decisions, usually departing from the ideal, that must be made in the conduct of research.

To aid the student in this decision-making process an attempt to nurture what might be called the "statistical imagination"—an ability to come to terms with the hiatus between the social world and the world of statistical-mathematical models—is encouraged. To do this I have chosen to focus upon the relationship between the level of measurement of the variable and the appropriate statistical tool(s). Acknowledging that other criteria for choosing statistical techniques could be stressed it was believed that, in general, the level of measurement is one of the most important criteria. Consequently, I systematically proceed from descriptive statistics (graphic techniques, central tendency, dispersion) to inferential statistics (parameter estimation and hypothesis testing) using this concept to pare down to those tools that are most legitimate. In the hypothesis testing chapters I reiterate for each statistical test the ideal-typical steps that are implicit in the research process. Such reinforcement should prove most helpful for understanding the underlying generic logic of this division of statistics.

The inclusion of the adjective "social" in the title is didactic in that virtually all examples use social science concepts. At various points throughout the writing of the manuscript I was tempted to depart from tradition and title the book "Sociometrics" since the suffix "metrics" refers to the measurement process and the prefix "socio" designates the root of the discipline of sociology. Had I done this it would have carried with it the same connotations of econometrics, biometrics, and psychometrics. Although I did not choose this route, the essence of the chapters brings to front stage the extreme importance of measurement in sociological empirical investigations.

Both parametric and nonparametric data processing procedures are included as are descriptive and inferential statistics. Several pedagogical aids have been included in this edition. The "key" terms, concepts, etc., are italicized in the textbook; you should pay particular attention to them. Every discipline has standardized meanings for its basic conceptual tools. The *Glossary* (Appendix C) in the rear of the text should be helpful to you in mastering these ideas. I also include two sections at the end of each chapter: (1) "Important Concepts Discussed in This Chapter", and (2) "Review Questions" (with answers in the rear of the text). I suggest you "work through" these sections to help you assess how well you've grasped the chapters' contents. Finally, "A Review of Some Math Basics" appears in Appendix B.

In short, the purposes of this text are to acquaint social science students with the *logic* of statistics, the *computation* and *interpretation* of statistical *techniques*, and their *uses* and *abuses* (what is sometimes called "statistical doublespeak". A personal goal is to combat "innumeracy", the mathematical counterpart of illiteracy. In the process my hope is that you become "statistically literate" and a critical thinker regarding statistical information.

Various persons have assisted me in completing this textbook. John Hecker of Stipes Publishing L.L.C. has been a pleasure to work with. His dependability and encouragement of this project have been outstanding. Connie Harrison, also of Stipes, has been invaluable in the completion of this book. Thanks to my friend Greg Walker for assisting me in numerous ways in teaching statistics. Finally, a special gratitude to my wife, Patsy, for her support.

I am grateful to the literary executor of the late Sir Ronald A. Fisher, F.R.S., to Dr. Frank Yates, F.R.S., and to Longman Group Ltd., London, for permission to reprint Tables III and V from their book *Statistical Tables for Biological, Agricultural, and Medical Research* (6th edition, 1974).

Normal, Illinois   W. M. Leonard II
September 1995

CONTENTS

†

CHAPTER 1

AN OVERVIEW OF SOCIAL STATISTICS

*Statistical thinking will one day be as
necessary for efficient citizenship as the
ability to read and write.*

                                        H. G. Wells

By the time you have opened this book you will have been using and consuming statistical information for a long time, perhaps since you began to speak. Statistical statements are ubiquitous. For example:

- A recent Gallup Poll found that about *43 percent* of the American public approve of the President's performance in office.
- The unemployment *rate* as of yesterday's Bureau of Labor Statistics report was hovering around 7½ percent.
- The *probability* of rain today was set at 40 percent during last evening's news broadcast.
- Those of Hispanic descent will become the *modal* minority group in the United States in the twenty-first century (circa 2050).
- The *median* age of the homeless is about 40.
- A sociology of sport study found a *statistically significant difference* between the prize monies of professional male and female golfers.
- In a study of the effectiveness of deterrence theory a comparison of states with the death penalty (capital punishment) and those without the death penalty found no *statistically significant differences* in homicide rates.

- Research conducted in the sociology of law found that minority group status *correlated* with differential treatment in the judicial system.
- A study of the effects of busing upon student achievement concluded that it *varies* according to the conditions under which it is introduced, that is, planned versus unplanned and how it is carried out by the administrators and teachers.
- According to some social psychological research the best *predictors* of altruistic behavior are situational variables.
- The Uniform Crime Report *statistics* reveal significant *variations* in the crime rate of different segments of the population, for example, age, sex, race, birthplace, region, and socioeconomic status.

The point of all this is that you have been exposed, maybe even inundated, to statistical information. The mass media (newspapers, television, radio, magazines, etc.), advertising, and sports have familiarized us with different kinds of statistics. However, this familiarity is sometimes more apparent than real in the sense that these statistics are not always interpreted or understood correctly. Often one must be able to reach beneath the surface to really comprehend a statistical datum since a reported figure may not be or mean what it looks like on the surface. In short, statistics are subject to misuse, or even abuse, and misinterpretation, what is sometimes called "statistical doublespeak."

The quotation with which this book began is didactic in that knowing some sound statistical principles will help us evaluate the increasingly numerical world in which we reside. In that sense, statistical thinking and statistical literacy become necessities.

In this chapter you will be provided an overview of social statistics. Specifically, a short historical excursion will be presented along with a couple of definitions of the field of statistics. In addition we will establish a few basic statistical concepts and indicate some reasons why statistics can be important to you.

STATISTICS YESTERDAY AND TODAY: A BRIEF HISTORY

The foundation of modern statistical analysis has either a long or a short evolution depending on one's perspective. If one thinks of statistics as a summary collection of "state-facts"[1] (births, deaths, and the like), it can be traced to antiquity. For example, the Book of Luke (chapter 2) reports that Joseph and Mary's pilgrimage—and the subsequent birth of Jesus Christ—2,000 years ago was undertaken so that they might be counted for census/taxation purposes. On the other hand, if one

---

[1] From an *etymological* standpoint, statistics, a word coined in a British publication in 1770, emerged from a concern with vital information—such as births, deaths, and marriages—about the state; hence, the term *stat-istics*. The observation that it was referred to as political or state arithmetic in the seventeenth century suggests its affinity with political structures.

chooses to focus on the "probability side," statistics has a more recent origin. Let us look at some of the contributions that statistics' intellectual predecessors have made. For a more extensive treatment of the history of statistics in the social sciences, see Camic and Xie (1994).

In the seventeenth and eighteenth centuries the notoriety of statisticians/mathematicians came to the fore. The story goes that during that period gamblers, particularly the French nobility, asked mathematicians to develop principles that would improve their odds of winning in games of chance like dice and cards. It is reported that Bernoulli (1654–1705) and Demoivré (1667–1754) were among the first mathematicians to be asked for their services. Demoivré is credited with developing the equation for the *normal curve*—about which more will be said in future chapters—in the 1730s. Laplace (1749–1827) and Gauss (1777–1855), two other mathematicians, applied probability principles to the study of astronomy and were given credit, which proved to be fallacious, for the discovery of the normal curve of errors.

The Belgian statistician Quételet (1796–1874), whom some have called the father of the quantitative method in sociology, was a keen social observer and applied statistics to the investigation of social and educational phenomena. In particular, he utilized quantification in citing the stability of the number of crimes from year to year. He asserted that these regularities could be used as a basis for predictions—in a manner similar to the National Safety Council's prediction that so many deaths will take place on our highways during a given holiday season. In Quételet's (1908: 83) own words:

Thus we pass from one year to another . . . seeing the same crimes produced in the same order, and calling down the same punishments. . . . We might ennumerate in advance . . . how many will be forgers, how many will be prisoners; almost we can ennumerate in advance the births and deaths that should occur (F. H. Hankins).

Another major historical figure in the evolution of statistics was Sir Francis Galton (1822–1911), a man believed by some to have had the greatest influence upon statistics in the social sciences. He is credited with developing the concept of *correlation*—the degree of agreement between two (or more) variables—and the concept of *centiles* or *percentiles*. In Galton's later years he and the mathematician Karl Pearson (1857–1936) collaborated and were responsible for deriving some of the correlation and regression[2] equations utilized today.

In the latter 1800s James McKeen Cattell (1860–1944) and Edwin L. Thorndike (1874–1949), two famous American psychologists, began to make use of quantitative procedures in psychology and education.

Up to the twentieth century the bulk of statistical applications was geared to

---

[2]Regression or regression analysis is a statistical procedure for predicting the exact value(s) of a specified variable from a knowledge of the value(s) of another variable(s). This technique is discussed in Chapter 13.

large samples ($n > 30$).[3] Sir Ronald Aylmer Fisher (1890–1962) is one of the key persons in developing what today is called *small sample statistical theory*, although his contributions include mathematical statistics, experimental design and analysis, and genetics and eugenics as well.

An oft forgotten individual is the Reverend Thomas Bayes (1702–61) whose approach to statistics is referred to as *Bayesian* analysis. In brief, he argued that many of the difficulties in classical statistical analysis were rooted in the definition of probability as relative frequencies. Instead, he expanded the definition of probability to include subjective considerations. In any event, his influence in statistics is being felt, despite his death in 1761.

Having briefly traced two sources of statistics—(1) descriptive information of a political/economic/demographic nature, and (2) mathematical probability considerations—let us turn to a more contemporary sociological view. Social science research makes use of two broad categories of methodologies: (1) *qualitative* research methods are those which emphasize describing, interpreting, and observing human behavior whereas (2) *quantitative* research methods stress measurement, quantification, statistical, and numerical aspects of behavior.

The use of statistical modes of analysis in sociology is of recent vintage. Research in the sociology of science (Camic and Xie, 1994) has revealed that European statistical methods were incorporated into the fledgling social sciences— sociology, anthropology, economics, and psychology—during the latter part of the first quarter of the twentieth century at Columbia University. Of interest, although the leaders in the four disciplines—Giddings, Boas, Moore, and Cattell—adopted statistical methodologies in an attempt to adhere to the canons of "acceptable" scientific practice, statistical techniques were virtually non-existent in the natural sciences. Each field adapted statistics to meet its own object(s) of study. Sociology changed more rapidly between the end of World War I and the Great Depression than during any other period. The case study—statistics controversy emerged then and led to bitter polemics over which was the better approach for understanding sociological phenomena. Sociologists of the stature of W. I. Thomas, F. Znaniecki, and the Lynds lined up on the case study side while Giddings, Chapin, Ogburn, and Rice advocated the merits of the statistical approach. Although the role of statistics in social analysis is unprecedented today, we need only look at qualitative methodologists to assure ourselves that the spirit of the issue is far from dead. Those who express a reluctance to use quantitative techniques argue that empathy, intuition, subjective understanding, insight, and the like are not easily amenable to quantification. Some still contend that statistics is debasing and dehumanizing in an already too-impersonal world. I subscribe to the saying, "Not everything that can be counted counts, and not everything that counts, can be counted." The position taken here is that statistics is a *tool* for understanding and is legitimate to use if and when such understanding is facilitated.

---

[3] The symbol n (or N) is regarded as a mathematical noun. It refers to the *number* of elements (cases and/or observations) in a set of data. The symbol "$>$" means *greater than*; "$<$" means *less than*. A more comprehensive review of mathematical notation is found in the "Review of Some Math Basics" section in Appendix B of this book.

DEFINING STATISTICS

Today **statistics** has two generic definitions: (1) when used as a plural noun it refers to *a summary of a collection of numerical facts,* for example, the total yardage gained by the Pittsburgh Steelers last year, the average IQ of college students, and the number (often expressed in terms of rates) of births, deaths, marriages, and crimes during a given time span; and (2) when used as a singular noun it refers to *a method or tool for dealing with data.*[4] Most commonly, it is this latter definition that conveys the contemporary usage of statistics and the one employed in this text. Formally speaking, then, *statistics may be defined as the general body of techniques for assembling, describing, and inferring something from numerical data.* To this writer statistics is best understood as a methodology or an ideology, or as a form of reasoning. Mueller et al. (1970: 5) provide the following statements.

Statistics, when competently cultivated by the social scientist, comprises much more than the manipulation of figures and formulas. Statistical procedures, when applied, consists in relating or fitting social data to the appropriate statistical formulas and equations.

The integration of mathematical/statistical models with social phenomena is what Mueller et al. call *statistical reasoning.* This text will aid you in discovering the *logic* underlying such reasoning, and will be made more explicit in Chapter 2.

The major purposes of statistics are contained within the terms assembles, describes, and infers. The oldest and most traditional use of statistics facilitated the reduction of large quantities of information to manageable and understandable form. The scores in Table 3.1 serve to illustrate this purpose. At first glance, it is virtually impossible to assess these data meaningfully. However, by arranging (assembling) the data into categories—Table 3.4—one can see at a glance some of the important characteristics of this distribution of scores. Closely related to the assembling function is a descriptive one. It is possible to describe some key characteristics of this distribution by computing an appropriate measure of central tendency such as the arithmetic mean (symbolized $\bar{X}$) and an appropriate measure of dispersion such as the standard deviation (symbolized s). These descriptive measures give us an idea of the typical score (central tendency) and how much the individual scores depart (dispersion) from the typical score in a distribution. In short, by assembling and describing the data they are easier to manage and comprehend. Finally, when the researcher wishes to go beyond a mere description of data, that

---

[4] The term statistics is often confusing since there are two generic definitions as well as a distinction between a statistic (a numerical characteristic of a *sample* of observations) and a parameter (a numerical characteristic of a complete set, technically called a *population,* of observations).

is, when interest is with generalizing from the data at hand to some broader entity, the inferential branch of statistics becomes functional.

It is conventional to deal with two broad functions of statistics. The first, just alluded to, is description or summarizing information to make it more usable. When researchers are inundated with masses of data that cannot be adequately or easily absorbed, they may reduce them to manageable portions by computing such descriptive measures (descriptive in that they describe or tell us something about the observations) as percentages, means, standard deviations, and correlation coefficients. This function of statistics is called **descriptive statistics.**

The second broad function of statistics deals with inducing or inferring properties of a population on the basis of known sample results. This mode of analysis is based directly on *probability* theory about which more will be said later. This function of statistics is labeled **inferential** (or **sampling**, or **inductive**, or **probability**) statistics.[5]

In much social research the descriptive function is subordinate to the making of valid and reliable *inferences* from data. In inferential statistics—as opposed to descriptive statistics—there are two very important methodological concepts: (1) the **population** (sometimes called the **universe** or **parent population**), and (2) the **sample.** For example, suppose we are interested in the number of students on campus who voted Republican in the last presidential election. Let us further assume that for practical (as well as theoretical) reasons, we find it virtually impossible to canvass every student. Since it's impossible to survey every student we take recourse to selecting a subset (sample) of the population that we are confident reflects, within a certain margin of error, the complete set (universe) of individuals in whom we are interested. It should be apparent that the sample per se is of no real interest; rather, we are interested in what it can tell us about our real concern, the population. How do we select a "good" sample? There are two salient statistical considerations: (1) the *representativeness* of the sample and the *adequacy* of the sample. The representativeness of a sample is the extent to which the characteristics of the population are genuinely reflected in the subset of data selected from the larger entity. The adequacy of a sample deals with the sample size—population size ratio. Sometimes it is symbolized as n (sample size) divided by N (population size), that is n/N, and referred to as the *sampling fraction*. In brief, a sample should be of a certain magnitude in order to maximize reliable and valid inferences. These two sampling considerations will be dealt with more extensively in future chapters. For the moment, inferential statistics is concerned with generalizing or inferring characteristics of the population from a subset of elements selected from that larger entity.

Two other related purposes of statistics are: (1) to study the infinite *variations* that exist in empirical data, for example, height, weight, attitude scores, abilities, and the like (it has even been argued that variation provides the founda-

---

[5]Some writers of statistics books say there are three broad functions: (1) description, (2) inference, and (3) drawing relationships or associations (correlations) between the variables. Since the third consideration is a description of the degree of relationship between the variables being examined, this writer prefers to incorporate it into descriptive statistics.

tion for statistics since, if all values of a data-set were identical, it would be superfluous to compute any type of statistic); and (2) to aid us in *decision making,* for example, if we wanted to determine the most effective teaching method, it would be possible to statistically compare achievement test scores of students taught by different instructional modes, say lecture versus discussion versus project, to see if any statistically significant differences emerge. Market research is designed to determine consumer's preferences for and usages of various products. Who decides what you see on television? The Nielsen ratings, conducted by one of the better known marketing research organizations, describe how many households watch various television shows and how such demographic characteristics as age, gender, race/ethnicity, and socio-economic status are related to these choices. The viewing habits of (typically) less than 1,500 carefully chosen households determine whether or not programs remain on the air. The ratings calculated by the organization provide some the key ingredients that are used to *decide* what you and I see on our television sets.

WHY STUDY STATISTICS?

A spontaneous reply to this query might be that to understand social research or to do research yourself requires at least a basic understanding of the fundamentals of statistical analysis.

Another, perhaps more basic, reason concerns you as a "critical thinker" of numerical information. We are swamped with tidbits of statistical information—four out of five dentists who recommend gum recommend . . .; nine out of ten physicians who suggest aspirin, recommend . . .; in independent laboratory studies it was found . . ., and so forth—information that the statistically (and methodologically) naive are likely to misinterpret and misunderstand. Many illustrations of the use of statistics can be reported. A classic example concerns psychologist Arnold Gesell's studies of infants whereby he established statistical norms for various motor and intellectual performances. Let's say that the norm for beginning walking is twelve months. Parents often become disturbed if their child passes that period without taking a first step. On the other hand, if a child walks at ten months the parents are sure they have an "advanced" child on their hands. The joker in all this is that as the *norms* have been popularized, the deviations from the average have somehow gotten lost. The point is that there is a range of time, perhaps 9–15 months, that encompasses "normal" development. Hence, because of the absence of a measure of dispersion, many parents have misinterpreted the data and perhaps run off frightened to their family pediatrician! In short, in daily affairs all of us are inundated with facts and information easily misconstrued without some rudimentary knowledge of statistics. Hence, statistics is not primarily a matter of plugging numbers into formulae and performing rote computations. It is a way of thinking and questioning.

In addition to these reasons for studying statistics there are two others. First, with the boom in graduate education, students are often required to design and execute their own experiments, and such tasks are intricately interwoven with the statistical treatment of data. Second, training in statistics is training in the scientific method. One often thinks of science as a game, a game, like other games, that requires its players to obey the rules. While science, like other games, has many rules, one very important one is that of **objectivity**. Even though statistics is not a panacea, the proper understanding of and abiding by its rules is one way of eliminating the pervious *bias* that may enter social research.

SOME BASIC STATISTICAL CONCEPTS

There are several important concepts for which we will have immediate use:

1. **Population (universe** or **parent population)**—a complete set of individuals, objects, or events; that is, it is all those elements of interest to the researcher. For example, all students at Illinois State University, all citizens of voting age, all gainfully employed females.

2. **Sample**—a subset of elements selected from the population. To illustrate, some students at Illinois State University, some citizens of voting age, some gainfully employed females. How the some is selected is vitally important and will be treated in the discussion of sampling.

3. **Data**—numbers or measurements or scores collected from the units of analysis. While the unit of analysis, or case, may vary, usually the unit is the individual and the data may consist of individual heights, weights, IQ scores, and the like.

4. **Variable (or variate)**—a characteristic or phenomenon which may take on different values, for example, weight, height, attitude scores. Frequently a distinction is made in statistics between *quantitative phenomena* (in which case the term **variable** applies) and *qualitative phenomena* (in which case the term **attribute** applies). Examples of attributes include sex, for example, male, female; ethnicity, for example, White, Asian-American, African-American, Hispanic; and religion, for example, Protestant, Catholic, Jew. With attributes, unlike variables, there is usually a distinction of "kind" rather than of true numerical differences.

   Variables can de defined in a number of ways, but one distinction (that will be used frequently in this book) is between **independent (causal)** and **dependent (effect)** variables. If one were interested in differences in cognitive dissonance scores by sex (male and female), dissonance would be the dependent or effect variable. That is, it's something attributed or due to something else, in this case gender. Sex would be the independent or causal variable.

   Another important way of conceptualizing variables or attributes is in terms of their number of categories or classes. For example, sex (gender) has two subdivisions and is referred to as a **dichotomy** whereas religion or race as classified above is called a **polychotomy** or **manifold classification**.

5. **Constant**—this refers to a value that never changes, for example, pi = 3.1417. Some statistical formulae—Spearman's rho and Kruskal-Wallis test—employ a constant.

6. **Parameter**—a numerical characteristic of a *population,* designated by Greek letters, in contrast to a statistic. The mean age of *all* Illinois State University students would be a parameter and designated μ.

7. **Statistic**—a numerical characteristic of a *sample,* designated by Roman letters, that is used as an estimate of its corresponding population parameter. The mean age of a sample (*some* but not all) of Illinois State University students would be a statistic and designated $\overline{X}$.

An example will clarify the interrelationships among some of these statistical concepts. Suppose you are a student of formal organizations and wish to study lower level bureaucrats' attitudes toward top management in the home office of the State Farm Insurance Company. Instead of studying the entire bureaucratic structure (the population), you select a certain number of bureaucrats (the sample) and ask them whether their attitudes are favorable, unfavorable, or undecided toward top management. The variable being studied is attitudes toward management. The data consist of all the attitudinal information gathered from the sample of persons. If you compute a summary measure of the bureaucrats' attitudes, like the mean score, you would be computing a statistic, which is an estimate of all bureaucrats' attitudes, the latter being a parameter.

PRACTICAL USES OF STATISTICAL ANALYSIS

The collection and analysis of statistical data can be put to numerous practical uses. Here we will consider some of the myriad possibilities:

1. The data can be *graphically* presented. Graphs, tables, and figures, the concern of Chapter 3, provide us with a "picture" of our data.

2. The *central tendency* or *average* can be calculated. The various measures of central tendency provide us with an idea of the "typical" value in a constellation of observations. Chapter 4 will discuss this concept and the different types of averages.

3. The *dispersion* or *spread* of scores from the typical score can be determined. Through the calculation of measures of dispersion (or variation) we are provided with information that permits us to determine how observations spread out from the center of a distribution. Chapter 5 will discuss this concept and different ways of computing dispersion measures.

4. Scores taken from different distributions can be directly compared when *transformed* into a common standard. Chapter 6 will discuss this operation under the heading of z scores (*standard scores*).

5. We can generalize from a sample of observations to a larger set of observations. This is the major concern of the chapters entitled "Inferential Statistics," Chapters 7 and 8, which puts forth the logic, and subsequent chapters (9, 10, and 11) which deal with specific inductive techniques.

6. The relationship, quantitatively speaking, between variables can be com-

puted. The concept of *association* or *correlation* will be the focus of Chapters 12 and 13 in this text.

7. A logical extension of correlational analysis is *regression analysis*. In regression, we predict a person's status on one variable (*Y*) on the basis of another (*X*). This procedure will be highlighted in Chapter 13.

The chapters that follow are organized in a systematic manner. To the researcher, statistics comprise but one component, albeit a very important one, of the research act. In conveying some notion of the gestalt of this process, Chapter 2 is devoted to a discussion of the foundations of statistical analyses. This framework is predicated on the important interrelationships among theory, methodology, measurement, and statistics. The theory of measurement or the meaning that numbers have when assigned to observations is the backbone of the logic underlying the contents of this book.

Once these building blocks have been laid we move into a discussion of descriptive statistics for summarizing and describing *univariate* (single variable) distributions (Chapters 3, 4, and 5). The normal curve exposition (Chapter 6) is a bridge between the descriptive statistics chapters and the inferential statistics chapters (Chapters 7, 8, 9, 10, and 11). Inferential statistics, as we will see, is concerned with two subtopics—parameter estimation (Chapter 7) and hypotheses testing (Chapters 8, 9, 10, and 11).

Then, in Chapters 12 and 13 we will return to descriptive statistics again, although this time the concern is with describing *bivariate* (two variables) distributions. The location of this material was deemed to logically appear after the inferential statistics chapters because the statistical test of significance for association (correlation) coefficients presumes an understanding of the rationale of hypotheses testing.

Finally, a brief summary of what has transpired through the various chapters of the text is reiterated in the last chapter (Chapter 14).

SUMMARY

In this chapter we discussed some of the ways in which you have already been a consumer of statistical information and then presented a brief overview of the evolution of statistics. Toward this latter end a consideration of the forbearers' contributions to modern-day analysis was reviewed along with a statement of statistics current status in sociology.

Statistics was formally defined as the *general body of techniques for assembling, describing, and inferring something from numerical data*. The two broad functions, description and inference, of statistics were discussed.

A listing and discussion of some of the reasons for studying statistics were examined from a practical and academic standpoint.

Finally, several key statistical concepts were dealt with and some of the practical uses of statistics were briefly mentioned.

IMPORTANT CONCEPTS DISCUSSED IN THIS CHAPTER

Statistics

Descriptive statistics

Inferential statistics (sampling, inductive, probability)

Population (universe, parent population)

Sample

Objectivity

Data

Variable (variate)

Attribute

Independent (causal) variable

Dependent (effect) variable

Dichotomy

Polychotomy (manifold classification)

Constant

Parameter

Statistic

REVIEW QUESTIONS

1. The term *statistics* may be considered as either a singular or plural noun. In what way does this observation have importance in the field of statistics?

2. The major purposes of statistics are contained within the terms assembles, describes, and infers. Explain.

3. What is the difference between descriptive and inferential statistics?

4. What are some of the practical reasons why a basic knowledge of statistical techniques is helpful in cultivating "statistical literacy"?

5. How does the statistician define the concepts: (a) population, (b) sample, (c) data, (d) variable, (e) parameter, and (f) statistic? Think of an illustration of how these statistical terms can be interrelated.

6. What contribution(s) did the following persons make in the development of statistics? (a) Bernoulli, (b) Demoivre, (c) Laplace, (d) Gauss, (e) Quételet, (f) Galton, (g) Pearson, (h) Cattell, (i) Thorndike, (j) Fisher, and (k) Bayes.

7. Does there exist any controversy in the application of statistics to sociological pheno-mena?

*

1

FOUNDATIONS OF STATISTICAL ANALYSES

CHAPTER 2

SOCIAL THEORY, METHODOLOGY, AND STATISTICS

The purpose of this chapter is to show some of the interconnections among theory, methodology, and statistics in the social research process. To accomplish this, it will be necessary to dabble in the philosophy of science. Although theory and research comprise integral and complementary components, the tendency of higher education to compartmentalize courses into theory, research, and statistics often leaves the student somewhat ignorant of their interrelationships. The objective here is to make these connections explicit. To accomplish this it will be necessary to outline the relationships among theoretical propositions, empirical hypotheses, measurement, and mathematical models. To achieve this goal the works of Blalock (1979: chap. 2; 1968: chap. 1) and Wallace (1969: preface) will be drawn upon.

A dominant analytical mode in the behavioral sciences is sometimes called the **hypothetico-deductive method.** The hypothetico-deductive process constitutes a merger of deductive and inductive reasoning. Logic (e.g., syllogism) and mathematics are illustrations of deductive or analytical thinking while sociology and political science (empirical disciplines) exemplify inductive reasoning. According to Palumbo (1969: 3):

Deductive reasoning makes assumptions and then derives consequences or conclusions from them analytically. The vehicle used is the concept, an abstraction, an idea, several steps removed from what can be observed with the senses. When a number of concepts have been interrelated in lawlike generalizations, we have a theory through which predictions about the world are made and tested empirically. Inductive reasoning is the process of moving from observations of events in the world to more general statements. Its principal vehicle is measurement, or the operational definition of abstract concepts. Through the inductive method, concepts are explicated or further clarified, and theories are confirmed, modified, or refuted.

This method, diagrammed in Figure 2.1, indicates one form social research takes, namely, to test hypotheses logically derived from theories of behavior. The hypotheses (propositions or variable relationships we wish to study empirically) tested in the social research act must be understood in a *probabilistic* framework. That is, there exist few, if any, relationships which may be labeled **determinate** (or a **deterministic hypothesis**). When a change in one variable *always* occurs because of a change in another variable, a deterministic relationship is evident. Boyle's law in thermodynamics is a case in point. It states that for relatively low pressures, the pressure of a gas kept at a constant temperature varies inversely with the volume of the gas. However, most social hypotheses are **stochastic** in nature. A stochastic relationship is one that occurs quite frequently or on the average but not always. The relationship between annual salary and years of formal schooling is stochastic in that, on the average, the more years of schooling one has the higher is one's salary. But, salary does not automatically increase with an increase in academic training, although it is likely to go up. The processes involved in transiting from theory to actual research hypotheses and from these hypotheses to probability statements bearing upon both theory and hypotheses are indirect. In fact, the linkages between the various strata are so elusive that professional disagreements frequently arise.

Wallace (1969: ix) provides one the best visual schemes for understanding the various components of scientific sociology. He maintains that sociology, as a scientific enterprise, may be thought of as consisting of five parts: (1) Methods, (2) Theories, (3) Hypotheses, (4) Observations, and (5) Empirical Generalizations. His visual scheme is presented in Figure 2.1. It must be remembered that this visual paradigm is an "ideal type," since in the actual conduct of social research the five components frequently overlap and the sequence of steps is not invariable (see discussions of inductive and deductive research). In this chapter our basic concern will be with the first half (moving clockwise) of the scheme, that is, with the "Theories, Hypotheses, and Observations" constituents. Also, we will deal with the "Scaling and Measurement" dimension which is a link between observations and empirical generalizations.

THE CONNECTION BETWEEN THEORIES AND HYPOTHESES

Often students think that knowledge about social behavior is out in the "real world" merely waiting to be collected. Such thinking belies the very active role the researcher must play in "creating" that knowledge. Particularly in a discipline with a host of abstract concepts, the ingenuity of the investigator becomes tremendously important as he or she attempts to establish concrete empirical indicators of the phenomena of central focus. Let us look at the modus operandi of the social researcher.

There exists a wide range of definitions of **theory**. For our purposes assume that it refers to a system of logically interrelated propositions which purport to explain social behavior. Sociological theories are frequently distinguished on the

FIGURE 2.1

The Components and Process of Scientific Sociology

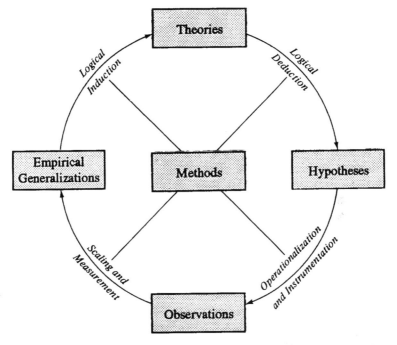

*Reprinted from Walter L. Wallace, SOCIOLOGICAL THEORY (Chicago: Aldine Publishing Company, 1969); copyright (c) 1969 by Walter L. Wallace. Reprinted by permission of the author and Aldine Publishing Company.

basis of their scope, for example, grand (macro) theory as in conflict theory and functionalism, middle range as found in Robert K. Merton, and micro (elementary) as in symbolic interactionism.

When we begin to design a research project to test hypotheses derived from our social theories, several decisions must be made before the test can actually be made. Assume you are interested in assessing the relationship between socio-economic status (SES) and ethnocentrism. Obviously, a decision must be made concerning how you will determine a person's SES and ethnocentrism. Since individuals do not wear tags that are valid and reliable indicators of these concepts, we must look elsewhere. Consulting the social stratification literature informs us that there are three reasonably good ways of determining a person's social class. They are: (1) the *reputational method* in which individuals rate or rank others in terms of where they think these others fall on the socioeconomic status ladder, (2) the *subjective method* in which individuals identify the social position to which they believe they belong, and (3) the *objective method* in which various indices, for example, income, education, occupation, are used by the investigator to determine a person's social class. The crux of the matter is that the three methods do not necessarily yield a consensus, that is, a person's social class position is in part a function of the method used. Ethnocentrism, too, would have to be carefully defined for research purposes since, like SES, there exist alternative ways of measuring it. Conceptually, ethnocentrism is defined as the tendency for people to use their own sociocultural group as a measuring stick for evaluating other sociocultural group practices. By extension it implies an attachment of the labels "proper," "natural," and "correct" to one's own beliefs and behavior modes and the labels of "improper," "unnatural," and "incorrect" to deviations from this standard. *What must be done for research purposes is to translate the concept ethnocentrism into operations or indicators.* Adorno et al. in their classic work, *The Authoritarian Personality* (1950), devised a series of items (*E*-scale) purportedly measuring this theoretical concept. For example, responses of subjects to items like "Certain religious sects who refuse to salute the flag should be forced to such a patriotic action or else be abolished" were used as indicators of ethnocentrism.

In the preceding paragraph we've been talking about the importance of **operational definitions**,[1] that is, the importance of making explicit the manner or mode in which concepts such as SES and ethnocentrism are measured. Imagine what could happen if I hadn't made explicit, that is, operationally defined, the classification of your variables. If I used the reputational approach while you used the objective approach, the potential for lack of consistency between studies exists, even though the concept we both measured is the same. In brief, an operational definition spells out the exact procedures used in measurement. It may be considered a detailed set of instructions for classifying the phenomena of interest. The reason operational definitions are necessary stems from the fact that most ordinary definitions—named **theoretical definitions**—are defined in terms of other concepts supposedly already understood (these concepts supposedly already understood are called **primitive concepts** or **axioms**). To illustrate primitive conceptualization look at Euclidean geometry where the concepts of point and line are undefined but the concepts of angle, triangle, and rectangle are defined in terms of the primitive, that is, undefined, concepts. Let us look at some examples of operational definitions: an operational definition of "weight" would indicate how the object is (or was) to be weighed; an operational definition of one's desire to relate to persons of different ethnic groups might include the use of a Bogardus' social distance scale; and an operational definition of status might include the use of a composite index of an individual's occupation, salary, and education.

---

[1] Operationism came into modern science about 1927 and was championed by Percy W. Bridgman. This principle asserts that the validity of a scientific finding or theoretical construct is contingent upon the operations involved in arriving at that finding or construct. In sociology a major advocate of this position was George A. Lundberg (1895–1966).

The point is simply this: in any science two different definitions or languages are used, the theoretical and the operational (Blalock, 1979: chap. 2).[2] Many of the sociologists' basic concepts, for example, role, norm, social status, social structure, social system, group, integration, organization, society, culture, institution, value, attitude, deviance, interaction, socialization, conflict, stratification, mobility, and power, are of a highly abstract nature and, consequently, present a measurement problem. Since such concepts have no ultimate meaning, they must be reduced to specific empirical indicators, which is what operationalization is all about. Diagrammatically, Figure 2.2 is helpful in grasping the logic of conceptualization and operationalization. Epistemic rules (Northrop, 1947; Dumont and Wilson, 1967) link the concept with its empirical referent (real world). Not all sociological concepts are so elusive. Many of the demographic variables (age, sex, race, regional residency) are not highly abstract and, consequently, are easier to measure.

FIGURE 2.2

The Link between a Concept and the Real World

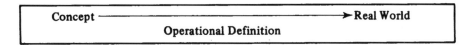

The methodological question is whether or not there is a foolproof way of determining if a given operational definition really measures the theoretically defined concept. The answer to this query is a clear and resounding "NO!" The reason the answer is "No" is that concepts must be operationally defined for research purposes, and many concepts can be defined in a number of different ways. There is at least one recommendation for increasing confidence in a research outcome. The replication of studies has not been particularly popular but it does enable one to determine what consistencies exist. Two subtypes of replication are: (1) *exact*, and (2) *conceptual*. Exact replication involves only a minor change in the research design, for example, if the same measures of SES and ethnocentrism were used to test respondents in different states. Conceptual replication entails an operational definition change, that is, instead of employing the objective method of determin-

---

[2]There are a variety of ways of stating these two different definitions. Northrop (1947) refers to what Blalock calls "theoretical definitions" as concepts by postulation and "operational definitions" as concepts by intuition. Bierstedt (1959) refers to real versus nominal definitions respectively, and Coombs (1953) refers to genotypic and phenotypic concepts. Another frequently used notion for an operational definition is the concept index. This term (index) carries the implication that the procedures used give an imperfect indication of some underlying variable which is not directly measurable. In other words, there is both an underlying variable and an indicator of that variable. One final point, Blalock implies there are two distinct ways of defining the same concept whereas Northrop chooses to refer to two different kinds of concepts.

ing SES the subjective approach might be used. If the different operational indicators of a concept are relatively consistent (one thrust of *triangulation*), then one's confidence in the outcome is enhanced. Although conceptual replications help to avoid the criticism of "one methodology" studies, the nature of the social world and the research modus operandi produce few absolute and unchanging truths. According to Northrop (1947), the only way of associating the two concepts is by convention or common agreement; researchers must agree that a given operational definition is an acceptable indicator of the theoretical definition to which it refers. Bridgman (1938), the champ of operationism, maintained that the two kinds of definitions should be associated on a one-to-one basis—if you change the operation you should change the concept. In terms of our previous example this would mean that the different methods of determining a person's social class are not all measuring the same phenomenon. Although there is some merit to this extreme position, it does pose as somewhat unrealistic in the social sciences at the present time.

Given this dilemma what can we do? It is important to define operationally the concepts being tested. Not all variables (or concepts) need or can be operationalized. But concepts which haven't been operationally defined should not be permitted to appear in statements purporting to be testable. If this occurs, the questions raised by the hypotheses will be virtually meaningless and lead to futile debate (Blalock, 1979: 11–14). In terms of Wallace's visual model we have made explicit the link between theories and hypotheses and the link between hypotheses and observations.

MEASUREMENT

We have seen that the processes involved in moving from theory to hypotheses are not direct. Similarly, the selection of an appropriate mathematical or statistical model to be used in research involves a number of decisions. This process is so important that Anderson and Zelditch (1975: vi) say, "The central problem of the application of statistics is in the relation of model to practical circumstance."

A germane question at this juncture is this: What do we mean by **measurement**? In part, the confusion surrounding the idea of measurement stems from our implicit tendency to think in terms of quantitative scales. Does the number "2" always imply a quantity larger than "1"? The answer is, of course, no, if we are dealing with telephone numbers, or street addresses, or football jersey numbers. The use of numbers in these cases is merely to identify or categorize the different phenomena. Consider this illustration. If we rank three individuals, assigning "1" to the tallest, "2" to the middle person, and "3" to the shortest, does the height of the first person plus the height of the second person equal the height of the third person? Once again, the answer is "No!" One conceptual distinction statisticians make to avoid this confusion involves the concepts **numerals** and **numbers**. *Numerals* refer to symbols used to classify or order events—no arithmetical operations are implied. *Numbers,* in contrast, may involve arithmetical manipulations.

This distinction is more than academic since many of the "numbers" we confront daily, for example, zip codes, telephone numbers, do not have the arithmetical properties we ordinarily ascribe to them. Since confusion surrounds the use of numerals and since they can be used to name (nominal numerals), to represent position in a series (ordinal numerals), and to represent quantity (interval/ratio numerals), a precise definition of measurement is necessary (Runyon and Haber, 1976: 19–20).

Probably the broadest and most widely used definition of measurement comes from S. S. Stevens (1946).[3] He notes that "measurement is the assignment of numerals to objects and events according to rules." This definition expresses the basic nature of measurement. Let's take an example from the diving events in Olympic competition. As we know, the judges rate the contestants on numerous dimensions. Does this constitute measurement? To answer this query let us refer back to Stevens' definition. The judges assign values or numerals (perhaps 1 to 10) to objects (in this case divers' performances) according to the instructions (in this case whatever rules they are expected to abide by). Since the operations involved conform to Stevens' definition we have an illustration of measurement.

Levels of Measurement

Statistics texts traditionally discuss four levels of measurement (nominal, ordinal, interval, and ratio) to emphasize the point that *data contain different information depending upon how scores/values are assigned.* These different strata provide the basic conceptual foundation in this text for choosing the most appropriate statistical techniques for discovering the meaning of statistical observations. It should be borne in mind that others (Sarle, 1995) consider in-between measurement levels such as a log-interval scale and an absolute scale. However, in basic statistics these latter concerns are not ordinarily important.

The notion of "levels of measurement" refers to the *relationships between categories* of a variable. For a nominal variable like gender, there are two categories (male and female) that are simply different. For an ordinal variable such as social class, there are any number of categories—upper, middle, lower versus upper, middle, working lower, and so forth—but in all instances the categories can be located on a continuum from high to low or more to less on such dimensions as power,

---

[3] *Measurement theory* is a branch of applied mathematics that is useful in measurement and data analysis (Sarle, 1995). The fundamental idea of measurement theory is that measurements are not the same as the attribute being measured. Hence, if you want to draw conclusions about the attribute, you must take into account the nature of the correspondence between the attribute and the measurements. Measurement theory helps us to avoid making meaningless statements. A typical example of such a meaningless statement is the claim by the meteorologist on the local TV station that it was twice as warm today as yesterday because it was 40 degrees Fahrenheit today but only 20 degrees yesterday. This statement is meaningless because one measurement (40) is twice the other measurement (20) only in certain arbitrary scales of measurement, such as Fahrenheit. The relationship "twice-as" applies only to the numbers, not the attribute being measured (temperature).

privilege, and prestige. For interval/ratio variables like temperature and years of formal schooling, respectively, we can talk in terms of clearly defined units of measurement. With standardized measurement units we can talk in terms of *magnitudes* of difference such as a high school graduate has had twice as much formal schooling as a grammar school graduate.

There are several distinct levels of measurement, each with its own rules and properties. These strata are cumulative, meaning that it is legitimate to drop back one or more levels but *not* move up in analyzing our data. These levels of measurement refer to the manner in which we've operationalized and assigned numbers to the concepts in question. The four conventional levels are as follows:

1. Nominal or Classificatory Level of Measurement. The most basic level of measurement is the **nominal** or **classificatory level of measurement,** and often the data are technically referred to as **attributes** (or **frequency data,** or **enumerative data,** or **categorical data**) rather than as variables. A formal definition of this type of measurement is *the assignment of numbers or other symbols to classify an object, event, or characteristic.* If numbers rather than symbols are used in the classification process, it is important to remember that they are not used in the quantitative sense. There are numerous examples of this type of measurement, for example, the psychiatric classifications of neurotic and psychotic, numbers on license plates, social security numbers, basketball jersey numbers, the various hues on the color spectrum. In sociology many of the social structural variables, for example, sex, race, and religion, conform to the requirements of nominal level measurement.

Although classification is the major operation involved in constructing a nominal level variable, such a classification or measurement procedure should be **inclusive** as well as **mutually exclusive.** An inclusive classification scheme must enable the researcher to categorize each and every case. Inclusiveness means that the classification scheme must be exhaustive. For example, suppose you construct a questionnaire which request respondents to check their marital status with one of the following codes: married _____ divorced _____ separated _____ . If a respondent were single there would be no category to check. As a rule, each and every respondent must have a category within which to respond. With more complex items this inclusive dimension is accomplished by adding an "other," "don't know" (symbolized D/K), or "no answer" (symbolized N/A) category.

Mutually exclusive categories are, likewise, important in constructing a nominal level variable. Mutually exclusive categories permit the researcher to classify, unambiguously, a case into a single category. If a variable had two categories, "married" and "one or more children," a precise classification of an individual that was married and who had children would not be possible since, logically, the person could be placed in both categories. Variables at *any* level of measurement should meet the criteria of exhaustiveness and mutual exclusiveness.

What is the mathematical criterion for constructing a nominal level variable? The outstanding mathematical property is an equivalence (symbolized by " = ") relationship. The mathematical properties of this *equivalence relation* are reflexive, symmetrical, and transitive. *Reflexive* means $X = X$ for all values of X; *symmetrical* means if $X = Y$, then $Y = X$; and *transitive* means if $X = Y$ and $Y = Z$, then $X = Z$.

This means that all the elements placed in a given category are, for analytical purposes, considered identical (or equivalent), despite the fact that the elements may differ on other characteristics. To exemplify this, consider sex. In category A we place all males while in category B we place all females. Obviously, men and women differ on innumerable characteristics other than sex, for example, height, weight, intelligence, manual dexterity, and so forth, but for our research purposes we disregard the individual differences on the remaining nonrelevant characteristics.

Some representative statistics for nominal variables that will be discussed in this book are the mode (measure of central location), index of qualitative variation and index of dispersion (measures of dispersion), contingency coefficient (measure of association), and the chi-square test (measure of statistical significance).

2.   *Ordinal or Ranking Level of Measurement.* In ordinal or ranking measurement we are able to make mathematical distinctions among the categories of our variables not possible with nominal measurement. The objects stand in some kind of relationship to each other and can be positioned at some point along a continuum, for example, small, medium, large; poor, good, excellent; few, many. An illustration of typically ordinally measured variables includes the Moh's scale in which precious gems are ranked in terms of hardness. In sociology the concept of social class is of this nature, for example, upper class, middle class, lower class; also, grades for academic performance (e.g., A, B, C, . . . F).

What are the formal properties of an ordinal variable? Since the measurement levels are cumulative, in addition to the relation of equivalence ($=$), we add the relationship of *greater or less than* ($>$ or $<$). The mathematical properties of the relationship of less than or greater than are irreflexive, asymmetrical, and transitive. *Irreflexive* means that it is not true for any X that $X > Y$; *asymmetrical* means that if $X > Y$, then $Y \not> X$; and *transitive* means that if $X > Y$ and $Y > Z$, then $X > Z$. This means that the algebra of inequalities is applicable to the data manipulation. One easy way to grasp the meaning of the ranking level is to think of the finish in a horse race. Very likely (assuming no ties) it is possible to distinguish the order of finish, that is, win, place, show, and so forth, but not how much the orders differ. In other words, the gap between win and place is not necessarily the same as the gap between place and show and show and the rest of the field.

The construction of ordinal variables occurs in three basic ways (Anderson and Zelditch, 1975: 35–38) through the use of: (1) judges, (2) counting unequal elements, and (3) the frequency of occurrence. To illustrate the use of judges your attention is called to the role of judges in the Olympic diving competition mentioned previously. An example of counting unequal elements is the typical objective (true-false or multiple choice) test. Although professors ordinarily count the number of items answered correctly, it is understood that the various items represent the acquisition of knowledge unequally. In other words, the individual questions are not equal with respect to a *unit of knowledge*. The Guttman scaling technique, a methodological device for scaling attitudes, would illustrate the third manner in which ordinal variables can arise. A discussion of Guttman scaling is beyond the scope of this book, but the interested student may consult one of many methodology texts for a more thorough explication.

Some representative statistics for ordinal variables that will be discussed in this book are the median (measure of central tendency), interquartile range (measure of dispersion), Spearman's rho (measure of association), and Mann-Whitney U test (measure of statistical significance).

3. Interval Level of Measurement. The first truly quantitative level of measurement is the **interval level of measurement.** It is the stratum that "matches" our ideas of numbers. In fact, nominal and ordinal measurement are often referred to as *qualitative* whereas the interval and ratio levels are called *quantitative*. Since the theory of measurement has a cumulative dimension to it, an interval scale may be defined as one that has all the properties of an ordinal scale, namely " = " and " > and < ," plus the distance between any two numbers on the scale is of a known size. It's important to remember that, technically speaking, the zero point and the unit of measurement are *arbitrary*. Examples of interval measurement are temperature (remember that absolute zero is a $-273°$ on the Kelvin scale and not the arbitrary $0°$ on the Centigrade or on the Fahrenheit), calendar time, and Likert's equal-appearing interval scale. Notice that these examples (temperature, calendar time) have standard units of measurement. Temperature is comprised of degrees; calendar time can be fractioned into hours, days, weeks, and months. The interval level of measurement is highlighted by these standardized measurement units accompanied by an arbitrary origin.

What are the formal properties of interval measurement? In addition to the relation of equivalence (" = "), of greater than or less than (" > or < "), we are able to specify the ratio of any two intervals. Since the operations and relations of interval measurement are such that the differences in the scale are isomorphic (identical) to the structure of arithmetic, we can legitimately add, subtract, multiply, and divide without doing a disservice to the data. There is a compelling reason for attempting to devise interval measures since the information that these scores contain adds increasing amounts of valuable statistical information and provides us with a broader selection of statistical tools.

Some respresentative statistics for interval variables that will be discussed in this book are the arithmetic mean (measure of central tendency), standard deviation (measure of dispersion), Pearsonian product-moment correlation coefficient (measure of association), and the z, t, and F tests (measures of statistical significance).

4. Ratio Level of Measurement. The "highest" level of measurement is the **ratio level of measurement.** Although the physical sciences often have variables at this level, the social sciences have relatively few. Examples of ratio variables include weight (ounces, pounds, grams), length, and the Kelvin scale. In sociology, some of the demographic variables, for example, income, age, and years of formal education, conform to this level.

What are the formal properties of ratio measurement? These scales have all the elements of interval measurement ("=," ">" or "<," known ratio of any two intervals) plus the existence of a *true zero point* which means it is possible to know the ratio of any two scale values. A defined origin is a very important theoretical advantage since it represents the complete absence of what is being measured. In sociology, many of the major concepts when translated into variables do *not* have this property. Zero, or no, social class, attitude, group, culture, social structure are meaningless. On the other hand, zero inches and zero pounds are theoretically meaningful. One way of understanding the differences between the levels of measurement is to consider some practical examples. Let us distinguish ordinal from interval/ratio measurement first, then interval from ratio measurement.

To illustrate the fundamental difference between ordinal and interval/ratio measurement consider the work of gemologists. Since the hardness of precious stones affects both appearance and durability, jewelers follow what is called the Moh's Scale of Hardness. This is a scratch hardness scale which determines to what degree minerals can or cannot be scratched with hardness points or plates. On this scale, quartz is ranked as 7, sapphire at 9, and diamond at 10. The various gem substitutes (artificial, man-made stones) for diamonds rank 6½–7 for synthetic rutile, 5–6 for strontium titanate, 8¼ for YAG or synthetic garnet, and 9 for synthetic sapphire. But this scale is highly misleading for diamonds are many times harder than sapphires. On an *absolute scale* (ratio level measurement), if quartz is 7 and sapphire is 9 in hardness, diamonds would be 42.4! Different investigators have demonstrated diamonds to be from 5 to 140 times as hard as their nearest neighbor. From a statistical standpoint, the observations of gemologists attest to the potential loss of information when interval/ratio measurements are reduced to ranking ones as well as to the intrinsic differences between these measurement scales.

The fundamental distinction between interval and ratio levels of measurement resides in the nature of the origin or zero point. One way of comprehending the difference between interval and ratio measurement is to think of measuring something from the floor (ratio measurement since the floor may be thought of as having a 0 point) and the top of a table (assuming you do not know the distance between the floor and table). In the former case you know the ratio of any two scale points whereas in the latter you know the ratio between any two intervals. One of the best examples this writer has seen of the distinction between interval and ratio measurement can be illustrated as follows. Can we say that 20° C is twice 10° C? Or 40° C is twice 20° C? The answer is no for the following reason. The zero point on the C scale is arbitrary, that is, it does not represent the complete absence of heat. You will recall from physics that absolute zero—or the absence of heat—is −273°. Hence, by observing Figure 2.3 you can see that 40° is not twice 20° or that 100° is not twice 50°.

FIGURE 2.3*

Relationship of Various Points on a Centigrade Scale to Absolute Zero

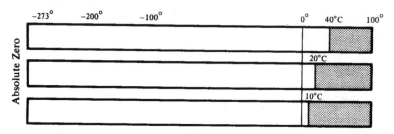

* Reprinted from Richard P. Runyon and Audrey Haber, FUNDAMENTALS OF BEHAVIORAL STATISTICS (Reading, Mass: Addison-Wesley Publishing Company, 1976), copyright (c) 1976 by Runyon and Haber. Reprinted by permission of authors and Addison-Wesley Publishing Company.

Some of the representative statistics for ratio measurement that will be discussed include the geometric mean (measure of central location) and the coefficient of variability (measure of dispersion).

It is salient to mention here that many textbooks, including this one, in statistics frequently treat the interval/ratio levels together since once a standardized measurement unit has been established, a zero point (at least arbitrary) is also established. As a consequence, statistical techniques for variables conforming to these levels are interchangeable in a practical sense, although it is important to be cognizant of the theoretical differences between these two levels of measurement.

Levels of Measurement and Appropriate Statistical Techniques

The four levels of measurement form a *cumulative* scale. The cumulative nature of this scale means that it is legitimate to drop back one or more levels in analyzing our data. Table 2.1 depicts this relationship. Remember that, even though it's permissible to drop down a level for whatever reasons, it is generally best to use the highest level possible since, in general, statistics at higher levels are more powerful[4] than statistics at lower levels and make greater use of the intrinsic mathematical character of the variables. On the other hand, it is generally not appropriate to use a statistical technique at a higher level than the level at which the data were defined since the mathematical assumptions underlying the statistical tool are not consistent with the original assignment of numbers.

---

[4] Power has a specialized statistical meaning that will be discussed in the chapter on inferential statistics. Here it is not intended to convey its unique statistical interpretation.

TABLE 2.1

Levels of Measurement and the Appropriate Statistical Techniques to Use

If you have:	Then use:
(1) ratio data	(1) ratio, or interval, or ordinal, or nominal statistics
(2) interval data	(2) interval, or ordinal, or nominal statistics
(3) ordinal data	(3) ordinal or nominal statistics
(4) nominal data	(4) nominal level statistics

Present Status of Measurement

The role of measurement in any science is far from a moot academic exercise. Every discipline tangles with delineating its major variables and the appropriate methods to investigate them. Beginning in 1932 and extending for a seven-year period, a renowned committee of the British Association for the Advancement of Science debated the problem of measurement. This deliberation failed to reach consensus on what is meant by the term measurement. In 1946 an authoritative statement, albeit controversial, was published by S. S. Stevens who maintained that the key issue was semantic, that is, the problem surrounded the *meaning* of measurement. In that article Stevens classified different measurement scales and indicated the statistical techniques appropriate for the different levels of measurement.

Following Stevens' article, two conflicting schools of thought emerged. Those who have strong affinities with Stevens' thinking (Champion, 1970; 1968; this writer) were advocates of the *weak measurement* school. The basic tenet of this position is that the level of measurement of one's variable(s) places certain restrictions upon the choice of appropriate statistical techniques. In opposition to this position is the *strong statistics* school which maintains that the formal properties of the different measurement levels should *not* categorically influence the choice of statistical tests.

The strong statistics position has been stressed and empirically supported to some extent by several students of measurement (Baker, Hardyck, and Petrinovich, 1966; Lord, 1953; Burke, 1953; Boneau, 1961; and Labovitz, 1967). Stevens' critics say that his position is correct only insofar as descriptive statistics is concerned. They loudly and clearly disagree with his stance when inferential statistics (particularly the *t* and *z* tests of significance) is concerned. Although the number of sources cited above appears to favor the strong statistics school, Stevens (1968) and Champion (1968) are not completely convinced of their critics' position. The position subscribed to by this writer is not an adamant one but, at the same time, is more in line with that of the weak measurement school than that of the strong statistics branch. Stevens' *schemapiric view* (1968) provides a summary of this writer's position:

Measurement provides the numbers that enter the statistical table. But the numbers that issue from measurements have strings attached, for they carry the imprint of the operations by which they were obtained. Some transformations on the numbers will leave intact the information gained by the measurements; other transformations will destroy the desired isomorphism between the measurement scale and the property assessed. Scales of measurement therefore find a useful classification on the basis of a principle of invariance: each of the common scale types (nominal, ordinal, interval, and ratio) is defined by a group of transformations that leaves a particular isomorphism unimpaired.

. . . Therein lies the primacy of measurement: it sets bounds on the appropriateness of statistical operations.

The nature of measurement theory has been subject to considerable controversy. However, most of the polemic surrounds the use of interval measurement since there is little doubt that we have nominally measured variables and little doubt that we do not have an abundance of ratio-measured variables. Since, all things being equal, we want to use the most powerful statistics possible, the disagreement usually boils down to whether ordinal or interval measurement provides the most appropriate mathematical models for data currently employed in the behavioral sciences. In actual practice statistics appropriate to interval variables continue to be widely used—with or without the mathematical requirements being met. To the extent a statistical test can be demonstrated to be *robust* (that is, some test assumptions can be violated without doing too much "damage" to the data analysis and its interpretation) this argument must be tempered. Nevertheless, there does seem to have been an increase in the use of statistics appropriate to ordinal variables. Tests at the nominal and ordinal levels are called *nonparametric tests* (a misnomer) whereas those at the interval and ratio levels are termed *parametric tests.* More will be said about these in future chapters.

The crucial role of measurement in sociology, or any social science for that matter, cannot be overstated. Measurement theory shows that strong assumptions are required for certain statistics to provide meaningful information about reality. Measurement theory encourages people to think about the meaning of their data. It encourages critical assessment of the assumptions behind the analysis. It encourages responsible real-world data analysis. Mathematical statistics is concerned with the connection between inference and data. Measurement theory is concerned with the connection between data and reality. Both statistical theory and measurement theory are necessary to make inferences about reality.

For the beginning student of social statistics it is important to grasp the *logic* between levels of measurement and appropriate statistical techniques. To facilitate the comprehension of this rationale this writer has focused upon the fundamental relationship between measurement and statistics. However, for the serious student it is salient to point out the debates continue to occur.

Labovitz (1967) has argued that sociologists traditionally adhere to the "invariant properties of measurement scales and select only those relationship measures and inference procedures that are consistent with both the assumptions and the level of measurement met by the data." He maintains that certain assumptions *can* be violated without unduly jeopardizing the conclusions, and, if not done, may actually lead to a wasting of information. While he treats several statistical issues beyond the scope of this book, he does demonstrate the utility of assigning numbers to ordinal data and then using interval level statistics for their analysis. One further comment worthy of reiteration is that the leap from a nominal to an ordinal level is much greater than the jump from ordinal to interval. Champion's reply (1968) to Labovitz's position is in disagreement and more in line with the position of this text. In any event, students who wish to resolve the polemic are encouraged to peruse the arguments of measurement theorists and decide for themselves.

To lighten this issue a reading of Lord's (1953) pithy exposition of the statistical treatment of football numbers is highly recommended. Furthermore, at least one behavioral statistician believes the level of measurement polemic can be further refined by talking of two measurement levels. According to Sarle (1995), it may be well to distinguish between the following levels of measurement, the *qualitative*, which includes the nominal level of measurement, and the *quantitative*, which includes the ordinal, interval, log interval, ratio, and absolute levels of measurement. This distinction is conceptualized in Figure 2.4.

FIGURE 2.4

Scales of Measurement in Terms of Their "Strength"

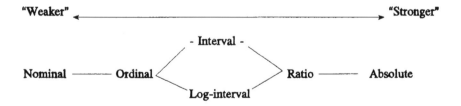

ORGANIZATION OF BASIC SOCIAL STATISTICS
AND FUTURE CHAPTERS

The threads that tie the fundamentals of social statistics together are: (1) *Levels of Measurement*, (2) *Graphic techniques*, (3) *Measures of central tendency*, (4) *Measures of dispersion*, (5) *Measures of association*, (6) *Parameter estimation techniques*, and (7) *Measures (or tests) of significance*. The text will proceed systematical filling in Figure 2.5. Notice that we have followed the convention of locating the independent variable along the horizontal axis (in this case levels of measurement) and the dependent variables (graphic techniques, measures of central tendency, measures of dispersion, measures of association, parameter estimation techniques, and measures of significance) along the vertical axis. In effect, we are maintaining that *the appropriate statistical technique(s) is/are dependent upon the level of measurement of the variable(s)*.

FIGURE 2.5

Appropriate Statistical Techniques by Levels of Measurement

Appropriate Statistical Techniques		*Levels of Measurement*		
		Nominal	*Ordinal*	*Interval/ Ratio*
Descriptive Statistics	Graphic techniques Measures of central tendency Measures of dispersion Measures of association			
Inferential Statistics	Parameter estimation Measures of significance			

The level of measurement is *not* the only consideration in selecting statistical tools. However, it is one of the most important criteria. When a numeral has been assigned to an object or event, the meaning of that score and the statistical techniques appropriate depend upon the intrinsic information it contains. **Variables** may be distinguished in at least three different ways: (1) level of measurement; (2) continuous-discontinuous; and (3) their role, that is, independent, intervening, dependent, in the social research process. Some statistical techniques compel the researcher to look at dimensions other than the level of measurement.

IMPORTANT CONCEPTS DISCUSSED IN THIS CHAPTER

Hypothetico-deductive method	Nominal or classificatory level of measurement
Determinate or deterministic hypothesis	
	Attributes (frequency, enumerative, or categorical data)
Stochastic hypothesis	
Theory	Inclusive
Operational definitions	Mutually exclusive
Theoretical definitions	Ordinal or ranking measurement
Primitive concepts (axioms)	Interval level of measurement
Measurement	Ratio level of measurement
Numerals	Variables
Numbers	Levels of Measurement

REVIEW QUESTIONS

1. The hypothetico-deductive method is a dominant analytical mode in the behavioral sciences. Combining this approach with Wallace's wheel diagram, explain how social theory, methodology, and statistics are interconnected.

2. Why are operational definitions essential in social research?

3. Blalock says any science contains two different definitions, theoretical and operational. What are the implications of these different terms?

4. What do we mean by measurement? In what ways do nominal, ordinal, interval, and ratio levels of measurement differ?

5. Explain the relationships between statistical techniques and levels of measurement. Why does the level of measurement influence the selection of appropriate statistical tools?

6. The text refers to a polemic between the weak measurement and strong statistics schools of thought. To what do these terms refer? How are they important to you as a student of statistics?

7. What are the threads that tie the fundamentals of statistics together?

*

2

DESCRIPTIVE STATISTICS: UNIVARIATE DISTRIBUTIONS

3

FREQUENCY DISTRIBUTIONS AND THEIR GRAPHIC REPRESENTATION

The information that results from empirical studies is usually a collection of numbers, technically called *data*.[1] The data must be put in a form that facilitates the investigator's purposes. The classification and description of these numbers is a step toward making the data more meaningful and manageable. In this chapter some of the conventions for organizing or assembling and describing raw data will be discussed using Figure 3.1 as an organizing scheme. Following through with the logic developed in Chapter 2, notice that the level of measurement of the variable gears us to select the appropriate graphic technique(s).

FIGURE 3.1

Graphic Techniques by Levels of Measurement

Appropriate Statistical Technique	Levels of Measurement		
	Nominal	*Ordinal*	*Interval/Ratio*
Graphic techniques	Bar graph Pie diagram	Bar graph Pie diagram Boxplot	Frequency and percentage polygons Frequency and percentage histograms Cumulative frequency and cumulative percentage polygons (ogives) Line graph Stemplot

---

[1] The word data is plural. Data *are* described using some of the techniques discussed in this text. A single statistical observation (or score) is called a *datum* (singular of data).

To understand the logic behind distributions and graph construction it is necessary to reiterate some of the distinguishing characteristics of variables. In addition to the level of measurement theme, there is also a difference between variables in terms of *scale continuity*. Some variables are *continuous* while others are *discontinuous* (technically called *discrete*). Imagine the variable of weight. Theoretically, individuals' heaviness or lightness could be fractionated indefinitely, as depicted in Figure 3.2a. The counterpart of a continuous variable is a discrete variable, that is, the measurement of the variable can only come in whole number or integer form. To illustrate, consider family size: there can be no families with fractional sizes like 2½, 3¼, and so forth. Instead, it must come in whole number form as depicted in Figure 3.2b.

A moment's reflection indicates that there is no such thing as a continuous nominal variable since it's a logical impossibility. However, there are discrete interval/ratio variables such as family size. In carrying through the logic of statistical analysis it is important to remember that the graphic technique(s) one chooses must be selected with a clear understanding of the meaning of the numbers assigned to the data as well as to their scale continuity.

FIGURE 3.2

Illustration of Continuous and Discrete Variables

(a)

Weight:
Continuous Variable

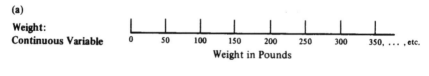

Weight in Pounds

(b)

Family Size:
Discrete Variable

Number in a Family

FREQUENCY DISTRIBUTIONS OF DATA

A **frequency distribution** is an arrangement or classification or assemblage of data showing the frequency of occurrence of the different categories of the variable. The construction of frequency distributions plays an important role in statistical analysis, and in this chapter we demonstrate the construction of frequency distributions for *continuous* data along with some of the main rules for creating them. A frequency distribution for *discrete* data can be found on p. 381.

Let us assume that you are a teacher and have administered an examination to 116 students. You grade all the exams and record the number of correct answers each student made on a 70-item test. These data appear in Table 3.1. The variable "number of correct answers" is an illustration of an interval/ratio level variable that is also discrete. Undoubtedly, the helter-skelter arrangement of your exam scores in Table 3.1 leaves you befuddled. However, you must eventually assign letter grade equivalents to the raw scores so you decide you may as well get started making some sense out of the exam scores.

TABLE 3.1

Exam Scores (Number of Correct Answers) Made by 116 Students

33	64	57	43	45	52	52	52	47	55	56	53
65	32	62	45	49	52	60	52	48	55	55	53
66	54	57	49	45	60	59	53	50	56	61	53
66	32	62	49	49	51	52	60	50	61	61	53
37	54	62	49	51	60	59	60	50	61	61	63
40	62	43	49	49	60	47	60	56	56	53	53
40	62	43	49	51	59	52	58	50	53	61	53
64	62	46	49	51	51	48	58	56	55	55	42
64	62	46	49	51	58	50	58	56	61	56	41
64	62	43	49	51	51	59	41				

Some Steps in Organizing Data

As a first step you decide to *rank order* the scores. A rank ordering entails arranging the information from the highest to the lowest (or vice versa) score as has been done in Table 3.2. An arrangement of this kind is called a **rank order distribution or an array** of scores. After completing this step you find that certain characteristics of these scores emerge, for example, at a glance you can see the highest or maximum (66) and lowest or minimum (32) scores, and the frequency of their occurrence is easily determined by counting the number of entries of each number. To illustrate, a score of 66 occurs twice and a score of 32 occurs twice. Technically speaking, each of these scores has a frequency of two.

As a second step you decide to construct an **ungrouped frequency distribution**. Technically speaking, this is an arrangement of the data showing the frequency of occurrence of different values of the variable, in this case the number of correct answers. Since clerical errors can easily crop up in constructing such distributions, it is advisable to create the table in two stages. First, the raw scores are *tallied*, that is, a mark is made to indicate that the score has been registered. Secondly, the tallies are then converted into frequency counts. In Table 3.3 an ungrouped frequency distribution appears. This distribution of scores is "ungrouped" because the scores have not been collapsed into categories, that is, there are as many *classes* as there are score values. The number of times a particular score occurs is called the **frequency** of the score, represented by the lowercase f. After completing this step, you can see that the original raw data have become more manageable and comprehensible.

TABLE 3.2

Rank Distribution (an Array) of Exam Scores Shown in Table 3.1

66	62	61	59	56	55	53	51	50	49	45	40
66	62	61	59	56	55	53	51	50	49	45	40
65	62	61	59	56	54	53	51	50	49	45	37
64	62	60	59	56	54	52	51	49	49	43	33
64	62	60	58	56	53	52	51	49	48	43	32
64	62	60	58	56	53	52	51	49	48	43	32
64	61	60	58	56	53	52	51	49	47	43	
63	61	60	58	55	53	52	51	49	47	42	
62	61	60	57	55	53	52	50	49	46	41	
62	61	60	57	55	53	52	50	49	46	41	

TABLE 3.3

**Ungrouped Frequency Distribution of Exam Scores from
Table 3.1 with as Many Classes as Score Values**

Score	Tallies	f	Score	Tallies	f	Score	Tallies	f
66	I I	2	54	I I	2	42	I	1
65	I	1	53	⊤⊢⊣ I I I I	9	41	I I	2
64	I I I I	4	52	⊤⊢⊣ I I	7	40	I I	2
63	I	1	51	⊤⊢⊣ I I I	8	39		0
62	⊤⊢⊣ I I I	8	50	⊤⊢⊣	5	38		0
61	⊤⊢⊣ I I	7	49	⊤⊢⊣ ⊤⊢⊣ I	11	37	I	1
60	⊤⊢⊣ I I	7	48	I I	2	36		0
59	I I I I	4	47	I I	2	35		0
58	I I I I	4	46	I I	2	34		0
57	I I	2	45	I I I	3	33	I	1
56	⊤⊢⊣ I I	7	44		0	32	I I	2
55	⊤⊢⊣	5	43	I I I I	4			

As a third step, you decide to construct a **grouped frequency distribution**. The "grouped" nature of this distribution means that the scores are collapsed into categories so that, for example, all the scores (see Table 3.4) within a range of 31 to 33 are contained therein. In other words, all scores with values of 31, 32, and 33 are classified together. While the number and width of the categories are somewhat arbitrary, there are some conventions to follow. One practical recommendation is to use intervals that are neither too large nor too small. Large intervals, particularly, can produce a grouping error problem (a loss of precision); and this potential dilemma is discussed later in the chapter.

At this junction in constructing a grouped frequency distribution two questions arise: (1) How many categories should there be? and (2) How wide, that is, how many different scores should be contained within a category? The answer to both queries is not absolute, but there are some practical guidelines. Somewhere around fifteen class intervals often permit a manageable and meaningful data arrangement. To obtain this, determine the range (R) for the data. This can be easily computed by using formula (3.1):

$$\text{range} = H - L + 1 \tag{3.1}$$

where: H = highest (or largest) score in the distribution
    L = lowest (or smallest) score in the distribution

In our example, $H = 66$ and $L = 32$, hence the range is:

$$66 - 32 + 1 = 35$$

By dividing the range by the optimum number of intervals, we determine the *width* of the interval. The width of the values of the variable is called the **class interval**. In our example, $35 \div 15 \approx 2$ (approximately)[2] which is the desirable width for our class intervals. Notice that the lowest interval (31–33) has a width of 3, not 2. (The reason for choosing a class interval width of 3 and not 2 concerns certain advantages that accrue to odd number intervals and is explained below.) The class interval is designated by the symbol i.[3] There is nothing sacred about fifteen class intervals; rather, the optimum number should be determined by the nature of the problem and the type of questions you wish to answer (or ask) about the data.

Both questions raised above can be dealt with in a single operation. Formula (3.2) combines both steps:

$$i = \frac{H - L + 1}{K} \tag{3.2}$$

[2] In symbolic notation the expression "$\approx$" means "is approximately equal to."

[3] The class interval, designated i, will be used to refer to the class interval itself and the width of the class interval. To avoid confusion, the context in which i is presented will explicate how it is to be used.

where: i = width of class interval
H = highest score
L = lowest score
K = desired number of class intervals

Substituting our data into formula (3.2):

$$i = \frac{66 - 32 + 1}{15}$$

$$i \approx 2 \text{ (approximately)}$$

The lowest class interval should be *identical with or less than* the smallest score in the original data. In the present example the lowest interval begins with one less than the smallest score. Then each successive class interval is a multiple of the desired width. As a general rule the width of all class intervals should be the same since computational problems occur if this convention is not adhered to. One additional suggestion that facilitates further operations is that the class interval, if feasible, should be odd, that is, the width should be an odd number like 3, 5, 7, 9, and so forth. The reason for this is simply that if midpoints are to be determined, then with an odd class interval size the midpoints will be whole numbers and not decimals (or fractions).

Percentage Distributions

Students often find it easier to think in terms of percentages than in terms of absolute frequencies. It is possible and often leads to easier comprehension if a frequency distribution is converted into a **percentage distribution.**[4] This is accomplished by dividing the *frequency* in each class interval by the total number of scores and multiplying each result by 100. In Table 3.4 this has been done. For example, the percentages of exam scores in class interval 31–33 is [3/116](100) or 2.6; for class interval 49–51 the percent is [24/116](100) or 20.7. The percentages of all class intervals are contained in Table 3.4 and will be used later in constructing a percentage polygon.

In Chapter 1 we said that one function of statistics entails reducing data to more meaningful and manageable forms. The construction of the various frequency and percentage distributions is a means to this end. In later chapters you will see that many statistical calculations can be made directly from data assembled in a grouped frequency distribution. In the following sections we will see how graphs can be constructed from these distributions also.

---

[4] To compute a percentage the following formula is used: $P(\%) = f_i/N(100)$, where f_i = frequency of cases and N = total number of cases. See Appendix B at the rear of this book for a review of this procedure.

TABLE 3.4

Grouped Frequency and Percentage Distributions of Exam Scores from Table 3.1

Class Interval (i)	Frequency (f)	Cumulative Frequency (F)	Percent (%)	Cumulative Percentages (cum %)	Midpoints
64–66	7	116 (N)	6.0	100.0	65
61–63	16	109	13.8	94.0	62
58–60	15	93	12.9	80.2	59
55–57	14	78	12.1	67.3	56
52–54	18	64	15.5	55.2	53
49–51	24	46	20.7	39.7	50
46–48	6	22	5.2	19.0	47
43–45	7	16	6.0	13.8	44
40–42	5	9	4.3	7.8	41
37–39	1	4	.9	3.5	38
34–36	0	3	0	2.6	35
31–33	3	3	2.6	2.6	32
Total (N) = 116			100.0		

EXACT LIMITS OF CLASS INTERVALS

Data may be thought of as having two forms: (1) **continuous** and (2) **discrete**. Consider the following examples. Suppose the average (median) family size[5] was 3.8 whereas the mean income was $41,116. A moment's reflection leads you to have second thoughts about the average family size figure. For one thing, you have never seen nor heard of an eight-tenths of a human being or of a human being who had two-tenths missing. The bugaboo here is that family size is a discrete variable, that is, not all values are possible, only whole numbers. A woman may have 0, 1, 2, 3, . . ., ∞ (fecundity) children but not .3 or 15.6. You get the point! The arithmetic average is correct, mathematically, but there is no empirical reality to which it corresponds. Income, the second example, is a continuous variable, that is, any value might theoretically be obtained (provided measurement is precise). Consequently, virtually any value—$10,011.02 or $115,118.19 ad infinitum—is possible.

Our measuring instruments, of course, are not perfect and usually it is expedient to round our data at some point. What this means is that *empirical data are*

---

[5] Technically speaking, family size is a discrete variable since families can only be reported with whole numbers; fractional size families are not possible. However, average family size is a different variable because the units of analysis are groups and not individuals. Ordinarily it is defined as a continuous variable characteristic of groups (Loether and McTavish, 1993: 24).

usually reported in discrete form but in many instances we can at least imagine that the recorded score represents a value falling within certain limits. These limits are usually taken as one-half the *unit of measurement* above and below the recorded score and are termed **exact limits.**[6] The reported limits, in contrast, are called **stated limits.**[7]

Consider the variable of weight with a class interval of 131–150. The stated limits are 131 and 150, but the exact limits, lower and upper, respectively, are 130.5 and 150.5. Although in practice the exact limits are rarely reported, they are used in graph construction as well as in the computation of certain statistics. One final point: *the distinction between exact and stated limits applies only to continuous data* since discrete data, by definition, only come in whole number (integer) form.

DISTRIBUTION OF OBSERVATIONS WITHIN A CLASS INTERVAL

There is a loss of information when individual scores are grouped into class intervals. This is called *grouping error.* This means that there is a certain loss of exactness, precision, and accuracy. In the construction of frequency distributions and graphs as well as in the calculation of certain statistics, it becomes necessary to make assumptions about the distribution of scores within the class intervals. There are two assumptions commonly made:

Assumption 1: The observations (scores) are *uniformly* (evenly or rectangularly) *distributed over the exact limits* of the interval. This assumption is used in constructing histograms and in computing various ordinal level statistics.

Assumption 2: The observations are *centered at the midpoint* of the interval. This assumption is made in constructing frequency polygons and in computing various interval/ratio level statistics.

The **midpoint** of an interval is its exact center. It can be obtained by adding one-half the width of the interval to the *lower exact limit* of that interval. Take the class interval 31–33 in Table 3.4. The width of the interval is 3 (31, 32, 33); one-half of 3 is 1½. We add 1½ to the lower exact limit which is 30.5. Hence, 30.5 + 1.5 = 32.0 which is the midpoint of that interval. The midpoint of any class interval can be calculated with the following formula (3.3):

$$\text{midpoint of class interval} = \frac{i}{2} + L \qquad (3.3)$$

---

[6]The exact limits of a score or interval are sometimes called *true limits, real limits, end values,* or *class boundaries* by various writers.

[7]The stated limits are sometimes called *integral limits, finite limits,* or *apparent limits* by various writers.

where: i = width of class interval
L = lower exact limit of class interval

Substituting our data for the 31–33 class interval into formula (3.3):

$$\text{midpoint of class interval} = \frac{3}{2} + 30.5$$

$$= 1.5 + 30.5$$
$$= 32$$

When a statistical technique uses the midpoint (assumption 2) for computational purposes, a certain amount of accuracy is lost. Technically this loss of accuracy is called *grouping error* and occurs because the midpoint of the class interval usually does not precisely represent all the scores within the interval. In many cases grouping error is negligible and facilitates further statistical computations.

GRAPH CONSTRUCTION

Graphs are geometrical or pictorial representations of data. The adage, "a picture is worth a thousand words," is somewhat appropriate here. In most **graph** construction we work with quadrant one of the **Cartesian coordinate system** devised by René Descartes (1596–1650), the French philosopher and mathematician. The **vertical axis** is conventionally labeled the Y axis and values along it are called **ordinate values.** When data are displayed in cross-tabular form (cross-tabulation is an arrangement of data in which one can determine the number of cases which fall *simultaneously* into two or more categories), the *dependent variable* is located along this axis. The **horizontal axis** is usually labeled the X axis and values along it are called **abscissa values.** When data are cross-tabulated it is the *independent variable* that is placed along this axis. These two axes, vertical and horizontal, intersect at right angles at a point called the *origin,* symbolized by O. It is helpful to think of each axis as a *number line.* Figure 3.3 portrays the relationship among these graph components.

In all graph construction neatness as well as technical accuracy is important. Standard arithmetic graph paper is recommended and will facilitate neatness. The importance of technical accuracy can be inferred by examining the graphs appearing in Figure 3.4. These two graphs were constructed from the identical raw data! They are called "Gee-Whiz" charts. They illustrate how graphs can be used for deceptive purposes. The technical error is the elimination of the zero frequency on the ordinate of Figure 3.4a. Without the zero point the reader fails to see the information in a wider perspective and consequently may misconstrue its interpretation. To avoid such chaos and minimize erroneous interpretation, statisticians have also adopted a **three-quarter high rule.** In practice this means that the vertical axis should be laid out so that its length is roughly three-quarters the length of the horizontal axis. The adoption of this convention along with the placement of zero on the ordinate is strongly recommended since it minimizes subjective factors and even personal biases in graph construction and interpretation.

Figure 3.5 is to be used for understanding the construction of a numerically accurate graph but one that produces a distorted impression of the data. Figure 3.5a is correct in the sense that the three-quarter high rule is part of the graph design. Figures 3.5b and 3.5c demonstrate what can happen if the X and Y axes are elongated: Figure 3.5b suggests a much more gradual change than is the impression conveyed by Figure 3.5c.

FIGURE 3.3

Components of the Cartesian Coordinate System

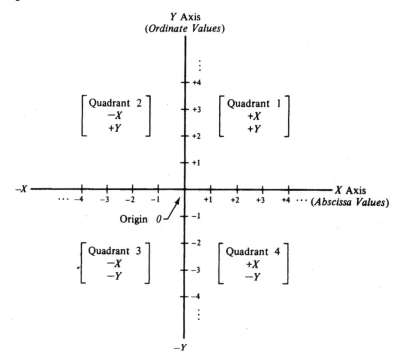

TYPES OF GRAPHS

There exists many different types of graphs and graphing techniques. We will concentrate on some of those more commonly used and will construct several different graphs for the data in Table 3.4. Ordinarily only a single technique would be employed, but by examining different graphic techniques for the same data a comparison of their assets and liabilities is encouraged. Graphing devices are important to the statistician because they are helpful in understanding the **shape** or **form** of a distribution of scores.

FIGURE 3.4*

Government Payrolls Up or Stable?

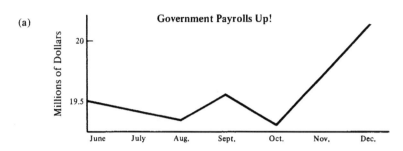

(a)

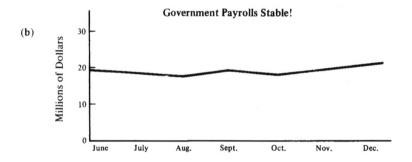

(b)

*Reprinted from Darrell Huff, HOW TO LIE WITH STATISTICS (New York: W. W. Norton and Company, Inc., 1954): copyright (c) 1954 by Darrell Huff, Reprinted by permission of author and W. W. Norton and Company, Inc.

Frequency and Percentage Polygons

A **frequency polygon** is a visual depiction of a frequency distribution. In constructing one, assumption 2 is made about the distribution of scores within the class intervals. It is customary to place the *frequency values* (designated *f*) along the *Y* axis and the *midpoints* of all class intervals along the *X* axis. Look at Figure 3.6. We place our frequencies beginning with 0 (where the two axes intersect) along the vertical axis. How do we know how many frequencies to list? We refer back to the original frequency distribution—Table 3.4—and see that the maximum frequency is 24 (see interval 49–51). This is the key to how many frequencies we will list. Notice that a frequency of 26 has been added even though there is no interval that has a frequency that corresponds to it. This is often done to provide the reader with a better overall perspective of the distribution of scores. We place the midpoints of each class interval along the horizontal axis beginning with the lowest, in this case

FIGURE 3.5

Hypothetical Data Illustrating Distortion in Graphing

Raw Data	
Scores	Frequency
15	2
14	2
13	1
12	1
11	3
10	4

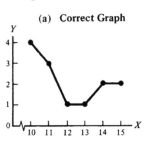

(a) Correct Graph

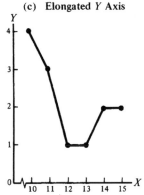

(c) Elongated *Y* Axis

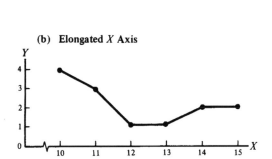

(b) Elongated *X* Axis

31–33, and ending with the highest (64–66). To complete the graph we extend the straight line to the base of the abscissa by locating an interval above and below our data. Sometimes the graph is broken with a swiggly mark (⸮ or ‖ or Ƨ). This indicates that the graph did not begin at zero (see abscissa in Figure 3.6). Since we employ assumption 2 in constructing a frequency polygon we place a dot *above the midpoint of each interval,* the dot located in terms of the *frequency* of occurrence of the scores in that interval, and connect all points with a straight line. In short, the *f* and midpoint are coordinated. When the frequency polygon is correctly—and neatly—constructed and labeled we have a visual image of the frequency distribution.

Instead of plotting the *frequencies* of each class interval, it is often desirable to plot the *percentage* of cases in the respective intervals. That is, the % and midpoint are coordinated. In doing this a **percentage polygon** is constructed. Figure 3.7 is a percentage polygon for the data in Table 3.4. The only change in the graph construction is that percents are placed along the ordinate. Again, dots are placed above each class interval's midpoint corresponding to the *percent* of cases in the respective intervals and the dots are connected by straight lines. The purpose of graph construction, again, is to make it easier to think about our data and see the shape or form of the data distribution.

FIGURE 3.6

Frequency Polygon

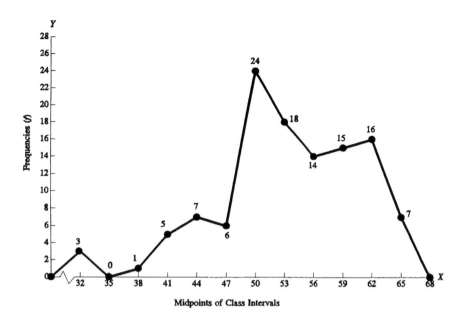

Midpoints of Class Intervals

Frequency and Percentage Histograms

Some equate a **histogram** and a **bar graph** whereas technically the histogram is appropriate for continuous data and the bar graph for discrete data. We will distinguish the two on these grounds. A histogram is a graph particularly useful for continuous variables since the columns are not separated and this highlights their underlying scale continuity. With interval/ratio variables histograms are most appropriate. On the other hand, with nominal variables the bar chart or bar graph should be used since the categories of the variable are separate and distinct. Technically, because there is no underlying scale continuity with nominal variables, the bars should not be contiguous. With ordinal variables a histogram may be employed but the categories should be arranged in their naturally occurring order with, ideally, the bars separated.

A **frequency histogram** is a graph in which the frequencies (f) are represented by areas in the form of bars. It differs from the frequency polygon in that it is constructed using assumption 1. Whereas the frequency polygon plots points above the midpoints of the class intervals, the histogram takes the *exact limits* (both upper and lower) into account. In Figure 3.8 you can see that bars or rectangles including the exact limits of the class intervals are constructed to correspond with the frequency of cases in the various intervals. It provides us with a picture of our data, a picture similar to that of the frequency polygon.

Instead of constructing a frequency histogram we may construct a **percentage histogram**. Figure 3.9 is a percentage histogram for the data in Table 3.4. The only change is that percents are placed along the ordinate. Again, rectangles including the exact limits of the class intervals are used.

FIGURE 3.7

Percentage Polygon

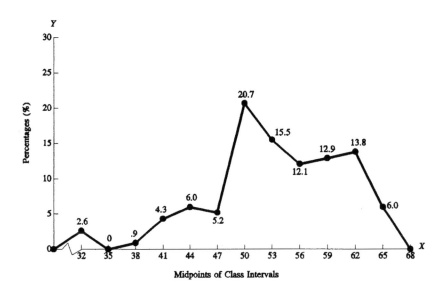

CUMULATIVE FREQUENCY AND CUMULATIVE PERCENTAGE
DISTRIBUTIONS AND THEIR GRAPHIC REPRESENTATION

Sometimes we are interested in the number (or percentage) of cases that are "greater than" or "less than" a specified value. (Remember that in a grouped frequency distribution our concern was with the frequencies *within* various class intervals per se.) This information can be readily obtained by preparing a **cumulative frequency distribution** through a process known as **cumulation**. The cumulative frequencies—designated by the uppercase "F" in Table 3.4—are obtained by adding

FIGURE 3.8

Frequency Histogram

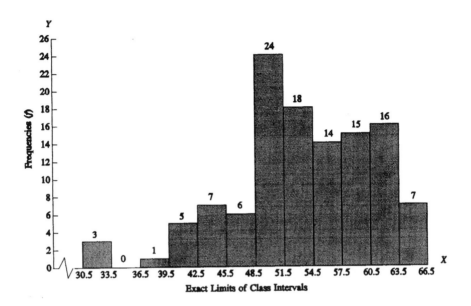

successively the individual class interval frequencies as indicated by the arrows in columns two and three of Table 3.4. In Table 3.4 we say that 78 cases fall below the upper exact limit of the class interval 55–57. That is 78 of the 116 cases fall below a score of 57.5. Similarly, 93 cases fall below a score of 60.5. When scores are arrayed from largest to smallest this interpretation holds. Cumulative frequencies are used in constructing ogives and in calculating certain statistics, for example the median and various fractiles.

Just as it is possible to convert a frequency distribution into a percentage distribution, it is possible to convert a cumulative frequency distribution into a **cumulative percentage distribution.** The procedure for doing this is to divide the *cumulative frequency* for the respective class intervals by N and multiply each result by 100 or by successively summing the individual class interval percentages as is illustrated with the use of arrows in the columns four and five of Table 3.4. To illustrate see Table 3.4. The cum % column represents a cumulative percentage distribution. The cumulative percentage of class interval 40–42 is obtained by dividing the cumulative frequency 9 by 116 and multiplying by 100 or [9/116](100) equals 7.8. Similarly, the cumulative percentage of class interval 52–54 is calculated by dividing 64 (cumulative frequency) by 116 (total number of observations) and multiplying by 100 to get rid of the decimal. This procedure is followed for all class intervals and enables one to say that, for example, 55.2 percent of the exam scores fell below a score of 54.5 or 80.2 percent of exam scores fell below a score of 60.5. As a check be sure that the last class interval (highest category) has N (in this case 116) and 100 percent entered adjacent to it. These cumulative percentages will be used in constructing a cumulative percentage polygon.

FIGURE 3.9

Percentage Histogram

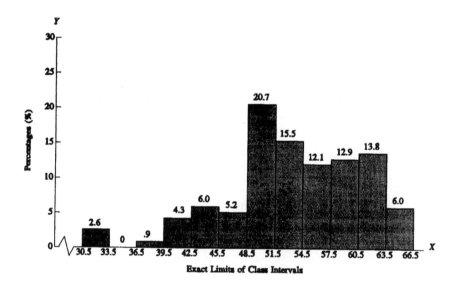

Exact Limits of Class Intervals

Cumulative Frequency and Cumulative Percentage Polygons (Ogives)

A **cumulative frequency polygon,** sometimes called an **ogive** or a **distribution curve,** is to a cumulative frequency distribution what a frequency polygon is to a frequency distribution. A cumulative frequency polygon graphically depicts the distribution of scores in a cumulative frequency distribution. Aside from the analogy, the ogive differs from the frequency polygon in a couple of respects. Instead of plotting points (or dots) corresponding to frequencies, we plot points corresponding to *cumulative* frequencies. Secondly, instead of placing the dots above the midpoints of the corresponding intervals, we plot dots at the *upper exact limits* of the corresponding intervals and then connect the dots with a straight line. A moment's reflection tells us what this permits us to do: at a glance, we can see, the number of cases above or below particular class intervals. The graph format remains identical to the frequency polygon except that along the Y axis we indicate cumulative frequencies (F) instead of frequencies (f) (see Figure 3.10). How do we know how many cumulative frequencies? Easy; the number of F's will correspond to the total number of observations. If the distribution of scores is "proper," then the ogive will take on an "S" shape, winding from the lower left to the upper right of the graph.

FIGURE 3.10

Cumulative Frequency Ogive

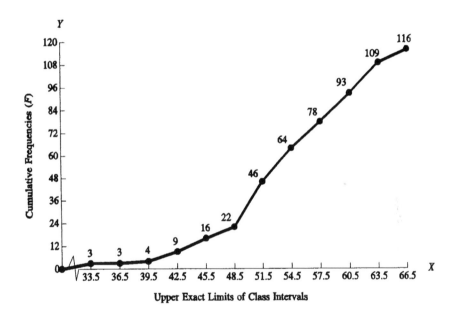

Instead of locating dots above the upper exact limits of the class intervals corresponding to cumulative frequencies we may place dots above the upper exact limits corresponding to *cumulative percents*. Figure 3.11 is a **cumulative percentage polygon (ogive)** for the data in Table 3.4. The only change is that the ordinate lists cumulative percents rather than cumulative frequencies. Once again, the purpose of an ogive is to facilitate our interpretation of the data.

FIGURE 3.11

Cumulative Percentage Ogive

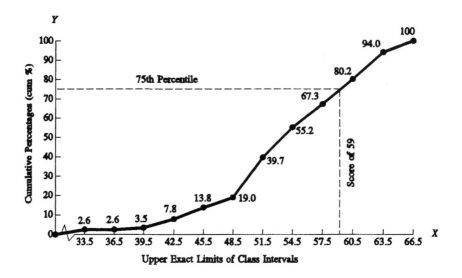

Line Graph

The **line graph** shows the values of a dependent variable for each category of another variable, usually but not always an independent variable. Time series analysis frequently uses this graphic technique as Figure 3.12 illustrates. Notice that in the example time (1995–2050) is represented on the abscissa and population increase in millions is plotted on the ordinate. Sometimes the line graph is referred to as a *trend line* because it deals with some phenomenon over a period of time. Figure 3.12 shows that the population will steadily increase and is projected to grow to about 392 million by 2050.

Stemplot

Another graphic technique for displaying data distributions is the *stemplot*. To construct a stemplot the scores are separated into two components: (1) a *stem* which consists of the leading digit(s) and (2) a *leaf*, the trailing digit. For the datum 33 in Table 3.1 the first digit, e.g., 3 is the stem; the second digit, 3, is the leaf. Whereas stems may have more than a single digit, leafs must only have a single digit. To facilitate constructing the stemplot, list the stems to the left of a vertical line and the leafs to the right of the line. Note, too, that both the leafs and stems are ordered. The completed stemplot for the data in Table 3.1 looks like this:

```
3 | 22
3 | 3
3 |
3 |
3 |
3 | 7
3 |
3 |
4 | 00
4 | 11
4 | 2
4 | 3333
4 |
4 | 555
4 | 66
4 | 77
4 | 88
4 | 99999999999
5 | 00000
5 | 11111111
5 | 2222222
5 | 333333333
5 | 44
5 | 55555
5 | 6666666
5 | 77
5 | 8888
5 | 9999
6 | 0000000
6 | 1111111
6 | 22222222
6 | 3
6 | 4444
6 | 5
6 | 66
```

A couple of variations that may be helpful in the construction of a stemplot include: (1) rounding the data so that the final digit can be treated as a leaf, e.g., 17.17 = 17.2, 88.34 = 88.3, etc. and (2) splitting the stems to avoid a confounding number of leafs on a given stem. Leafs between 0 and 4 could be located on one stem and leafs 5 to 9 on another. Both these variations are dependent on the researcher's decisions and are not absolute.

Using the split stem approach for the data in Table 3.1 produces the following stemplot:

```
3 | 223
3 | 7
4 | 001123333
4 | 5556677889999999999
5 | 00000111111112222222233333333344
5 | 55555666666667788889999
6 | 000000011111111222222234444
6 | 566
```

Notice in this approach the data are more compact and enable one to more easily determine the form of the data distribution.

A stemplot resembles a histogram turned on end. The length of each line corresponds to the number of cases in that category. The advantages of this graphic technique are that it: (1) records the actual values, (2) is fairly quick and easy to construct, and (3) presents the data in more detail (that is, avoids some of the problems associated with grouping). Its major disadvantage is that it is cumbersome with large data sets and therefore is best to use when the number of observations is small.

OTHER TYPES OF GRAPHS

The various frequency distributions and graphic techniques discussed above are most appropriate for interval/ratio level data. We will now consider some graphing techniques appropriate for ordinal and nominal level variables.

FIGURE 3.12
Line Graph Illustrating Population Growth in United States

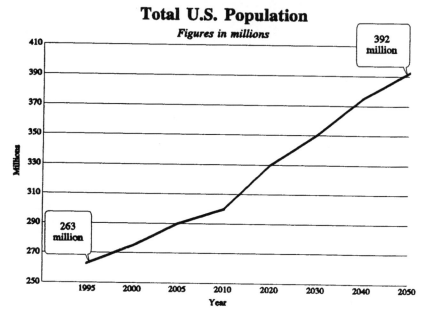

Bar Graph

Let us assume we've randomly selected 159 students from a university and asked them to identify the subculture (academic, collegiate, nonconformist, and vocational) to which they belong. Assume 42 percent said academic, 35 percent said collegiate, 14 percent said nonconformist, and 9 percent said vocational. We can depict this distribution of student subculture types using either the actual numbers or percentages. Let's use percentages. Along the ordinate place the subculture type and along the abscissa locate the percentages, equally spaced. If we did this we would have the **bar graph** shown in Figure 3.13. Note that in a bar graph the abscissa and ordinate entries can be reversed. The student subculture type could appear along the horizontal axis and the percentage of each type along the vertical axis. Were we to do this Figure 3.14 would emerge. Both of the bar graphs in Figures 3.13 and 3.14 are technically correct and, usually, only one would be constructed. Notice that the bars are separated—no order is assumed in the construction of nominal level variables—rather than contiguous so that the impression of an underlying scale continuity is avoided.

FIGURE 3.13
Bar Graph Illustrating Percentage Distributions of Subculture Types

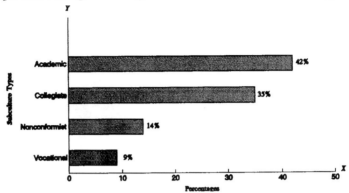

FIGURE 3.14
Bar Graph Illustrating Percentage Distributions of Subculture Types

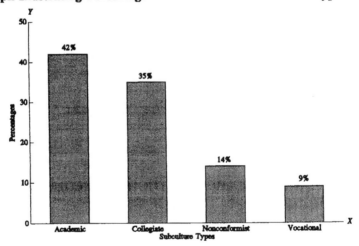

Pie Diagram

The **pie diagram** is a device frequently found in the media and is relatively easy to interpret. The total pie is equal to *N* (the total number of observations under consideration) or 100 percent and it is "sliced up" or divided into proportional segments to portray where the different pieces go or the contribution a given segment makes to the total. The projected population by race (in percents) in 2050 is White (52.5), Hispanic (22.5), Black (14.4), Asian (9.7), and American Indian (.9) Let us create a pie diagram, Figure 3.15, for this distribution.

FIGURE 3.15
Percentage Population by Race in 2050

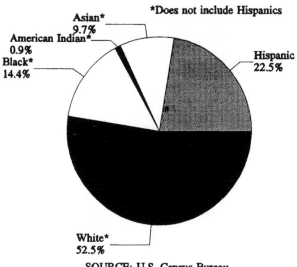

SOURCE: U.S. Census Bureau

HOW THE GRAPHIC REPRESENTATION OF FREQUENCY DISTRIBUTIONS DIFFER: TYPES OF CURVES

Frequency distributions and their graphic representations differ in several respects. Four of these important properties will now be discussed. These four dimensions convey a great deal about the distribution of any particular set of scores, and separate chapters will be devoted to the first two properties.

1.   Central Tendency

The **central tendency,** sometimes referred to as **central location,** is defined as the value of the variable(s) near the center of the distribution of scores. It is loosely called the *typical score* or *middlepoint.* Measures of central tendency are generically called **averages**. There are different averages, for example, mean, median, mode, for different levels of measurement, for example, interval/ratio, ordinal, and nominal, respectively. Figure 3.16 displays three frequency polygons that differ in terms of central location.

2. Dispersion

The **dispersion** of frequency distributions tells us how much or how little the scores cluster about the central value, that is, it gives us an idea of the spread or dispersion in a distribution. Statistics of this genre are termed *measures of dispersion* or *measures of variation*. There are different measures of dispersion, for example, index of qualitative variation, interquartile range, standard deviation, for different levels of measurement. When combined with measures of central tendency they give us a fuller picture of the major statistical characteristics of the distribution of scores. Figure 3.17 graphically depicts three frequency distributions that are the same in central location but differ in terms of variation. Note that if the values cluster close to the center, as in curve *A*, there is little variability, and if they spread out, as in curve *C*, there is a relatively large amount of variability.

3. Skewness

Skewness refers to the asymmetry of the graphic portrayal of a frequency distribution. There are two basic types of skewness: (1) **positively skewed distributions**—see *A* in Figure 3.18—in which the distribution is asymmetrical and the larger frequencies tend to concentrate at the bottom end (far left) of the scale and the smaller frequencies at the top end (far right), and (2) **negatively skewed distributions**—see *C* in Figure 3.18—in which the larger frequencies tend to concentrate at the right side and the smaller frequencies at the left side of the graph. The reference point for determining the skewness of scores is the normal curve—see *B* in Figure 3.18—which is symmetrical, that is, there's no skew to it. An aid to determining the *direction* of skewness is that it is the longer *tail* of the curve which determines the type and not the location where the scores concentrate. This "aid" conforms with the mathematicians' practice of calling the right end of the number line "positive" and the left "negative."

4. Kurtosis

Kurtosis refers to the "flatness" or "peakedness" of one distribution in relation to another. The reference point, as in skewness, is the normal curve which is technically referred to as **mesokurtic** (see *A* in Figure 3.19). If a curve is more peaked than the standard, it is called **leptokurtic** (see *C* in Figure 3.19); if less peaked or flatter than the standard, it's called **platykurtic** (see *B* in Figure 3.19).

FIGURE 3.16

Three Frequency Polygons with Different Averages

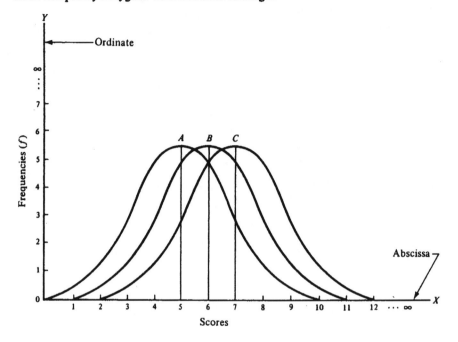

FIGURE 3.17

Three Frequency Polygons with Different Dispersions

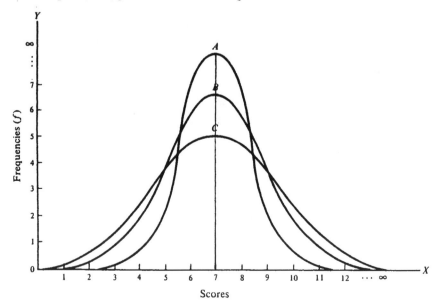

FIGURE 3.18

Three Frequency Polygons Differing in Skewness

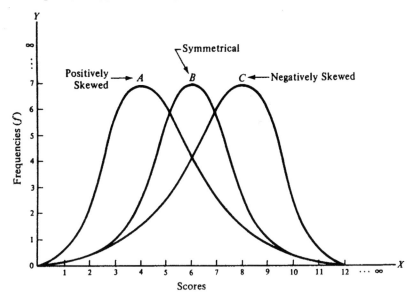

FIGURE 3.19

Three Frequency Polygons Differing in Kurtosis

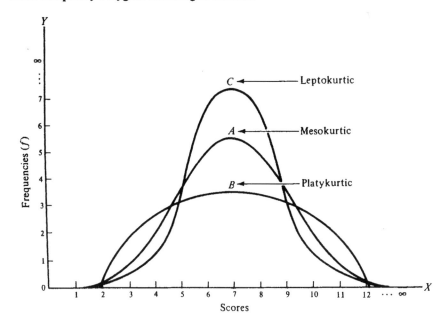

SUMMARY

In this chapter we've talked about the construction of frequency and cumulative frequency distributions and percentage and cumulative percentage distributions as well as graphs that represent these distributions. Some of the commonly used graphs discussed were the frequency (and percentage) polygon, cumulative frequency (and cumulative percentage) polygon (ogive), histogram, line graph, stemplot, bar graph, and pie diagram.

Four important properties of frequency distributions were discussed: namely, 1) central tendency, 2) dispersion, 3) skewness, and 4) kurtosis. Each of these dimensions was graphically portrayed in a series of diagrams.

IMPORTANT CONCEPTS DISCUSSED IN THIS CHAPTER

Frequency distribution

Rank order distribution (array)

Ungrouped frequency distribution

Frequency

Grouped frequency distribution

Range

Class interval

Percentage distribution

Continuous data

Discrete data

Exact limits

Stated limits

Midpoint

Graph

Cartesian coordinate system

Vertical axis (Y)

Ordinate values

Horizontal axis (X)

Abscissa values

Three-quarter high rule

Shape or form
  (of a distribution)

Frequency polygon

Percentage polygon

Frequency histogram

Percentage histogram

Cumulative percentage distribution

Cumulative frequency distribution

Cumulation

Cumulative frequency polygon (ogive or distribution curve)

Cumulative percentage polygon (ogive)

Line graph

Bar graph

Pie diagram

Central tendency (central location)	Kurtosis
Averages	Mesokurtic
Dispersion	Leptokurtic
Skewness	Platykurtic
Positively skewed distributions	Stemplot
Grouping error	Number line
Negatively skewed distributions	

REVIEW QUESTIONS

1. Social psychologists often develop data-gathering instruments to measure attitudes toward different social objects. Below are hypothetical cultural diversity scores for a sample of 100 university students. Your objective is to present these data in a more meaningful and understandable way.

127	123	115	120	98	115	120	121	105	110
134	109	81	89	108	85	150	109	124	128
110	118	97	107	119	127	126	119	113	145
124	148	119	90	130	111	115	103	123	131
112	112	101	124	142	135	104	122	138	116
138	129	122	114	118	95	107	112	80	103
119	117	106	98	99	106	114	125	118	146
94	136	113	121	120	101	133	94	126	114
125	83	104	100	154	92	112	109	130	120
116	127	101	109	88	140	102	115	141	132

   a. Construct a grouped frequency distribution for these data using 80–84 as the lowest class interval and indicate the midpoint of each interval.
   b. Construct a stemplot for these data using the split stem approach.

2. Suppose you wish to present this information to a lay audience. One way of making the data easier to grasp is to construct various graphs.
   a. Prepare a frequency polygon for these data.
   b. Prepare a frequency histogram for these data.

3. Instead of working with the frequencies you wish to present cumulative frequency information.
   a. Construct a cumulative frequency polygon (ogive) for the data in question 1.

4. Sometimes it is helpful to convert frequency data into percentages.
   a. Prepare a percentage polygon.

b. Construct a percentage histogram.

c. Prepare a cumulative percentage polygon (ogive).

5. For the data below perform the following operations:

Class Interval (i)	Frequency (f)	Cumulative Frequency (F)	Percent (%)	Cumulative Percentages (cum %)	Lower and Upper Exact Limits	Midpoints (m)
76–80	2					
71–75	2					
66–70	4					
61–65	5					
56–60	8					
51–55	10					
46–50	10					
41–45	11					
36–40	9					
31–35	6					
26–30	7					
21–25	4					
16–20	5					
11–15	2					
	$N = 85$					

a. How many score units wide are the class intervals?

b. Add a cumulative frequency column.

c. Add a percentage distribution column.

d. Add a cumulative percentage column.

e. Indicate the upper and lower exact limits of all intervals.

f. Indicate the midpoints of all intervals.

6. Using the data in question 5 above, construct a—

a. Frequency polygon.

b. Percentage polygon.

c. Cumulative frequency polygon (ogive).

d. Cumulative percentage polygon (ogive).

e. Frequency histogram.

f. Percentage histogram.

7. Sociologists have suggested that the American class structure can be divided into six categories—capitalist, upper middle, lower middle, working class, working poor, and under class—with 1 percent, 14 percent, 30 percent, 30 percent, 22 percent and 3 percent of Americans in these respective categories. Display these data using the bar graph and pie diagram.

*

CHAPTER **4**

MEASURES OF CENTRAL TENDENCY

Statisticians have observed several important properties of frequency distributions and have devised quantitative methods for describing them. Three of these features are: (1) *central tendency* or the clustering of scores around some central value, (2) *variation* or the dispersion of the scores about the center point, and (3) *form* or *shape* which refers to the kurtosis and symmetry or skewness of a frequency distribution.[1] Mathematically, these characteristics of frequency distributions can be summarized quantitatively by employing *index numbers*. An index number is a quantity derived from a series of statistical observations and used as an indicator of some condition or property like central tendency and variability. In this chapter our interest will be confined to computing measures of central tendency, in the next chapter measures of dispersion will be explored, and in chapter 6 form or shape.

An important goal of statistical analysis is to enable us to make quantitative statements about our data. While a frequency distribution represents an organization of data and a graph represents the data pictorially, both are somewhat limited in making quantitative statements about the distribution of scores or in the comparison of two or more distributions. Our ability to make quantitative statements about the data is facilitated by the calculation of **measures of central tendency (typicality** or **central location)**. Furthermore, such indices as central tendency and dispersion are consistent with the data reduction function of statistics in which a group of numbers can be represented by a much smaller set of numerical measures.

---

[1] The discussion of skewness and kurtosis will be limited to verbal descriptions. However, summary quantitative measures of skewness and kurtosis can be computed. For coverage of computational procedures for skewness, sometimes called beta-one (β_1), and kurtosis, sometimes called beta-two (β_2), see Norusis (1995).

Measures of central tendency are commonly called **averages**. This latter nomenclature, as we will see, is problematic. Since there are different kinds of averages, it is possible to "lie" with statistics by choosing the one that best suits your vested interests. The advertising industry is fond of this technique. To highlight the ambiguity of the concept "average," consider the following hypothetical episode. The CEO (chief executive officer) of a large corporation proudly reports at the company's annual awards banquet that the average salary supplement of the firm's top salespeople is $14,615. One salesperson disputes this claim and charges that the average bonus was only $5,000. To clear up this inconsistency the company commissions a statistician to examine the data and the statistician confidently asserts that the average supplement is $8,000.

Who is lying? The fact of the matter is that no one is lying. The truth is that all three parties were using a *different* measure of central tendency or a different average. To unfold the dilemma consider the frequency distribution appearing in Table 4.1. The **arithmetic mean** is the sum of all values divided by thirteen, hence, $190,000 \div 13 = \$14,615.38$. The **median** is a positional average obtained by locating the middle score, for example,

(1)	(2)	(3)	(4)	(5)	(6)	(7)
$5,000	$5,000	$5,000	$5,000	$5,000	$5,000	$8,000

(8)	(9)	(10)	(11)	(12)	(13)
$8,000	$10,000	$17,000	$17,000	$50,000	$50,000

With thirteen scores we count up to the seventh score and that score is the median, in this case, $8,000. The score that occurs most often is the **mode**, and in this example the mode is $5,000. There is even a fourth measure of central tendency, the *midrange*. It is the average of the maximum and minimum. Here, the midrange value would be $27,500 or $5,000 + $50,000 divided by 2. Even though none of the parties deliberately lied, your understanding that averages come in different varieties will protect you from deceit and will enable you to become a more astute interpreter of statistical information.

This chapter will be organized in two ways: (1) in terms of the most appropriate measure(s) of central tendency at the different levels of measurement (see Figure 4.1), and (2) in terms of whether the data are grouped or ungrouped. This chapter is organized in such a fashion that upon completing it, Figure 4.1 will make intuitive sense.

A NOMINAL MEASURE OF CENTRAL TENDENCY

Mode *(Mo)*

At this level of measurement, alternatives to the mode are nonexistent. With nominal level data, the **mode**, defined as *the most frequently occurring score, category, or value*, is the most appropriate measure of typicality.

TABLE 4.1

Hypothetical Salary Supplements of Thirteen Salespeople

Salary Supplement	Frequency
$50,000	2
17,000	2
10,000	1
8,000	2
5,000	6
	N = 13

FIGURE 4.1

Measures of Central Tendency by Levels of Measurement

Appropriate Statistical Technique	Levels of Measurement		
	Nominal	Ordinal	Interval/Ratio
Measures of central tendency	Mode	Median	Arithmetic mean Geometric mean Harmonic mean

Mode (Mo$_U$) for Ungrouped Data. Ungrouped data are those in which class intervals have not been employed; instead, a listing of the raw scores or values is all that is available. Let us assume that we have selected 100 persons on the street and have asked them to indicate their religious affiliation (in terms of Protestantism, Catholicism, and Judaism). Sixty-six indicate they are Protestants, 30 indicate they are Catholic, and 4 indicate they are Jewish. What is the mode for these data? Since the mode is defined as the most frequently occurring category, in this case Protestantism (frequency = 66) is the *modal category.* In this hypothetical survey if 45 passersby had indicated their religious affiliation as Protestant and 45 had indicated their religious affiliation as Catholic, we would have had a *bimodal* distribution, that is, there would have been two categories that had equally large frequencies. It is possible to have *trimodal* and even *multimodal* distributions. A convention adopted by statisticians is to mention any category that comes within 5 percentage points of the actual mode.

Mode (Mo$_G$) for Grouped Data. Grouped data are those in which the scores have been collapsed into class intervals. With grouped data, the mode is defined as *the midpoint of the interval with the largest frequency,* that is, the center of the most frequently occurring class interval. In Table 4.2 the mode is 50 (the midpoint of the class interval with the exact limits of 48.5 to 51.5).

TABLE 4.2

Grouped Frequency Distribution of Exam Scores from Table 3.1

Class Interval (i)	Midpoints (m)	Frequency (f)	x'	fm	fx'	Cumulative Frequencies (F)
64–66	65	7	+5	455	35	116
61–63	62	16	+4	992	64	109
58–60	59	15	+3	885	45	93
55–57	56	14	+2	784	28	78
52–54*	53	18	+1	954	18	64
49–51†	50	24	0	1,200	0	46
46–48	47	6	−1	282	−6	22
43–45	44	7	−2	308	−14	16
40–42	41	5	−3	205	−15	9
37–39	38	1	−4	38	−4	4
34–36	35	0	−5	0	0	3
31–33	32	3	−6	96	−18	3
Total (N) = 116				$\Sigma = 6{,}199$	$\Sigma = 133$	

*Interval within which N/2 case falls.
†Modal category.

The modes calculated for both ungrouped and grouped data above are termed *crude modes* in contrast to a more *refined mode* which is computed in formula (4.1):

$$\text{refined mode}_G = L + \left[\frac{D_1}{D_1 + D_2} \right] i \tag{4.1}$$

where: L = lower exact limit of class interval containing mode
D_1 = the difference between the frequency of the modal class interval and the frequency of the class interval *below* the modal category
D_2 = the difference between the frequency of the modal class interval and the frequency of the class interval *above* the modal category
i = width of class interval

Substituting the data in Table 4.2 we compute the refined mode to be:

$$\text{refined mode} = 48.5 + \left[\frac{18}{18 + 6} \right] 3$$

$$= 48.5 + \left(\frac{18}{24}\right) 3$$
$$= 48.5 + (.75) \, 3$$
$$= 48.5 + 2.25$$
$$= 50.75$$

The refined mode *pulls* the modal value in the direction of the adjacent class interval with the greater frequency and, in our example, the refined mode is pulled toward the higher class interval with a frequency of 18 rather than toward the lower class interval with a frequency of 6.

AN ORDINAL MEASURE OF CENTRAL TENDENCY

Median (*Mdn* or *Md*)

With ordinal level data, the **median** is the most appropriate measure of typicality. It is defined as *the score in a distribution that divides the observation in the middle.* In other words, one-half of the observations lie above that point, one-half lie below it. Technically speaking, the median is a member of the *quartile statistics* family. Furthermore, it is a special percentile, the 50th.

The quartile statistics, better termed *quantile statistics* or *fractile measures*, are used to partition scores or values in a distribution. Included in this family are *percentiles* (which divide scores into 100 equal parts), *deciles* (which divide scores into 10 equal parts), and *quartiles* (which divide scores into 4 equal parts). This family of statistics may be used to determine the relative position of any given value in an array and is important for a couple of reasons: (1) fractiles are standardized measures of position independent of the metric system used or of the substantive type of data, and (2) they are independent of the shape or form of the distribution (Mueller, Schuessler, and Costner, 1970: 127).

Median (Mdn$_U$) for Ungrouped Data. There are two general ungrouped data situations that you may confront: (1) an *odd* number of scores, and (2) an *even* number of scores. Consider the following number series:

$$80, \ 75, \ 60, \ 45, \ 18$$

With an odd number of scores arranged from largest, for example, 80, to smallest, for example, 18, the median is simply the middle score. (This process, as we have reported earlier, is known as creating an *array* or rank ordering of scores.) In this case 60 is the median. One-half the observations are below it while one-half are above it. Consider the following series:

$$80, \ 80, \ 80, \ 80, \ 80, \ 80, \ 15$$

Once again the median in an odd series is the middle score or 80 in the above example, or $(N + 1)/2 = (7 + 1)/2 = 4$, the fourth score in the array. In the formula $(N + 1)/2$, N refers to the number of scores and the 1 and 2 are constants. Consequently, using this formula for the first odd number series we would have $(5 + 1)/2 = 3$. The end result, "3," means to count up to the third score in the array and, in this case, the number 60, the median for these ungrouped data.

With an even number of scores the median is the arithmetic mean of the two adjacent middle scores. Consider the following numbers:

$$1, 2, 3, 4, 4, 5, 5, 6, 7, 8$$

The two middle scores are 4 and 5. The mean of 4 and $5 = 4.5$ or $9/2 = 4.5$.

In determining the median for ungrouped data it is absolutely essential that the scores be *arrayed*. Suppose we failed to arrange the scores from high to low (or vice versa) and we attempted to find the median for the three numbered series below:

(1) 75, 60, 18, 45, 80
(2) 80, 80, 80, 15, 80, 80, 80
(3) 1, 2, 3, 4, 7, 8, 5, 5, 6, 4

In series (1) the median is not 18 but 60; in series (2) the median is not 15 but 80; and in series (3) it is not 7.5 but 4.5.

Median (Mdn_G) for Grouped Data. Computing the median for grouped data involves several steps. Let us compute the median for the data in Table 4.2. The following steps are recommended:

1. Compute the *cumulative frequencies* by successively adding the individual class interval frequencies. Label this column F. For the median equation that follows, being with the smallest interval at the bottom of the table and end with the largest class interval at the top.

2. Determine one-half the number of scores by dividing N (total number of cases) by 2. This division provides us with the number of cases below the median score. In our example $N = 116$ and $116 \div 2 = 58$.

3. Find the class interval in which the middle case falls by looking at the F column and determine the *exact limits* of that interval. In our example the class interval in which the 58th case falls is 52–54 and the exact limits extend from 51.5 to 54.5.

4. *Interpolate*[2] to find a value on the scale above and below which one-half the total number of cases fall (if the cumulative frequency in a class interval exactly equals $N/2$, then the upper exact limit of that interval is the median value). To interpolate, computational formula (4.2) for the median is used:

$$Mdn_G = L + \left(\frac{\frac{N}{2} - F}{f}\right) i \quad or \quad L + \left[\frac{(N)(P) - F}{f}\right] i \quad (4.2)$$

where: L = the lower exact limit of the class interval containing median ($N/2$) case
N = total number of cases
F = cumulative frequency up to but *not* including the cumulative frequency of the class interval which contains the median ($N/2$) case
f = frequency of class interval containing median
i = width of class interval containing median
P = percentile of interest expressed as a proportion; in the case of the median P = .5

In our example the lower exact limit (L) of the interval containing the median is 51.5. The total number of cases is 116 and 116/2 or ($N/2$) = 58. The sum of all frequencies (F) below the lower exact limit of the interval containing the median is 46. The frequency (f) of the interval containing the median is 18. The width of the class interval (i) is 3 (52, 53, 54). Substituting these values into formula (4.2):

$$Mdn_G = 51.5 + \left[\frac{58 - 46}{18}\right] 3 = 53.51$$

The middle of our distribution, then, is 53.51. One-half the scores fall above 53.51 and one-half the scores fall below 53.51.

The median, as we've noted, is the 50th percentile. By making some minor modifications in formula (4.2) it is possible to compute any percentile, or fractile as we call it in the next section.

---

[2]*Interpolation*, sometimes called *intercalation*, is a process for ascertaining the equivalency of some unstated term inserted between two succeeding terms. In the case of the median we must interpolate to find a median value within the class interval containing the $N/2$ case on the assumption that cases are *evenly spread out* within that interval. With only minor revisions in formula (4.2) any fractile can be calculated. Sometimes the median or other fractiles are calculated on data that do not meet the assumption noted above. While there are occasions where this is done one must be cautious of the interpretation of the statistic in light of the mathematical infraction.

Computing Fractiles

Many of the standardized tests such as ACT, SAT, MCAT, DAT, GREs, and IQ measures report an individual's score in percentiles. *Percentiles* are probably the most common type of **fractiles**, this latter concept being a generic one implying a point on a measuring scale that divides the total set of scores into known proportions. In addition to percentiles, other fractiles in use are *deciles* (which divide a distribution into 10ths), *quintiles* (5ths), and *quartiles* (4ths). A fractile is a rank of a particular score that represents the percent of cases in a reference group that scored *at or below* the one cited.[3] For illustrative purposes, if one's scores on the verbal dimension of the GRE was recorded at the 80th percentile, this means that 80 percent of the reference group (perhaps all senior level college students) scored at or below the score under consideration.

There are two typical fractile questions frequently encountered. One is to find the raw score at a given percentile. The other is to find the percentile rank of a given raw score. Percentiles can be computed from a grouped frequency distribution, and we will now demonstrate the calculation of these two typical fractile questions.

Computing the Raw Score at a Given Percentile. Suppose we are interested in determining the score in Table 4.2 at the 75th percentile. Any percentile, including this one, can be computed by employing formula (4.3). The initial step is to determine (N) (P), then substitute the appropriate terms in a manner analogous to that of the median.

$$\text{score at selected percentile} = L + \left[\frac{(N)(P) - F}{f} \right] i \qquad (4.3)$$

where: L = the lower exact limit of the class interval containing the percentile score of interest

N = total number of cases

P = percentile of interest expressed as a proportion

F = cumulative frequency up to but *not* including the cumulative frequency of the class interval which contains the percentile of interest

f = frequency of class interval containing percentile of interest

i = width of class interval containing percentile of interest

Substituting our data into formula (4.3):

[3] Actually there are two different ways of defining the meaning of percentiles. A common interpretation is the *less than* one. The other definition is the *less than or equal to* approach. Take the hypothetical illustration of the score on the verbal component of the GREs that was at the 80th percentile. The former interpretation is that the particular score exceeded 80 percent of the reference group or that 80 percent of the scores were *less than* this one. The latter interpretation is that 80 percent of the scores were *less than or equal to* this one. It is helpful in interpreting percentiles to be cognizant of these nuances of meaning.

$$\text{score at selected percentile} = 57.5 + \left[\frac{116(.75) - 78}{15}\right]3$$

$$= 57.5 + \left(\frac{87 - 78}{15}\right)3$$

$$= 57.5 + \left(\frac{9}{15}\right)3$$

$$= 57.5 + (.6)\,3$$

$$= 57.5 + 1.8$$

$$= 59.3$$

The score at the 75th percentile in Table 4.2 is 59. This score is *interpreted* as follows: 75 percent of the class taking the examination made a score at or below 59. On the other hand, 25 percent of the class made a score above 59.

Computing the Percentile Rank of a Raw Score.   Let us now answer the second common query in dealing with percentiles. This is the reverse operation of computing the raw score at a selected percentile. To demonstrate the reversibility of these operations let us determine the percentile rank of a score of 59.3. Since we already know that a score of 59.3 is equivalent to the 75th percentile this counterpart transformation should provide a check on our first calculation. The following formula (4.4) is utilized. The primary step is to start substituting with the value of X_i.

$$\text{percentile of a selected raw score} = \frac{F + \left(\frac{X_i - L}{i}\right)f}{N} \times 100 \tag{4.4}$$

where: F = cumulative frequency up to but *not* including the class interval containing the raw score of interest
X_i = raw score whose percentile rank is to be computed
L = score at the lower exact limit of the class interval containing X_i
f = frequency of class interval containing X_i
i = width of class interval
N = total number of cases

Substituting our data into formula (4.4):

$$\text{percentile of a selected raw score} = \frac{78 + \left(\frac{59.3 - 57.5}{3}\right)15}{116} \times 100$$

$$= \frac{78 + \left(\frac{1.8}{3}\right)15}{116} \times 100$$

$$= \frac{78 + (.6)15}{116} \times 100$$

$$= \frac{78 + 9}{116} \times 100$$

$$= \frac{87}{116} \times 100$$

$$= .75 \times 100$$

$$= 75$$

The percentile rank of a score of 59 is the 75th, and this computation corroborates our earlier contention about the reversibility of formulas (4.3) and (4.4).

Notice that in the *cumulative percentage ogive (polygon)* constructed for these data in Chapter 3 (Figure 3.11) it is possible to determine the percentile rank of a score as well as the score at a given percentile rank merely by inspection. In other words, with a cumulative percentage polygon it would not be necessary to calculate the percentile rank of a score or the score at a percentile rank since both could be obtained by an examination of the graph. This is accomplished by extending a horizontal line from the 75th percent point on the ordinate to the ogive and then drawing a vertical line (perpendicular) to the abscissa where the scores are located. See Figure 3.11 for an illustration of this procedure.

INTERVAL/RATIO MEASURES OF CENTRAL TENDENCY

Arithmetic Mean ($\overline{X}$)

The most common measure of location for interval/ratio level data is the **arithmetic mean**. It is defined as *the sum of all scores in a distribution divided by the total number of cases.*

Arithmetic Mean ($\overline{X}_U$) for Ungrouped Data. Suppose we had the following five scores:

$$X_1, X_2, X_3, X_4, X_5, \ldots, X_N$$
$$10, 12, 15, 8, 20$$

The equation for the arithmetic mean for *ungrouped* scores, formula (4.5)[4], is:

$$\overline{X}_U = \frac{\Sigma X_i}{N} \tag{4.5}$$

[4] A more explicit notation for "ΣX_i" is "$\sum_{i=1}^{N} X_i$." The *subscript* "$i = 1$" means we begin adding with the first score, for example, $10 = X_1$, $12 = X_2$, $15 = X_3$, . . . , and $20 = X_N$; and the *superscript* "N" means we terminate adding after the last score. In summary "$\sum_{i=1}^{N} X_i$" means we sum all quantities X_1 through X_N (or $X_1 + X_2 + \ldots + X_N$). Refer to Appendix B for a review of the grammar of mathematical notation. The mean could also be computed: $\overline{X}_U = \frac{1}{N}\Sigma X_i$. For our example, $\frac{1}{5}(65) = 13$.

where: $\bar{X}$ = read "bar X" (the nearly universal symbol used to designate the
          arithmetic mean for a sample)[5]
          Σ = sum all quantities that follow (summation operator)
          X_i = any score in a distribution, for example, 10, 12, 15, 8, 20
          N = total number of cases

Substituting our values into formula (4.5)[6]:

$$\bar{X} = \frac{65}{5} = 13$$

The arithmetic mean for the ungrouped data is 13.

Arithmetic Mean ($\bar{X}_G$) for Grouped Data. Let us assume that we have the distribution of scores in Table 4.2 and are asked to compute the arithmetic mean. The following steps are recommended:

1. Calculate the *midpoints* of all class intervals. You will recall that the midpoint of a class interval is one convention used to represent all values within the interval. In Table 4.2 midpoints are noted by *m*.

2. Multiply each midpoint by the corresponding frequency of scores occurring in the interval. This procedure means that each class interval is weighted by its frequency of occurrence. In Table 4.2 *fm* designates this operation.

3. Sum the products of the midpoints multiplied by frequencies, Σfm.

4. Divide this sum by N (total) to obtain the arithmetic mean, $\Sigma fm/N$.

Let us systematically follow these steps for the data in Table 4.2. The first step is to calculate the midpoints for each class interval. Beginning at the bottom we have an interval 31–33. The midpoint is determined by adding one-half the width of the interval (in this case 3 ÷ 2 = 1.5) to the lower exact limit (in this case 30.5). Hence, 1.5 + 30.5 = 32 or the midpoint of the bottom interval. The second interval is 34–36. To the lower exact limit (in this case 33.5) we add one-half the width of the interval (in this case 1.5). Consequently, 33.5 + 1.5 = 35 or the midpoint for the interval 34–36. We proceed in this fashion until we've determined the midpoints for all intervals.

The second step is to multiply each midpoint by its corresponding frequency. The midpoint of the bottom interval is 32 and the frequency is 3; therefore, 32 × 3 = 96. The second interval has 35 as its midpoint and 0 as its frequency, therefore,

---

[5] Although *M* is sometimes used by statisticians. Note, too, $\bar{X}$=sample mean; μ = population mean.

[6] Earlier in this text (Chapter 1) we made a distinction between two important statistical concepts: (1) *parameter* and (2) *statistic*. You will recall that a parameter is a numerical characteristic of a universe designated by Greek letters and a statistic is a characteristic of a sample designated by Roman letters. The symbol for the mean of the population is μ (the Greek letter mu) and its sample counterpart is $\bar{X}$. Since, in most cases, we make computations from sample data we will use the notation appropriate for sample statistics. In inferential statistics we will use statistical notation for parameters and statistics and will explain then why, how, and when the distinction is important.

35 X 0 = 0. We proceed in this fashion until we have completed this operation for all class intervals.

The third step is to add together all of the computations in step two, that is, 96 + 0 + 38 + 205 + 308 + 282 + 1,200 + 954 + 784 + 885 + 992 + 455 = 6,199.

The final step is to divide this sum, 6,199, by the number of cases, 116. Hence, 6,199 ÷ 116 = 53.44.

The formula for these operations, formula (4.6), is:

$$\overline{X}_G = \frac{\Sigma fm}{N} \tag{4.6}$$

where: $\overline{X}$ = arithmetic mean.
  Σ = sum all quantities that follow (summation operator)
  f = frequency of class interval
  m = midpoint of class interval
  N = total number of cases

Substituting our data into formula (4.6):

$$\overline{X}_G = \frac{6,199}{116} = 53.44$$

Coding Method

The so-called "long method" for computing the arithmetic mean for grouped data can be shortened by using a coding operation. This latter procedure starts with an *arbitrary origin* or *reference point* and to ascending class intervals positive successive integers are attached and to the descending class intervals negative successive integers are attached. The "short method" will be illustrated for the data in Table 4.2. The steps are as follows:

1. Attach a zero in a column labeled x' (x prime) to any class interval. Although any class interval can be used, it is desirable to use one of the middle intervals since it will reduce the calculations that follow. It is the *midpoint* of the class interval that is the arbitrary origin, and this value will be used in formula (4.7).

2. To the ascending class intervals, for example, 52–54, 55–57, 58–60, 61–63, and 64–66, attach values of +1, +2, +3, +4, and +5. In general, affix *step deviations* of +1, . . . , +N for all *ascending* class intervals. To the descending class intervals, for example, 46–48, 43–45, 40–42, 37–39, 34–36, and 31–33, attach values of −1, −2, −3, −4, −5, and −6. In general, affix step deviations of −1, . . . , −N for all *descending* class intervals.

3. Find the products of the respective frequency times x' values and record these outcomes in an fx' column.

4. Sum the fx' column *algebraically* (see footnote 7) and substitute into formula (4.7).

$$\overline{X}_S = \text{midpoint} + \left[\frac{\Sigma fx'}{N} \right] i$$

where: $\bar{X}_s$ = arithmetic mean (short method using coding procedures)
$\Sigma fx'$ = sum of fx' products
N = total number of cases
i = width of class interval

Hence,

$$\bar{X}_s = 50 + \left(\frac{133}{116}\right) 3$$

$$= 50 + (1.15)\, 3$$

$$= 50 + 3.45$$

$$= 53.45$$

As we would expect, the short and long methods of computing the arithmetic mean for grouped data yield virtually identical values.

Mean of Combined Groups ($\bar{X}_w$): Averaging Means

Suppose that equivalent forms of a social psychology exam are administered to three different sections of the course. For simplicity's sake, assume that $\bar{X}_1 = 60$ (the mean of section 1), $\bar{X}_2 = 50$ (the mean of section 2), and $\bar{X}_3 = 40$ (the mean of section 3). Let us further assume that the number of students in each class varies, for example, $n_1 = 10$ (number of students in section 1), $n_2 = 60$ (number of students in section 2), and $n_3 = 30$ (number of students in section 3).

We want to know the overall mean for all groups combined. It may come as a surprise that the mean of combined groups *cannot* be determined by simply adding the individual means and dividing by the number of groups (assuming the groups are of *unequal* sizes). Since the number of students varies from one group to the next we must weight each section mean by the number of students in that section. The formula (4.8) for the mean of combined groups is:

$$\bar{X}_w = \frac{n_1\bar{X}_1 + n_2\bar{X}_2 + n_3\bar{X}_3 + \ldots + n_n\bar{X}_n}{N \text{ or } n_1 + n_2 + n_3 + \ldots + n_n} \qquad (4.8)$$

where: $\bar{X}_w$ = weighted mean (for combining groups)
n_1, n_2, n_3, n_n = number of subjects in groups 1, 2, 3, and n, respectively
$\bar{X}_1, \bar{X}_2, \bar{X}_3, \bar{X}_n$ = mean of groups 1, 2, 3, and n, respectively
$N = n_1 + n_2 + n_3 + n_n$ (all subjects considered)

Substituting our data into formula (4.8):

$$\bar{X}_w = \frac{10(60) + 60(50) + 30(40)}{10 + 60 + 30} = 48$$

Forty-eight is the mean of the three groups combined. In this example, had we simply added the three means (60 + 50 + 40) and divided by 3 we would have computed it to be 50.

If the groups are all *equal* in size, for example, $n_1 = n_2 = n_3 = n_n$, then the mean of combined groups *can* be computed by adding the individual means and dividing by the number of groups. For example, if we had the following data: $n_1 = 5$ and $\overline{X}_1 = 6$, $n_2 = 5$ and $\overline{X}_2 = 7$, and $n_3 = 5$ and $\overline{X}_3 = 8$, the mean of the three groups combined would be $6 + 7 + 8 \div 3$ or $21 \div 3 = 7$. Had we computed it the long way, the same answer would have resulted: $5(6) + 5(7) + 5(8)$ divided by $N(5 + 5 + 5) = (30 + 35 + 40)/15 = 105 \div 15 = 7$.

Some Important Properties of the Arithmetic Mean

The arithmetic mean belongs to a family of statistics used in advanced calculations. It is one of the *moment statistics*, and a brief discussion of the **moment system** is in order before proceeding.

The Moment System. When data are interval/ratio in nature it is often useful to describe them in terms of their balance around some central location. Average deviations (of scores from the mean) are traditionally referred to as *moments*, and an analogy can be drawn between the mean of a distribution of scores and the fulcrum of a seesaw when the seesaw is in a state of balance. The algebraic sum of the moments (on both sides) will produce a state of "balance" or equilibrium. A deviation score, sometimes called a **mean deviate**, is symbolized by x and is equal to:

$$x = X_i - \overline{X}$$

where: x = deviation score
X_i = any raw score in a distribution
$\overline{X}$ = mean of the distribution of scores

The moment system with which statisticians are generally concerned is comprised of four moments. The **first moment** (m_1) is the average of all deviations in a distribution from the mean of that distribution or:

$$m_1 = \frac{\Sigma(X_i - \overline{X})}{N} = \frac{\Sigma x}{N} = 0$$

Since the algebraic sum of deviations about the mean is always zero, the first moment is always zero, as will shortly be illustrated.

The **second moment** (m_2) is the average of the sum of the squares of the deviations from the mean and is called the variance, symbolized as:

$$m_2 = \frac{\Sigma(X_i - \overline{X})^2}{N} = \frac{\Sigma x^2}{N} = s^2$$

The **third** (m_3) and **fourth** (m_4) **moments** are the average of the third and fourth power (in mathematics *power* represents the product obtained by multiplying a quantity by itself a certain number of times, for example, the third power of 3 is 27 (3 × 3 × 3) and symbolized 3^3) of the deviations from the mean, or, respectively:

$$m_3 = \frac{\Sigma(X_i - \bar{X})^3}{N} = \frac{\Sigma x^3}{N}$$

and

$$m_4 = \frac{\Sigma(X_i - \bar{X})^4}{N} = \frac{\Sigma x^4}{N}$$

The third (m_3) and fourth (m_4) moments provide the statistician with a measure of skewness and kurtosis, respectively. The advantage of the moment system is two-fold: (1) even powers, as in m_2 and m_4, eliminate negative signs but, of course, odd powers, as in m_1 and m_3, do not; and (2) higher powers are more sensitive to extreme scores and will emphasize larger deviations from the mean (Loether and McTavish, 1993: 146–148).

With the moment system providing a backdrop, the two important properties of the mean should be more easily understood.

1. *Algebraically*[7], *the sum of the deviations of each score from the mean* (**sum of deviations from the mean**) *will always be zero.* Symbolically, $\Sigma(X_i - \bar{X}) = 0$. Let us illustrate why this is the case. Assume we have five scores: 5, 4, 3, 2, 1. The arithmetic mean is $\Sigma X_i/N = 15/5 = 3$. If we subtract the mean from each individual score, for example, (5 − 3 = 2), (4 − 3 = 1), (3 − 3 = 0), (2 − 3 = −1), (1 − 3 = −2), and sum these deviations, 0 results. So what? This suggests that the arithmetic mean is analogous to the fulcrum on a seesaw. It balances the scores on both sides but is sensitive to extreme scores, that is, it will be pulled toward the extremes, if they are not balanced on both sides. Algebraically this relationship can be proved as follows:

$$\begin{aligned} \Sigma(X_i - \bar{X}) &= \Sigma X_i - \Sigma \bar{X} \\ &= N\bar{X} - N\bar{X} \\ &= 0 \end{aligned}$$

Furthermore, since:

$$\bar{X} = \frac{\Sigma X_i}{N}$$

it follows that $\Sigma X_i = N\bar{X}$.

---

[7] This is an opportune time to distinguish between algebraic and absolute values. The magnitude of a number, disregarding its direction, is called its *absolute* (or *arithmetic* or *numerical*) value. The magnitude of a number with due regard to direction is termed its *algebraic* (or *directed* or *signed*) value.

The analogy between the mean and the fulcrum of a seesaw can be visualized in Figure 4.2. Using the data presented in Table 4.1 we employ stick figures, representing the number of persons with a given salary supplement, to construct a *pictograph* (figures representing a standard quantity).

FIGURE 4.2

The Mean as Analogous to the Fulcrum of a Seesaw

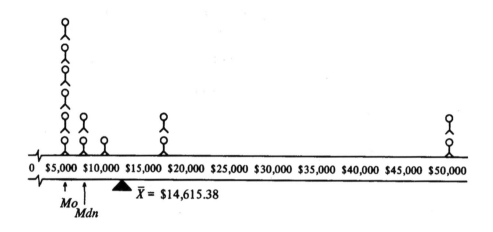

$$\bar{X} = \$14,615.38$$

Mo
  Mdn

TABLE 4.3

Illustration of Two Properties of the Mean

X_i	$\bar{X}$	$X_i - \bar{X}$	$X_i - 2$	$X_i - 4$	$(X_i - \bar{X})^2$	$(X_i - 2)^2$	$(X_i - 4)^2$
5	3	2	3	1	4	9	1
4	3	1	2	0	1	4	0
3	3	0	1	−1	0	1	1
2	3	−1	0	−2	1	0	4
1	3	−2	−1	−3	4	1	9
		$\Sigma = 0$	$\Sigma = 5$	$\Sigma = -5$	$\Sigma = 10$	$\Sigma = 15$	$\Sigma = 15$

$\Sigma(X_i - \bar{X}) = 0$

$\Sigma\left(\begin{array}{c}X_i- \text{any number other} \\ \text{than mean}\end{array}\right) \neq 0$

$\Sigma(X_i - \bar{X})^2 = \text{minimum}$

$\Sigma\left(\begin{array}{c}X_i-\text{any number other} \\ \text{than mean}\end{array}\right)^2 \neq \text{minimum}$

2. *The sum of the squared deviations of each score from the mean (***sum of squared deviations from the mean***) is less than the sum of the squared deviations*

about any other number. Symbolically, $\Sigma (X_i - \overline{X})^2$ = minimum. This is known in statistics as the **principle of least squares.** Let's prove this for our data: $5 - 3 = 2$ and $2^2 = 4$; $4 - 3 = 1$ and $1^2 = 1$; $3 - 3 = 0$ and $0^2 = 0$; $2 - 3 = -1$, and $-1^2 = 1$; $1 - 3 = -2$ and $-2^2 = 4$. Add them together: $4 + 1 + 0 + 1 + 4 = 10$. Try doing this for any number other than the mean and a sum larger than 10 will be produced. Again, so what? This important aspect of the mean is called the *least squares* property (it is that measure of central location which makes the sum of squared deviations around it minimal) and is of great theoretical importance in more sophisticated statistical computations. In addition, it is used in curve-fitting in regression analysis. Table 4.3 illustrates these two very important characteristics of the mean.

SPECIAL USE MEASURES OF CENTRAL TENDENCY

The Geometric and Harmonic Means (*GM* and *HM*)

Two less commonly used measures of central tendency are: (1) the **geometric mean,** defined as *the nth root of the product of a set of scores;* and (2) the **harmonic mean,** defined as *the reciprocal of the arithmetic mean of the reciprocals of the scores.* These measures of central tendency are not frequently found in the behavior sciences at the present time. The sociology subspecialty of demography sometimes has occasion to employ these statistical techniques.

The geometric mean (*GM*) is symbolized as follows:

$$GM = \sqrt[N]{(X_1)(X_2)(X_3)\ldots(X_N)}$$

To illustrate, the geometric mean of 18 and $2 = \sqrt[2]{(18)(2)} = \sqrt[2]{36} = 6$; the geometric mean of 3, 3, and $3 = \sqrt[3]{(3)(3)(3)} = \sqrt[3]{27} = 3$. This measure of typicality is used to average rates of change, assuming that such change has been constant. It cannot be used if any value is zero or negative.

Population analysts often use this mean to find the size of a city's population at the midpoint of a time interval. Suppose we wished to determine the population of Normal, Illinois, for the year 1995. The decennial census estimated it to be 50,000 in 1990 and 70,000 in 2000. To do this we may use the geometric mean:

$$
\begin{aligned}
GM &= \sqrt[2]{(50{,}000)(70{,}000)} \\
&= \sqrt[2]{3{,}500{,}000{,}000} \\
&= 59{,}161
\end{aligned}
$$

Assuming constant growth the population in the city would be calculated to be 59,161 in 1995.

The harmonic mean (*HM*) is symbolized as follows:

$$HM = \frac{1}{\frac{1}{N}\left(\frac{1}{X_1} + \frac{1}{X_2} + \ldots + \frac{1}{X_N}\right)} = \frac{N}{\sum\left(\frac{1}{X_i}\right)}$$

For example, the harmonic mean of 2, 5, and 10 = 1/2 + 1/5 + 1/10; the sum of the reciprocals is 8/10 or 4/5; the *HM* is 3.75. This measure of location is used in averaging ratios and rates as well as employing time as a variable.

COMPARING MEASURES OF CENTRAL TENDENCY AND DECIDING WHICH TO USE

In addition to the level of measurement of our variable(s), other criteria are used in deciding which measure is most appropriate. The *purpose of the statistic* is of major importance in the selection process. For example, if interest were in the size of a population at the midpoint of an interval of time, the geometric mean would be preferred over the other averages. A second criterion is the *shape or form of the distribution*. As a rule, with skewed distributions the median is typically the most appropriate measure of central tendency. Income, because of its skewed nature, ordinarily calls for the median because this statistic is not susceptible to the sensitivities of extreme scores (as is the case with the mean).

Each of these measures of central tendency has certain advantages and disadvantages. Although in practice it is common to compute only one, the one that is most appropriate for the data at hand, sometimes computing all three will add some interesting interpretive features to the data.

Advantages and Disadvantages of the Mode

The major advantages of the mode are its simplicity and the fact that it is the only average appropriate for qualitative variables. In a grouped frequency distribution the mode can be easily determined by finding the midpoint of the most frequently occurring class interval. In an ungrouped frequency distribution it is the score (category or value) that occurs most often. Because it is the most probable value it is sometimes called the *probability average*.

The major disadvantages of the mode are its instability and its inability to be manipulated algebraically. It is based on a single score (or category) only and is likely to fluctuate considerably from one sample to another. To illustrate the instability of the mode consider Table 4.4. In Table 4.4a the modal age is 2 (the age category that occurs most frequently) and 1½ in Table 4.4b (the midpoint of ages 1–2). This example serves to point out how a minor change in the data arrangement affects the determination of the crude mode.

TABLE 4.4

Illustration of the Instability of the Mode

(a)			(b)		
Ungrouped Ages of Kindergarten Children			Grouped Ages of Kindergarten Children		
Ages	Frequency			Ages	Frequency
5	2			5–6	2
4	1			3–4	3
3	2			1–2	4
2	3				$N = 9$
1	1				
	$N = 9$				

Advantages and Disadvantages of the Median

The major advantage of the median is that, being a *positional average*—that is, it doesn't depend on the true numerical values of the scores—it lends itself to use with skewed distributions. When data are negatively or positively skewed, the median should be used because the mean is sensitive to the nature of the skewness (see properties of the arithmetic mean discussion). To illustrate suppose ten individuals made the following contributions to the United Fund:

Individual	Contribution
1	$10.00
2	.10
3	.10
4	.10
5	.10
6	.05
7	.05
8	.05
9	.05
10	.05
	$\Sigma = \$10.65$

The mode, median, and mean for these data are $0.05, $0.075, and $1.065, respectively. Notice that of the three measures of central tendency, the mean is most affected by the single extreme score ($10.00), that is, the mean is affected by the skewness of the data. On the other hand, the median, a positional measure, for an even number of values is the mean of the two middle scores or $.10 + $.05 =

$0.15 ÷ 2 = $0.075. The most frequently occurring value, $0.05, is the mode. For these data, the median and the mode are more representative of the average contribution than the mean is. Comparing each average (mode, median, mean) with the data permits us to choose the best one. This practice should be encouraged.

The major disadvantage of the median is that it is based on one score—the middle score only. Furthermore, it does not readily lend itself to use in inferential statistics because it cannot be algebraically manipulated.

Advantages and Disadvantages of the Mean

All things being equal, the mean is the most desirable measure of central tendency for several reasons. First of all, it uses all the information in a distribution whereas the median and mode use only the score of the middle case (median) or the most frequently occurring one (mode). Second, it is more easily manipulated algebraically, for example, in averaging several means. Third, it provides the basis for many calculations in inferential statistics.

The major disadvantage of the mean is the affect a skewed distribution has on the computed value. It may be helpful to demonstrate this feature of the arithmetic mean in relation to the median and mode. Figure 4.3 illustrates this relationship. Notice that, of the three measures of central tendency, the mean is most influenced by the skewed nature of the distribution, that is, it is *pulled* in the direction of the skew. On the other hand, the mode is located at the peak of the curve and the median occupies a position in-between the mode and arithmetic mean. Finally, in a symmetrical distribution the three indices of central tendency are identical in terms of their location.

FIGURE 4.3

The Relationships among the Mean, Median, and Mode in Skewed and Symmetrical Distributions

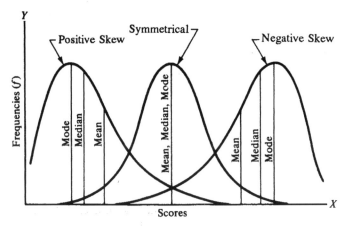

SUMMARY

In this chapter we have focused upon the computation, interpretation, advantages and disadvantages of the three most commonly used measures of central tendency. The mean, median, and mode are generally appropriate averages for interval/ratio, ordinal, and nominal data, respectively. However, for practical (ease of determination) and technical (skewness of distribution) reasons one should be flexible about the relationship between the level of measurement of the data and appropriate statistical techniques.

In addition, three less commonly used measures—weighted, geometric, and harmonic means—were mentioned along with an illustration of the calculation of each.

IMPORTANT CONCEPTS DISCUSSED IN THIS CHAPTER

Measures of central tendency (typicality, central location)

Averages

Arithmetic mean

Median

Mode

Fractiles

Mean of combined groups (weighted mean)

Moment system (m_1, m_2, m_3, m_4)

Mean deviate (x)

Sum of deviations from the mean

Sum of squared deviations from the mean (principle of least squares)

Geometric mean

Harmonic mean

Index numbers

Array

Midrange

REVIEW QUESTIONS

1. Assume you are interested in church attendance among the members of some Protestant denomination. You select a random sample of twenty persons from the official roll and ask each how many times he/she had been to a Sunday service during the last half year. You obtain the following hypothetical frequency counts of attendance.

10	26	14	11
12	20	13	0
4	18	12	8
6	17	2	10
7	15	10	9

a. Compute the arithmetic mean.
b. Compute the median.
c. Determine the mode.
d. Interpret the meaning of these different measures of central tendency.
e. Why are there differences among the three statistics?

2. A social psychology professor has three sections of introductory social psychology with 25,32, and 41 students in sections one, two, and three, respectively. Suppose the average score on the final exam is 47, 41, and 50 in sections one, two, and three, respectively. What is the average score for all sections combined?

3. The raw data in question 1 are organized into the following grouped frequency distribution.

Class Interval (i)	Frequency (f)
24–26	1
21–23	0
18–20	2
15–17	2
12–14	4
9–11	5
6–8	3
3–5	1
0–2	1
	$N = 20$

a. Calculate the arithmetic mean using:
   (1) The long method.
   (2) The short method (coding method).
b. Compute the median.
c. Determine the mode (refined and crude).
d. What differences are there between the raw score and grouped computations?
e. Why do such differences exist?

4. For the 100 original observations appearing in review question 1 in Chapter 3 compute the arithmetic mean.

5. For the grouped frequency distribution constructed in review question 1 in Chapter 3 compute the following:
a. Arithmetic mean.
b. Median.
c. Mode (crude).

6. What is the *HM* for 2, 4, & 8? What is the *GM* for 20 & 25?

CHAPTER 5

MEASURES OF DISPERSION

Measures of central tendency do not, in themselves, fully describe a frequency distribution. Although they locate the center of the distribution, they tell us nothing about how the scores are spread out or dispersed in relation to the center. To complement an average, a **measure of dispersion (variation, spread,** or **variability)** is essential. Let's say you have two distributions with 100 test scores in each, and both have a mean equal to 67. It's possible that distribution one has a small range, for example, highest score (H) equals 72 and lowest (L) equals 62, whereas distribution two has a large range, for example, $H = 107$ and $L = 25$. Without an idea of the variability in the two distributions one is likely to misinterpret the data. Or, to take a more mundane illustration, consider the dilemma of a basketball coach who has to decide on the player to occupy the fifth starting position. Suppose in the first five games of the season that two players have averaged 10 points per game. Player A has scored 8, 9, 10, 11, and 12 points in the first five games whereas player B has scored 2, 4, 10, 16, and 18 points in the same games. A measure of variability would be very important in this decision-making process even though the central tendency is identical.

Just as there are different kinds of averages (e.g., mode, median, mean, geometric mean, and harmonic mean), there are different *index numbers* of variation. This chapter, like the previous one, will be organized in two ways: (1) in terms of the most appropriate measure(s) of dispersion at the different levels of measurement, and (2) in terms of whether the data are grouped or ungrouped. Figure 5.1 provides the organizing scheme for this chapter.

FIGURE 5.1

Measures of Dispersion by Levels of Measurement

Appropriate Statistical Technique	Levels of Measurement		
	Nominal	Ordinal	Interval/Ratio
Measures of dispersion	Index of qualitative variation Index of dispersion	Interquartile range	Range Average deviation Standard deviation Variance Coefficient of variability

NOMINAL MEASURES OF DISPERSION

Nominal level measures of dispersion are techniques for *measuring* the variation of qualitative variables (attributes). Intuitively we know that the numbers assigned to attributes vis-à-vis the numbers inherent in interval/ratio variables are different. Whereas with interval/ratio data we deal with magnitudes, with nominal variables we count differences.

Imagine a fishbowl containing fifteen marbles. If all marbles are green no variation exists since the color of all marbles is the same. Similarly, if five marbles are green, five blue, and five red, maximum heterogeneity exists for the marble set. What this means is that the smaller the number of differences among a set of items, the more homogeneous is the set and the less the variation. Also, the larger the number of differences, the more heterogeneous is the set and the greater the variation. The index of qualitative variation and index of dispersion are based upon these principles.

Index of Qualitative Variation *(IQV)*

This nominal measure of dispersion (*IQV*) was derived by Mueller and Schuessler, two sociologists. It is a measure of the similarity (homogeneity) or dissimilarity (heterogeneity) in attribute data. The **index of qualitative variation** is defined as *the ratio of the total observed differences in attribute data to the maximum possible differences multiplied by 100.*

Let us examine the rationale for computing the ratio between the observed differences and the maximum possible differences in a set of data. To find the numerator, the total observed differences, a count of the differences between each item and every other item is calculated and then these values are summed. Computationally this means that the number of observations in each category is multiplied by the number of observations in every other category and these products are summed. To calculate the denominator of this ratio, the maximum possible differences, we norm on the maximum possible differences that could exist in a given data-set. This norming technique has the effect of controlling for the number of categories. To do this we imagine the total number of observations (N) to be evenly divided among the categories (K) of the variable. In other words, N/K provides the maximum differences in the respective categories. Formula (5.1) is as follows:

$$IQV = \frac{\text{total observed differences}}{\text{maximum possible differences}} \, (100)$$

$$= \frac{\Sigma \, n_i \, n_j}{\left[\dfrac{K(K-1)}{2}\right] \left[\dfrac{N}{K}\right]^2} \, (100) \qquad (5.1)$$

Assume you are interested in political sociology and want to know how much variation there is in students' political party affiliation. To accomplish your goal you randomly select 900 students and ask them to indicate their political party as either Republican, Democrat, or Independent. When the data are tallied you discover 200 students were Republican, 400 were Democrat, and 300 were Independent. You may use the index of qualitative variation to determine the degree of dispersion among students' political preferences. To do this the following steps are recommended:

1. Arrange the data in tabular form with two column headings: "Observed Frequencies" and "Maximum Possible Frequencies." This arrangement appears in Table 5.1.

TABLE 5.1

Table Arrangement for Computing *IQV*

Political Party Affiliation	Observed Frequencies	Maximum Possible Frequencies
Republican	200	300
Democrat	400	300
Independent	300	300
	$N = 900$	$N = 900$

2. To obtain the *total observed differences*, multiply the number of students observed in each category (political party affiliation) by the number of students in

every other category, for example, (200)(400) + (200)(300) + (400)(300), and sum the products. Doing this we have 80,000 + 60,000 + 120,000 = 260,000, which represents the total observed differences. Symbolically:

$$TOD = \Sigma n_i n_j$$

where: TOD = total observed differences
$\qquad$ n_i = the number of observations in the ith category
$\qquad$ n_j = the number of observations in the jth category
$\qquad$ Σ = summation operator

3. To obtain the *maximum possible differences* divide N (total number of observations) by the number of categories. This is done because it provides us with the maximum possible differences among the categories. Completing this operation, 900/3 = 300. The same multiplication-addition operation is performed for the column labeled "Maximum Possible Frequencies," hence (300)(300) + (300)(300) + (300)(300) = 270,000, which represents the maximum possible difference. Symbolically:

$$MPD = \left[\frac{K(K-1)}{2}\right]\left(\frac{N}{K}\right)^2$$

where: MPD = maximum possible differences
$\qquad$ K = number of categories of the variable
$\qquad$ N = total number of observations

Substituting our data:

$$MPD = \left[\frac{3(2)}{2}\right]\left(\frac{900}{3}\right)^2$$
$$= \frac{6}{2}(300)^2$$
$$= 3(90,000)$$
$$= 270,000$$

4. Substitute these values in formula (5.1):

$$IQV = \frac{260,000}{270,000}(100) = 96.30$$

What does 96.30 mean? Ninety-six percent of the total possible variation that could exist does exist. There is 96 percent of maximum heterogeneity among students with respect to political party affiliation. Since the IQV coefficient can vary between 0 percent and 100 percent, the higher the percent, the greater the variation and, the lower the percent, the less the variation.

The IQV is often used in comparative research. For example, assume we randomly select 900 students from a different university and, again, ask those chosen to indicate their political party preference. This time let's say 700 prefer an

Independent stand, 100 choose Republican, and 100 Democrat. Calculating the index of qualitative variation produces a value of 56 percent. We may say that there is more homogeneity (less variation) on the second campus than on the first.

Index of Dispersion (D)

The **index of dispersion** (D) is an alternative to *IQV* and, as such, is appropriate for qualitative variables. It is defined as *the ratio of the variation that does exist to the maximum variation that could exist*. Formula (5.2) for D is:

$$D = \frac{K(N^2 - \Sigma f^2)}{N^2(K - 1)}$$ (5.2)

where: D = index of dispersion
  N = total number of cases, observations, or scores
  K = number of categories into which data have been classified
  Σf^2 = frequency in each category squared, then summed

D varies between .0 and 1.0: the closer to 1 the greater the variation; the closer to 0 the less the variation.

It may be helpful to illustrate the logic behind D. To do this, examine Tables 5.2 and 5.3 which contain the outcome of a fictitious survey of 100 students' religious preferences, classified into five categories. We know intuitively that if maximum dispersion were present among the 100 students, there would be 20 students in each of the five categories (Table 5.3). On the other hand, if all students were concentrated into a single category (Table 5.2), there would be minimum variability. With maximum dispersion D would equal 1.0 and with minimum dispersion it would equal zero.

The index of dispersion is a ratio whose numerator and denominator are frequency counts of the number of pairs of scores. The denominator of formula (5.2) enables a calculation of the maximum number of unique pairs that *could* be created whereas the numerator permits a calculation of the actual number of pairs that *do* exist.

To illustrate the computation of D assume you survey a large sociology of religion class and the hypothetical data of religious affiliation given in Table 5.2 are obtained. Although this outcome is very remote, it can be used to "prove" formula (5.2). An inspection of the data permits us to conclude that there is absolutely no variation since all respondents indicated they were Protestant. The D coefficient should be zero in this illustration. To compute D the following steps are recommended:

1. After the different classifications of your variable have been listed with their respective frequencies, square each value in the frequency (f) column: $100^2 = 10,000$; $0^2 = 0$; $0^2 = 0$; $0^2 = 0$; and $0^2 = 0$. Create a new column f^2 where you list these products.

2. Sum the f^2 column. The sum of the f^2 column = 10,000.
3. Determine K, the number of categories. There are five: Protestant, Catholic, Jew, Unitarian, and Other.
4. Square N, the total number of cases: 100^2 = 10,000.
5. Determine $K-1$; in our example, $5-1=4$.

Substitute these values into formula (5.2):

$$D = \frac{5(10,000-10,000)}{(10,000)(4)} = .0$$

The computed D is .0 indicating no variation in our respondents' replies to the religious affiliation query.

TABLE 5.2

Table Arrangement for Computing D: Minimum Dispersion

Religious Affiliation	f	f^2
Protestant	100	10,000
Catholic	0	0
Jew	0	0
Unitarian	0	0
Other	0	0
	$N = 100$	$\Sigma f^2 = 10,000$

TABLE 5.3

Table Arrangement for Computing D: Maximum Dispersion

Religious Affiliation	f	f^2
Protestant	20	400
Catholic	20	400
Jew	20	400
Unitarian	20	400
Other	20	400
	$N = 100$	$\Sigma f^2 = 2,000$

To "prove" the other extreme of this variability measure assume the data given in Table 5.3 were obtained. Substituting the values obtained through steps 1 to 5 listed above:

$$D = \frac{5(10,000 - 2,000)}{(10,000)(4)} = 1.0$$

The computed D of 1.0 is, again, consistent with our inspection of the data indicating maximum dispersion.

ORDINAL MEASURES OF DISPERSION

Interquartile Range (Q)

Ordinal data present a unique problem with respect to the relationship between the level of measurement of a variable and the appropriate measure(s) of dispersion. To some statisticians (Loether and McTavish, 1993: 144) there is no specific variation measure for ordinal data. From a practical standpoint this means that techniques appropriate for interval/ratio or nominal level data are used, and if the former tools are used the distance notion is not meaningful.

Ordinal measures belong to a family of statistical techniques known as the *fractile statistics*. The **interquartile range,** one member of this family, is a measure of variation defined as *the distance between the first (Q_1) and third (Q_3) quartiles*. It is a type of range that covers the middle half or middle 50 percent of the cases in a distribution. Formula (5.3) for the interquartile range (Q) is:

$$Q = Q_3 - Q_1 \qquad (5.3)$$

Interquartile Range (Q_v) for Ungrouped Data. Suppose we had the following twenty-four scores:

   1   2   5   6   9   8   8   8   9   9   10   10   4   4   2   2   6   6   7   7   3   1   1   4

To calculate the interquartile range we must first create an *array* of these scores:

   1   1   1   2   2   ② 3   4   4   4   5   6   6   6   7   7   8   ⑧ 8   9   9   9   10   10
               Q_1 Q_3
       6th score   18th score

Then count up to Q_3, that is $3N/4$ or $3(24) \div 4 = 72 \div 4 = 18$, and count up to Q_1, that is $N/4$ or $24 \div 4 = 6$. Employing formula (5.3), the interquartile range for this ungrouped data-set is:

$$Q_3 = 8$$
$$Q_1 = 2$$
$$Q = 8 - 2 = 6$$

This means that the middle 50 percent of the scores has a range of 6. This example clearly demonstrates that the fractile (ordinal level) statistics are based upon their position in the data.

Interquartile Range (Q_G) for Grouped Data. To compute Q for grouped data we must determine how many scores it takes to make up one-fourth (or one-quarter) of the scores. The generic format for calculating Q is identical to that of the median, which is actually the second quartile (Q_2). To recognize its similarity to Q_2 (median) refer to Table 5.4. To calculate *any* quartile statistic from a grouped frequency distribution it is absolutely necessary to have a cumulative frequency column (F). To determine the first quartile (Q_1), formula (5.4) is employed:

$$Q_1 = LQ_1 + \left(\frac{\frac{N}{4} - F}{f} \right) i \qquad (5.4)$$

where: Q_1 = the first quartile
        LQ_1 = the *lower exact* limit of the class interval containing the $N/4$th case
        F = cumulative frequency up to but *not* including the cumulative frequency of the class interval which contains $N/4$th case
        f = frequency of class interval containing the $N/4$th case
        i = width of the class interval containing the $N/4$th case

TABLE 5.4

Grouped Frequency Distribution of Exam Scores from Table 3.1: Illustration of Computations of Interquartile Range and Inclusive Range for Grouped Data

Class Interval (i)		Frequency (f)		Cumulative Frequencies (F)
64–66	66.5 upper exact limit	7		116
61–63		16		109
58–60*		15		93
55–57		14	Q = 59.30−49.37	78
52–54		18	= 9.93	64
49–51†		24		46
46–48	range = 66.5−30.5	6		22
43–45	= 36	7		16
40–42		5		9
37–39		1		4
34–36		0		3
31–33	30.5 lower exact limit	3		3
	Total (N) = 116			

*Q_3 in this interval.
†Q_1 in this interval.

In our example (Table 5.4) the lower exact limit (LQ_1) of the class interval containing Q_1 is determined by dividing N (116) by 4. Since $116/4 = 29$ we locate the class interval as 49–51 because the 29th case lies in that class interval. The lower exact limit of this class interval is 48.5. The sum of all frequencies below the lower exact limits of the interval containing Q_1 is 22. The frequency of the class interval containing Q_1 is 24. The width of the class interval is 3. Substituting these values into formula (5.4):

$$Q_1 = 48.5 + \left(\frac{29-22}{24}\right) 3 = 49.37$$

To calculate Q_3, formula (5.5) is employed:

$$Q_3 = LQ_3 + \left(\frac{\frac{3N}{4} - F}{f}\right) i \tag{5.5}$$

where: Q_3 = the third quartile
LQ_3 = the *lower exact* limit of the class interval containing the 3N/4th case
F = cumulative frequency up to but *not* including the cumulative frequency of the class interval which contains 3N/4th case
f = frequency of the class interval containing the 3N/4th case
i = width of the class interval containing the 3N/4th case

In our example, the lower exact limit (LQ_3) of the class interval containing Q_3 is determined after dividing $3N$ by 4. Since $3(116) \div 4 = 348/4 = 87$ we locate the class interval as 58–60. The lower exact limit of this class interval is 57.5. The sum of all frequencies below the lower exact limit of the class interval containing Q_3 is 78. The frequency of the class interval containing Q_3 is 15. The width, once again, is 3. Substituting these values into formula (5.5):

$$Q_3 = 57.5 + \left(\frac{87-78}{15}\right) 3 = 59.30$$

Subtracting Q_1 (49.37) from Q_3 (59.30), that is, $59.30 - 49.37$, yields our inter-quartile range. In other words, 9.93 is the range that separates the middle half of the cases in our grouped distribution of scores.

Quartiles are special cases of fractiles and have a similar interpretation and computational format. The first quartile (Q_1) is the score point in a distribution at or below which a quarter (25 percent) of the cases fall and the third quartile (Q_3) is the score point at or below which three-quarters (75 percent) of the cases fall. The interquartile range avoids the problem often stemming from the use of the two extreme scores (range) in a distribution and usually is less subject to erratic variation. The relationships among the range, interquartile range, and the normal curve are diagrammed in Figure 5.2.

FIGURE 5.2

The Relationships among the Range, Interquartile Range, and the Normal Curve

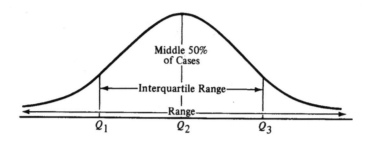

Sometimes it may be of interest to determine the *semi-interquartile range*, or *quartile deviation*, of a data-set. This is easily computed by dividing formula (5.3) by 2 or, symbolically: $(Q_3 - Q_1)/2$. Obviously, it is a value that encompasses one-half the interquartile range. The semi-interquartile range for the problem above is $9.93/2 = 4.965$.

INTERVAL/RATIO MEASURES OF DISPERSION

With interval/ratio measures of dispersion the concept of *distance* on a scale becomes meaningful. There are two general approaches to measurement at this stratum. The first concerns the spread, that is, the range of scores on the scale and may contain either the inclusive range (score range separating the highest and lowest scores) or intermediate ranges (interquartile range and interdecile range); and the second concerns the deviations of scores from a central value (average and standard deviations). Both of these generic types will now be discussed.

Range (R)

The **range** is the simplest variability measure to obtain and is defined as *the distance between the two most extreme scores in a distribution*. The range, like the mode, is easily determined by inspection, and this feature is its most important asset. However, its major limitation is its ignoring all other scores in a distribution except the two extreme ones.

Range (R_U) for Ungrouped Data. In a distribution of *ungrouped* scores, in which the observations have been arranged from high to low, the range may be defined as *the difference between the largest score and the smallest score plus one*. Formula (5.6) for the range is:

$$R_U = H - L + 1 \qquad (5.6)$$

where: H = the largest score in the distribution
L = the smallest score in the distribution

In a distribution that has 103 as the highest score and 30 as the lowest, the range is 74 or, substituting these values in formula (5.6):

$$R_U = 103 - 30 + 1 = 74$$

Another way of computing the range that avoids having to add one to the difference is to subtract the *lower* exact limit of the smallest score from the *upper* exact limit of the largest score. In formula (5.7) form:

$$R_U = UEL - LEL \qquad (5.7)$$

where: UEL = upper exact limit of largest score
LEL = lower exact limit of smallest score

Using the example above and employing formula (5.7) gives us:

$$R_U = 103.5 - 29.5 = 74$$

Range (R_G) for Grouped Data. When data are *grouped*, the range is the difference between the upper exact limit of the highest class interval and the lower exact limit of the lowest class interval. To illustrate, consider the data in Table 5.4. The highest class interval (64–66) has an UEL of 66.5, and the lowest class interval (31–33) has an LEL of 30.5. Subtracting the LEL of the lowest interval from the UEL of the highest interval using formula (5.7) yields a range of 36 (66.5 − 30.5 = 36).

One of the disadvantages of range measurements, either the total range or an intermediate range like Q, is that they represent the *extremes* or limits of variation and do not mirror the variation of the complete set of data. In other words, range measures describe the extremes of scatter but not the amount of variation of the entire aggregate. Consequently, measures of dispersion based upon the deviations of *all* scores from the center of the distribution are extremely important. The dispersion techniques (AD & s) to be discussed now are based upon deviations from the central tendency of a distribution.

Average Deviation (AD)

The *average deviation* is based upon the *absolute* deviations of scores from the center whereas the standard deviation is based upon the *squared* deviations of scores from the central tendency. Both of these procedures are designed to avoid the algebraic sum of deviations from the mean equaling zero, in which case it would be impossible to compute indices of variability.

Average Deviation (AD$_U$) for Ungrouped Data. The average deviation (sometimes called the **mean deviation**) is defined as *the arithmetic mean of the absolute differences of the mean from each score.* In formula (5.8) form it reads[1]:

$$AD(MD)_U = \frac{\Sigma |X_i - \overline{X}|}{N} \tag{5.8}$$

where: $AD(MD)$ = average deviation (mean deviation)
Σ = summation operator
X_i = raw score in the distribution

$\overline{X}$ = mean of the distribution
N = total number of scores
$|X_i - \overline{X}|$ = *absolute* value of $X_i - \overline{X}$

In general, the larger the average deviation, the greater the variability among the scores.

To illustrate the calculation of the mean deviation consider the data in Table 5.5. The following steps are recommended to compute the *AD*:

TABLE 5.5

Illustration of *AD(MD)* Computation for Ungrouped Data

Observation No.	X_i	$\overline{X}$	$|X_i - \overline{X}|$ or $|x|$
1	26	16	10
2	24	16	8
3	22	16	6
4	20	16	4
5	18	16	2
6	16	16	0
7	14	16	2
8	10	16	6
9	6	16	10
10	4	16	12
$N = 10$	$\Sigma = 160$		$\Sigma = 60$

1. After the scores have been arranged in tabular form, sum all scores (X_i's)

---

[1] An alternate way of symbolizing the average deviation is: $AD = \Sigma |x|/N$ where x is called a deviation x, that is, the mean has been subtracted from each score and these absolute deviations have been added together and divided by the number of observations. If you need to refresh your memory on the meaning of deviations in this context refer to the discussion of the moment system in Chapter 4.

and divide by N to determine the mean. If we add all X_i's ($26 + 24 + 22 + 20 + 18 + 16 + 14 + 10 + 6 + 4$) a total of 160 is produced. Dividing 160 by N (in this case 10) provides a mean of 16 ($\bar{X} = \Sigma X_i/N$ or $160/10 = 16$). Then add an $\bar{X}$ column.

2. Subtract the mean ($\bar{X}$) from each raw score (X_i) *disregarding the sign* (since we're concerned with absolute differences) and add. Doing this for our data: $26 - 16 = 10$; $24 - 16 = 8$; $22 - 16 = 6$; $20 - 16 = 4$; $18 - 16 = 2$; $16 - 16 = 0$; $14 - 16 = 2$; $10 - 16 = 6$; $6 - 16 = 10$; $4 - 16 = 12$. Adding these absolute deviations yields a value of 60.

3. Divide this sum, that is, $\Sigma |X_i - \bar{X}|$, by N, or $60 \div 10 = 6$. The average deviation for this data-set is 6.

What does an average deviation of 6 mean? It is interpreted as the average amount by which the scores in a distribution deviate from the distribution's mean. For example, 6 score units is the average deviation of the scores in Table 5.5. Since the AD lacks the standardization of another interval measure of dispersion (the standard deviation), it is not frequently used in statistical analysis. The standard deviation is ordinarily preferred because of its mathematical uses in other areas of statistics.

Average Deviation (AD_G) for Grouped Data. For grouped data, as in Table 4.2, the AD is computed identically except that it is the *midpoint* of each class interval from which the mean is subtracted. Then these absolute deviations are multiplied by the frequencies found within the respective class intervals. In our example, $65 - 53.44 = 11.56(7) = 80.92$; $62 - 53.44 = 8.56(16) = 136.96$; $59 - 53.44 = 5.56(15) = 83.40$; $56 - 53.44 = 2.56(14) = 35.84$; $53 - 53.44 = .44(18) = 7.92$; $50 - 53.44 = 3.44(24) = 82.56$; $47 - 53.44 = 6.44(6) = 38.64$; $44 - 53.44 = 9.44(7) = 66.08$; $41 - 53.44 = 12.44(5) = 62.20$; $38 - 53.44 = 15.44(1) = 15.44$; $35 - 53.44 = 18.44(0) = .00$; $32 - 53.44 = 21.44(3) = 64.32$. If these products are summed ($\Sigma = 674.28$) and divided by N (116) the average deviation is computed to be 5.81. It's interpreted in the same way as above: on the average, the scores in the distribution disperse from the mean by 5.81 score units.

There are affinities between the average deviation and the standard deviation. Computationally speaking, the standard deviation deals with the squared deviations between the mean and each score whereas the average deviation deals with the absolute differences between the mean and the scores. Both techniques sidestep the zero-sum-of-deviations property discussed with the arithmetic mean in the previous chapter (see Table 4.3).

Standard Deviation (s) and Related Concepts

To grasp the logic of the **standard deviation** there are several relationships that need to be identified. First of all, statisticians often distinguish *theoretical* from *computational formulae* on the grounds that the former facilitate conceptualizing (or thinking) about mathematical relationships but the latter facilitate the actual computation of the statistic. The advantages of computing formulae accrue when the researcher works with large amounts of data since unnecessary in-between operations are time-consuming and the various statistics may be computed directly from the raw data. Secondly, your attention is called to the *three-step procedure* for computing the standard deviation (for ungrouped data): (1) calculating the sum of squares, (2) dividing this value by N to obtain the variance, and (3) extracting the square root of the variance to obtain the standard deviation. Notice their interrelationships as you read the following discussion.

Sum of Squares. The sum of squares concept and computation are vitally important. It is symbolized Σx^2 and defined as the sum of the squared deviations from the mean. The basic formula is Σx^2, where x is a deviation score. To compute the sum of squares the computing formula (5.9) is recommended:

$$\text{sum of squares } (\Sigma x^2) = \Sigma X^2 - \frac{(\Sigma X)^2}{N} \tag{5.9}$$

For the data in Table 5.6 let us compute the sum of squares using formula (5.9)

TABLE 5.6

Illustration of Computation of Sum of Squares, Variance, and Standard Deviation

X_i	X_i^2	
2	4	$\text{sum of squares } (\Sigma x^2) = \Sigma X^2 - \dfrac{(\Sigma X)^2}{N} = 720 - \dfrac{(56)^2}{7}$
2	4	$= 272$
4	16	
6	36	$\text{variance } (s^2) = \dfrac{\Sigma x^2}{N} = \dfrac{272}{7}$
8	64	
14	196	$= 38.86$
20	400	
$\Sigma = 56$	$\Sigma = 720$	$\text{standard deviation } (s) = \sqrt{\dfrac{\Sigma x^2}{N}} = \sqrt{38.86}$
		$= 6.23$

Note that after squaring each X_i score   and placing it in column X_i^2 we sum both the X_i and X_i^2 columns and substitute into formula (5.9):

$$\text{sum of squares } (\Sigma x^2) = 720 - \frac{(56)^2}{7}$$

$$= 720 - \frac{3,136}{7}$$

$$= 720 - 448$$

$$= 272$$

Variance. With measures of dispersion, like measures of central tendency, a distinction between parameters, for example, σ (standard deviation) or σ^2 (variance), and statistics, for example, s (standard deviation) and s^2 (variance), is made. Since most data are sample data we will follow the convention of using notation for statistics.

The **variance,** symbolized by s^2, is simply the sum of squares divided by the total number of observations[2] or:

$$s^2 = \frac{\Sigma x^2}{N} = \frac{272}{7} = 38.86$$

One can see that the variance is nothing more than the average of the squared deviations from the mean.

Standard Deviation. The **standard deviation,** symbolized by s, is the square root of the variance or:

$$s = \sqrt{\frac{\Sigma x^2}{N}} = \sqrt{38.86} = 6.23$$

To illustrate the correspondence and relationships among the sum of squares, variance, and standard deviation, see Table 5.7.[3] Although the computing formulae for s^2 and s are different from those in Table 5.6, they produce identical values.

A cautionary word is in order concerning the calculation of the standard deviation using the raw score (computing formula) method. Notice that in the computing formula in Table 5.7 there are two similar-looking terms: ΣX^2 and

[2] For technical reasons the N in the denominator produces an underestimate of the population standard deviation. In Chapter 7 we will see that $N - 1$ will be used as a correction factor for this known biased estimate. As you might surmise, when N is large the correction factor does not make a great difference in the final value; however, when N is small it may produce a significant difference.

[3] One other related statistical concept in this context is the **quadratic mean,** symbolized QM. The standard deviation is actually the quadratic mean of the squared mean deviates. The formula for QM reads: $QM = \sqrt{\Sigma x^2 / N}$. For illustrative purposes consider the data in Table 5.8. The squared mean deviates appear in the far right column. The sum of these squared values equals 90. Substituting into the formula above we have: $QM = \sqrt{90/5} = \sqrt{18} = 4.24 = s$. The s could also be computed by $s = \sqrt{\frac{1}{N}\Sigma x^2}$. For our example, $\sqrt{\frac{1}{7}(272)} = 6.23$.

$(\Sigma X)^2$. The former expression represents the sum of the squares of each of the individual scores whereas the latter expression represents the square of the sum of the scores. A moment's reflection should convince you that it is impossible to obtain a negative sum of squares or standard deviation. In the event you do obtain a negative value check these two notations in particular.

TABLE 5.7

The Relationships among the Sum of Squares, Variance, and Standard Deviation

Concept	Statistical Notation	Basic Formula	Computing Formula (ungrouped data)
Sum of squares	Ns^2	Σx^2	$\Sigma X^2 - \dfrac{(\Sigma X)^2}{N}$
Variance	s^2	$\dfrac{\Sigma x^2}{N}$	$\dfrac{\Sigma X^2 - \dfrac{(\Sigma X)^2}{N}}{N}$
Standard deviation	s	$\sqrt{\dfrac{\Sigma x^2}{N}}$	$\sqrt{\dfrac{\Sigma X^2 - \dfrac{(\Sigma X)^2}{N}}{N}}$

Standard Deviation (s_u) for Ungrouped Data. The **standard deviation** (s), the most popular and mathematically useful interval/ratio measure of dispersion, is defined as *the square root of the arithmetic mean of the squared deviations from the mean.* To compute the standard deviation, the theoretical formula (5.10) is employed for *ungrouped* data:

$$s_u = \sqrt{\frac{\Sigma(X_i - \bar{X})^2}{N}} \qquad (5.10)$$

where: s = standard deviation

$\Sigma(X_i - \bar{X})^2$ = subtract the mean from all raw scores, square the difference and sum

N = total number of cases

Let's assume we have the set of scores given in Table 5.8 and wish to compute the standard deviation. The following steps are recommended:

1. After the scores have been recorded in tabular form, sum the individual scores and divide by N to determine the mean. In our example, $1 + 4 + 7 + 10 + 13 = 35/5 = 7(\bar{X} = \Sigma X_i/N$ or $35/5 = 7)$. Then create an $\bar{X}$ column.

2. Subtract the mean from each raw score and square these values. In the

present example, $1 - 7 = -6$ and $-6^2 = 36$; $4 - 7 = -3$ and $-3^2 = 9$; $7 - 7 = 0$ and $0^2 = 0$; $10 - 7 = 3$ and $3^2 = 9$; and $13 - 7 = 6$ and $6^2 = 36$.

3. Sum the $(X_i - \overline{X})^2$ computations (this value is the *sum of squares*) and divide by N. In our example, $90/5 = 18$. This quotient is the *variance*.

4. Take the square root of the quotient, for example, $\sqrt{18} = 4.24$. This is the standard deviation.

TABLE 5.8

Computation of Standard Deviation for Ungrouped Data

Observation No.	X_i	$\overline{X}$	$X_i - \overline{X}$	$(X_i - \overline{X})^2$ or x^2
1	1	7	-6	36
2	4	7	-3	9
3	7	7	0	0
4	10	7	3	9
5	13	7	6	36
$N = 5$	$\Sigma = 35$		$\Sigma = 0$	$\Sigma = 90$

$$\overline{X}_u = \frac{\Sigma X_i}{N} = \frac{35}{5} = 7$$

An alternative method for computing the standard deviation is expressed in formula (5.11). This formula is a *computational* one and will be related to the discussion of other statistics in this text.

$$s_u = \sqrt{\frac{\Sigma X_i^2 - \frac{(\Sigma X_i)^2}{N}}{N}} \tag{5.11}$$

where: s = standard deviation
ΣX_i^2 = the sum of all raw scores squared (the sum of squared scores)
N = total number of cases
$(\Sigma X_i)^2$ = the sum of the X_i column, quantity squared (the square of the sum of scores)

This computational technique deals directly with the raw scores. To use it, the following steps are recommended:

1. Square each raw score and sum these quantities. In our example, $1^2 = 1$, $4^2 = 16$, $7^2 = 49$, $10^2 = 100$, and $13^2 = 169$. The sum is equal to 335 ($1 + 16 + 49 + 100 + 169 = 335$).

2. Sum the raw scores, that is, $1 + 4 + 7 + 10 + 13 = 35$; square that quanti-

ty (35^2 = 1225) and divide by N, or 1225/5 = 245.

3. Subtract the value obtained in step 2 from the first quantity, or 335 − 245 = 90, and divide by N. Hence, 90/5 = 18.

4. Take the square root of this value: $\sqrt{18}$ = 4.24.

Standard Deviation (s_G) for Grouped Data. There exist two different ways of calculating the standard deviation for *grouped* data. One method is called the *long method* and utilizes the numbers as they appear in the original data. The second method is called the *short method* or *arbitrary origin method* or *mean deviation method.* Its use is recommended since it involves computations of smaller magnitudes and minimizes the chances of miscalculations. However, to appreciate the short method it is necessary to demonstrate the long method first. For the data in Table 5.9 we will compute the standard deviation by the long method. Several steps are necessary:

TABLE 5.9

Computation of Standard Deviation Using Midpoints: Long Method

Class Interval (i)	Frequency (f)	Midpoints (m)	fm	fm(m)
20–21	5	20.5	102.5	2,101.25
18–19	3	18.5	55.5	1,026.75
16–17	9	16.5	148.5	2,450.25
14–15	2	14.5	29.0	420.50
12–13	34	12.5	425.0	5,312.50
10–11	13	10.5	136.5	1,433.25
8–9	20	8.5	170.0	1,445.00
6–7	3	6.5	19.5	126.75
4–5	6	4.5	27.0	121.50
2–3	5	2.5	12.5	31.25
	$N = 100$		$\Sigma = 1,126$	$\Sigma = 14,469$

$$\overline{X}_G = \frac{\Sigma fm}{N} = 11.26$$

1. After the data have been properly grouped and arranged in tabular form, we compute the midpoints of all class intervals.[4]

2. Multiply the frequency of each class interval by its corresponding midpoint, for example, 5(20.5) = 102.5; 3(18.5) = 55.5; 9(16.5) = 148.5; . . . ; 5(2.5) = 12.5.

[4] In Chapter 3 a preference for odd size class intervals was expressed. With even number class intervals, as in Table 5.9, the midpoints contain decimals which often prove cumbersome. Such decimals (or fractions) can be avoided if odd size intervals are constructed.

3. Multiply the products in the *fm* column by their corresponding midpoints, that is, $102.5(20.5) = 2,101.25$; $55.5(18.5) = 1,026.75$; $148.5(16.5) = 2,450.25$; $\ldots$; $12.5(2.5) = 31.25$.

4. Sum the *fm* and *fm(m)* columns. The sums are 1,126 and 14,469, respectively. The sum of the *fm* column divided by N yields the arithmetic mean which is used in the equation.

5. Find the standard deviation using formula (5.12):

$$s_G = \sqrt{\frac{\Sigma fm(m)}{N} - \overline{X}^2} \tag{5.12}$$

$$= \sqrt{\frac{14,469}{100} - (11.26)^2}$$

$$= \sqrt{144.69 - 126.79}$$

$$= \sqrt{17.90}$$

$$= 4.23$$

While the former procedure is technically correct, the arithmetic operations involved become quite cumbersome. Hence, we will resort to a different procedure which involves **coding**.

In statistics the concept of coding is used in two generic ways to denote: (1) the substitution of simpler symbols for more complex values, or (2) the transformation of scores such that they become easier to handle (Mueller, Schuessler, and Costner, 1970: 132–133). Instead of using the midpoints of the class intervals we will use step deviations from an arbitrary origin.[5] Let us assume we have the frequency distribution given in Table 5.10. To compute the standard deviation, the following steps are recommended:

1. After the data have been properly grouped and arranged in tabular form, select an arbitrary origin near the middle of the distribution and attach a zero to that class interval. To the ascending class intervals place $+1, +2, +3, \ldots, +N$ until the intervals are exhausted. To the descending class intervals place $-1, -2, -3, \ldots, -N$ until the intervals are exhausted (see column 3 in Table 5.10).

2. Multiply the frequency of each class interval by its corresponding step deviation. In our example beginning at the top of the table, $(5)(5) = 25$; $(3)(4) = 12$; $(9)(3) = 27$; $(2)(2) = 4$; $(34)(1) = 34$; $(13)(0) = 0$; $(20)(-1) = -20$; $(3)(-2) = -6$; $(6)(-3) = -18$; $(5)(-4) = -20$. These computations appear in column 4 of Table 5.10.

3. Multiply the *fx'* products by their corresponding step deviations, for example, $(5)(25) = 125$; $(4)(12) = 48$; $(3)(27) = 81$; $(2)(4) = 8$; $(1)(34) = 34$; $(0)(0) = 0$; $(-1)(-20) = 20$; $(-2)(-6) = 12$; $(-3)(-18) = 54$; $(-4)(-20) = 80$. These values appear in column 5.

---

[5] The arithmetic mean (short method) in Chapter 4 also used a coding technique (see Table 4.2).

TABLE 5.10

Calculation of Standard Deviation for Grouped Data: Arbitrary Origin Method

(1) Class Interval (i)	(2) Frequency (f)	(3) Step Deviations (x')	(4) fx'	(5) fx'(x')
20–21	5	+5	25	125
18–19	3	+4	12	48
16–17	9	+3	27	81
14–15	2	+2	4	8
12–13	34	+1	34	34
10–11	13	0	0	0
8–9	20	−1	−20	20
6–7	3	−2	−6	12
4–5	6	−3	−18	54
2–3	5	−4	−20	80
	$N = 100$		$\Sigma = 38$	$\Sigma = 462$

4. Sum the fx' and $fx'(x')$ columns. The sums are 38 and 462, respectively. The summation procedure for column 4, fx', is an algebraic one.

5. Find the sum of squares (for grouped data) using formula (5.13):

$$\Sigma x^2 = i^2 \left[\Sigma fx'(x') - \frac{(\Sigma fx')^2}{N} \right] \qquad (5.13)$$

where: Σx^2 = sum of squares
i^2 = width of class interval, squared
$\Sigma fx'(x')$ = sum of column 5
$(\Sigma fx')^2$ = sum of column 4, quantity squared
N = total number of scores

Substituting our values into formula (5.13):

$$\Sigma x^2 = 2^2 \left[462 - \frac{(38)^2}{100} \right]$$

$$= 4 \left(462 - \frac{1,444}{100} \right)$$

$$= 4(462 - 14.44)$$
$$= 4(447.56)$$
$$= 1,790.24$$

6. Then substitute the sum of squares (in this case 1,790.24) into formula (5.14):

$$s = \sqrt{\frac{\Sigma x^2}{N}}$$ (5.14)

where: s = standard deviation
Σx^2 = sum of squares
N = total number of cases

Substituting,

$$s = \sqrt{\frac{1,790.24}{100}} = \sqrt{17.9024} = 4.23$$

As we would expect, both the long and short methods produce identical outcomes.

How Do We Interpret the Standard Deviation? According to Loether and McTavish (1993: 139), there are at least two different ways of interpreting the standard deviation apart from its actual value. First of all, both s and s^2 will be zero when all the scores are identical and will reach a maximum when scores are divided between the extremes of the scale. As you know, the extremes of a scale are reflected in the range, and for most distribution, the ratio of the range to the standard deviation is rarely smaller than two or greater than six. As a rule of thumb, the range is approximately six times the standard deviation. For the data in Table 5.10 the s was computed to be 4.23. The actual range was 20 (21.5 − 1.5). Note the relationship between the range and standard deviation. The rule of thumb above only holds for a large number of cases. In other words, the smaller the N, the fewer the number of standard deviations usually needed to include all the cases. Table 5.11 describes this relationship.

TABLE 5.11*

The Relationship between Sample Size and the Number of Standard Deviations Included in the Range

Sample Size	Number of s's Included in Range
5	2.3
10	3.1
25	3.9
30	4.1
50	4.5
100	5.0
500	6.1
1,000	6.5

* From N. M. Downie and R. W. Heath, *Basic Statistical Methods*, 4th Ed. (New York: Harper & Row Publishers, 1974), p. 60. Used with the kind permission of the authors and Harper and Row, Publishers.

Secondly, the standard deviation can also be interpreted in relation to the normal curve. In a normal distribution there is a constant proportion of scores between the mean and given standard deviation values from the mean. A standard deviation helps describe the normal curve. When data are normally distributed approximately 68 percent of the cases will fall within ±1 standard deviation; approximately 95 percent of the cases will fall within ±2 standard deviations; and nearly all cases (99 percent) within ±3 standard deviations of the mean. The full meaning of the standard deviation will become clearer when the normal curve is discussed in the next chapter.

Variance (s^2)

A very close relative of the standard deviation is the **variance,** defined as the *standard deviation squared.* The similarity of the variance to the standard deviation can be gauged by formula (5.15):

$$s_u^2 = \frac{\Sigma(X_i - \overline{X})^2}{N} \qquad (5.15)$$

where:

s_u^2 = variance (ungrouped)

$\Sigma(X_i - \overline{X})^2$ = the mean subtracted from each raw score in the distribution, the differences squared and summed

N = total number of cases

In the previous example, the standard deviation was 4.23. The variance is simply the standard deviation squared or s^2. In our example, $(4.23)^2 = 17.89$. The variance is of more theoretical importance than the standard deviation and is used in more complex statistical equations.

Coefficient of Variability (V)

The **coefficient of variability** (sometimes called the **variation ratio** or the **coefficient of relative variation**) is a measure of dispersion obtained by dividing the standard deviation by the mean. Formula (5.16) for V is:

$$V = \frac{s}{\overline{X}} \qquad (5.16)$$

where: V = coefficient of variability
s = standard deviation
$\overline{X}$ = mean

In actual research occasions arise where you may want to know if two groups are comparatively homogeneous. In such a case V is the suitable statistic. Let's say you want to compare two groups with respect to scores on the Medical College Admissions Test. In the one group the mean is 35 ($\overline{X}_1 = 35$) with a standard deviation of 5 ($s_1 = 5$) whereas in the other group, the mean is 42 ($\overline{X}_2 = 42$) and the standard deviation is 7 ($s_2 = 7$). Employing the coefficient of variability formula (5.16) for each group:

<table>
<tr><td align="center">Group 1</td><td align="center">Group 2</td></tr>
<tr><td align="center">$V = \dfrac{5}{35} = .14$</td><td align="center">$V = \dfrac{7}{42} = .17$</td></tr>
</table>

A comparison of the V's yields a much smaller difference than a comparison of the two standard deviations. However, it must be reiterated that there are relatively few cases in the social science literature where coefficients of variability are reported; this is in part due to their lack of defined limits.

COMPARING THE VARIOUS MEASURES OF DISPERSION

Each of the measures discussed in this chapter has certain advantages and disadvantages. Although in practice it is common to compute only one, the one that is most appropriate for the data at hand, sometimes computing several will add some insightful interpretive features to the data.

Advantages and Disadvantages of Nominal Measures of Dispersion

Probably the major advantage of these measures is that they provide us with some index of the variability in *attribute data*. This suggests that for virtually any data the computation of a measure of dispersion is possible. Their major disadvantage is that they cannot always be compared with each other. Furthermore, they lack the *standardized* property of the standard deviation.

Advantages and Disadvantages of Ordinal Measures

Acknowledging their uniqueness, these measures provide us with higher level statistics appropriate for describing variability characteristics of rank-ordered data. Moreover, they enable us to determine the position or point in a distribution of scores above and below which a specified number of cases fall.

The disadvantages of these measures is due to their being computed on the basis of *position* in a distribution. This means they do not use all the data as is the case with the interval/ratio measures of dispersion.

Advantages and Disadvantages of Interval/Ratio Measures of Dispersion

The major advantage of these statistics stems from their true metric qualities. It is legitimate to employ the numerous arithmetical operations available. In addition, they provide the foundation for some of the most advanced statistical calculations possible.

The key disadvantage, particularly in the behavioral sciences, is that data often do not meet the assumptions of interval/ratio level variables. This limitation is due to the level of measurement dimension and not to the statistics themselves.

Boxplot (Box-and-Whiskers Plot)

A *boxplot* is a graphic technique that enables visualizing the data distribution and, at the same time, contains summary descriptive statistics that facilitate understanding the data. The boxplot combines a pictorial display with a five-number—median, score at the first quartile, score at the third quartile, maximum, and minimum—summary of the data. Boxplots can be drawn either vertically or horizontally (what is done here). The lower boundary of the box is the score at the first quartile ($Q1$) and the upper boundary is the score at the third quartile ($Q3$). These values are sometimes called Tukey's hinges. Recall that this distance represents the interquartile range. The line inside the box is the median. Lines drawn from the edges of the box to the largest (i.e., maximum) and smallest (i.e., minimum) scores. Let us construct a boxplot for the data that appear in Table 3.4 since the five statistics necessary for its construction have been calculated.

The minimum is 32, $Q1 = 49.37$, $Mdn = 53.51$, $Q3 = 59.30$, and the maximum is 66. We locate a scale horizontally and plot the values along the horizontal axis (the height of the box is not meaningful).

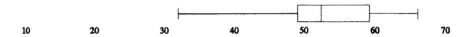

| 10 | 20 | 30 | 40 | 50 | 60 | 70 |

The boxplot reveals several statistical features of our data. The vertical line inside the box represents the median and provides us with an indicator of the central tendency of the data. If the data distribution is symmetrical this line should be equi-distant from the edges of the box. In most data distributions, if the data are positively skewed the location of the median will be closer to the bottom (left side) of the box and if negatively skewed the median will be closer to the top (right side) of the box. The length of the box is the interquartile range and reveals the variation in the middle fifty percent of the cases. Lines drawn from the ends of the box to the maximum and minimum values are called the "whiskers".

The advantage of the boxplot is that is combines the three important properties of distributions: (1) central tendency, (2) variability, and (3) form. It is a particularly helpful graph when comparing different distributions.

SUMMARY

In this chapter we have discussed and illustrated the computation of measures of variation. With the exceptions of IQV and D these statistics ideally require interval level data if they are to be meaningfully applied.

In social research the standard deviation has proved, when legitimately applicable, to be the most important dispersion measure. In completing this chapter we have dealt with the second important property of a distribution of scores (the first being that of central tendency). When variability measures are used in conjunction with central location indices, a more complete picture of one's data is revealed.

IMPORTANT CONCEPTS DISCUSSED IN THIS CHAPTER

Measures of dispersion (variation, spread, variability)

Index of qualitative variation

Index of dispersion

Interquartile range

Range

Average deviation (mean deviation)

Standard deviation

Sum of squares

Variance

Coding

Coefficient of variability (variation ratio, coefficient of relative variation)

Boxplot

REVIEW QUESTIONS

1. Suppose you are interested in the group dynamics tradition in social psychology. During the semester you keep a record of the number of times each person in a fifteen-member class makes a verbal contribution. From these data you intend to make some generalizations about class participation and sex of respondent (which you also have information on).

Student Number	Sex	X_i (Number of Times Participating)
1	F	40
2	F	38
3	M	37
4	F	36
5	M	33
6	F	33
7	F	32
8	M	31
9	M	29
10	F	27
11	M	25
12	F	24
13	M	23
14	M	22
15	M	20

a. Compute the sum of squares for the entire class.
b. Calculate the variance for the entire class.
c. Compute the standard deviation for the entire class.
d. Calculate the average deviation for the entire class.

2. Now, treating each sex separately:
   a. Compute the sum of squares for males and females.
   b. Compute the variance for males and females.
   c. Compute the standard deviation for males and females.
   d. Compute the average deviation for males and females.

3. Political sociologists are often concerned with comparing different student bodies on such things as political preferences. Suppose you obtained the following hypothetical sample data on voting outcomes on two different campuses.

	Campus 1	Campus 2
Republican	500	300
Democrat	100	50
Independent	600	425

a. Compute the index of qualitative variation for each campus.
b. Which campus is more politically homogeneous?

4. The grouped data below represent the number of questions answered correctly by twenty students on a fifty-item social stratification exam.

Class Interval (i)	Frequency (f)
42–44	2
39–41	3
36–38	4
33–35	5
30–32	3
27–29	2
24–26	1
	$N = 20$

a. Compute the standard deviation using both the long and short methods.
b. Calculate the variance for these data.
c. Determine the range.
d. Calculate the interquartile range.
e. What is the semi-interquartile range?
f. Compute the average deviation.

5. For the following data:

1	9	9	4	6	3
2	8	9	4	6	1
5	8	10	2	7	1
6	8	10	2	7	4

a. Determine the Range.
b. Construct a boxplot for these data. To do so, compute:
   (1) minimum   (4) first quartile
   (2) maximum   (5) third quartile
   (3) median

CHAPTER 6

THE NORMAL CURVE AND STANDARD SCORES

In this chapter the normal curve and standard scores and some of their applications will be considered. In some respects, the bell-shaped curve is a bridge between descriptive and inferential statistics. On the one hand, the normal curve is described by the mean and standard deviation (descriptive statistics), and on the other hand, it is one of the theoretical models used in hypothesis testing (which is a core of sampling or inferential statistics).

Abraham Demoivré (1667–1754) was among the first mathematicians to explore the properties of the **normal curve** (circa 1733). In fact, he developed the formidable mathematical formula (6.1) for the curve:

$$y = \frac{N}{\sigma\sqrt{2\pi}} \, e^{[-x^2/2\sigma^2]} \tag{6.1}$$

where: y = an ordinate at any point on the base line
N = the total number of cases
σ = the standard deviation of the distribution
π = 3.1416
e = 2.7183, the base of the system of natural logarithms
x = the deviation of a score from the mean

In addition to Demoivré, Gauss (1777–1855) and Laplace (1749–1827), early in the nineteenth century, further developed the concept and its probabilistic nature. Today the normal curve goes by a variety of different names such as *the curve of error, the bell-shaped curve, the Gaussian curve,* or *Demoivré's curve.* All of these terms refer to the same phenomenon.

A mathematical distinction between **parameters** and **statistics** is, again, in order. Parameters refer to the quantitative characteristics of a *population* and are

111

designated by Greek letters, for example, μ (population mean) and σ (population standard deviation). Statistics refer to quantitative characteristics of a *sample* and are designated by Roman letters, for example, $\bar{X}$ (sample mean) and s (sample standard deviation). By employing Greek letters to describe the normal curve we are considering it as a population or complete set of individuals, objects, or events.

Why is the normal curve important in statistics? There are two basic answers to this question. First, a large number of *empirical* distributions have been found to be approximately normally distributed. That is, if we were to graph these variables their shapes or forms would approximate the N.C. For example, the distribution of variables like weight, height, and IQ take on the shape of this curve. However, in reality, probably no distribution takes the *exact* form of the normal curve.

Secondly, the normal curve is important in the inferential side of statistical analysis. In other words, it has theoretical significance—not because many variables are approximately normally distributed but because the *sampling distribution* of various statistics is known or assumed to be normally distributed. The concept of sampling distribution is one of the most important terms in inductive statistics. It is used extensively in hypothesis testing in which the researcher compares his or her obtained results with the appropriate sampling distribution which describes the expected results. This notion will be discussed at length in the next few chapters, particularly in Chapter 7.

NATURE AND PROPERTIES OF THE NORMAL CURVE

The normal curve (abbreviated N.C.) is **symmetrical**. This means that it has two identical sides as depicted in Figure 6.1. If the curve were folded in the middle (ordinate in Figure 6.1a), the one side would be an exact replica of the other. However, not all symmetrical curves, for example, U-shaped or rectangular, are normal, as can be seen in Figures 6.1b and 6.1c.

The bell-shaped feature of the normal curve indicates that it has no skewness and it is also said to be *mesokurtic*. In short, there is no inclination for the distribution of scores to pile up on one side or the other of the center. Furthermore, since it is symmetrical and *unimodal*, the three measures of central location (mean, median, and mode) coincide. In Figure 6.1a the vertical line extending from the top of the curve to the base line is technically referred to as an **ordinate**. An ordinate (symbolized y) is a vertically drawn straight line from the base of the curve (abscissa) to some specified height or point along the contour of the curve. Ordinates will be discussed when the areas under the N.C. are presented.

The N.C. is **asymptotic**. This means that the ends (or tails) of the distribution extend toward infinity in both directions. They approach the horizontal axis (abscissa) but never quite touch it. In Figure 6.1a notice the *asymptote* labels. This asymptotic quality is very revealing in that it suggests that any score, event, or outcome is *theoretically* possible, although not highly probable.

The total area under the curve is defined as *unity* even though in the strict mathematical sense this is not true due to its asymptotic property. Sometimes the

N.C. is referred to as the **unit normal distribution** or the **standardized normal curve** and can be expressed in terms of percentages or areas as indicated in Figure 6.2. Note that the N.C. in Figure 6.2 is described in terms of two *parameters*, μ and σ. Notice that there is a *constant area* (proportion or percent of cases) between the mean and an ordinate which is a given distance from the mean in standard deviation units.

FIGURE 6.1

Symmetrical Nature of Normal Curve and Two Other Symmetrical Curves

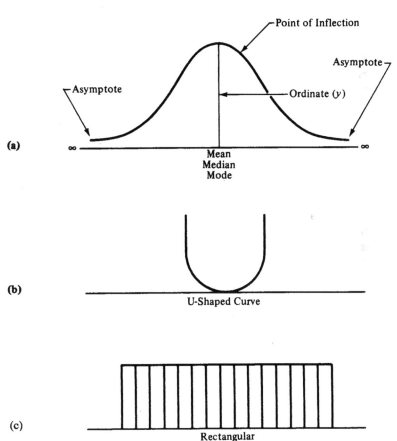

Let us look at some of the percentages or areas between the mean and various ordinates (see Figure 6.2). Thirty-four (34.13) percent of the cases fall between μ and $+1\sigma$ *or* -1σ; adding these together indicates that 68 (68.26) percent of the cases fall between μ and $\pm1\sigma$. Forty-seven and one-half percent of the cases fall within +1.96σ *or* −1.96σ; adding these together indicates that approximately 95 percent of the cases fall between μ and ±1.96σ. About 49 (49.5) percent of the cases fall between μ and +2.58σ *or* −2.58σ. Approximately 99 (99.02) percent of the area falls between ±2.58σ. It is worth reiterating that *practically* all cases fall within ±3σ from the mean, even though the tails of the curve extend to infinity.

FIGURE 6.2

The Unit Normal Distribution

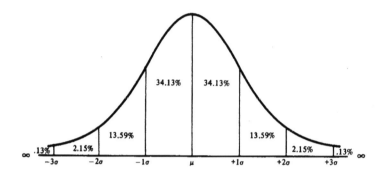

By examining the contour of the curve another salient property emerges. Notice that the slope of the curve adjacent to the central tendency (mean) falls rapidly and then becomes less and less steep. The point of maximum steepness is called the **point of inflection**. In a practical sense the contour of the curve suggests a heavy concentration of scores around the mean and a more sparse concentration of scores as one moves to the tails of the N.C. This aspect of the N.C. highlights its probabilistic nature, that is, the probability decreases as one moves along the base line away from the mean in either direction.

It should be noted that when scores are *skewed* these percentages (between mean and selected ordinates) will vary. Even in the most skewed distribution, however, it has been discovered that about 75 percent of the cases will fall between μ and ±2σ and approximately 90 percent between ±3σ. This observation is called **Chebyshev's Theorem** (or **Tchebycheff's inequality**) and is expressed as follows (Loether and McTavish, 1993: 140):

$$\begin{matrix} \text{minimum percent of cases} \\ \text{above and below the mean} \\ \text{in } \textit{any shaped} \text{ distribution} \end{matrix} = 100\left[1 - \left(\frac{1}{z^2}\right)\right]$$

Chebyshev's Theorem is applicable in inferential statistics and is an aid for interpreting the standard deviation as well. For many distributions the concentration of scores is even larger. For example, in *unimodal and symmetrical* distributions the minimum percent of cases above and below the mean becomes:

minimum percent of cases above
and below the mean of a *unimodal*, $= 100 \left[1 - \left(\dfrac{4}{9} \right) \left(\dfrac{1}{z^2} \right) \right]$
symmetrical distribution

This latter formula means that the minimum percentage of observations within ±2 standard deviations is 89 and not 75, and the minimum percentage of cases within ±3 standard deviations is 95 and not 90.

The *standardized* N.C. has a mean equal to zero ($\mu = 0$), and a standard deviation equal to one ($\sigma = 1$). *When the N.C. is standardized raw scores from different distributions may be expressed in comparable form.* To understand this a discussion of standard scores and their relationship to the N.C. will now be presented. These properties appear in Figure 6.3.

FIGURE 6.3

Mean and Standard Deviation of Standardized Normal Curve

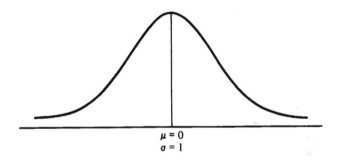

$\mu = 0$
$\sigma = 1$

NATURE AND PROPERTIES OF *z* SCORES

A *z* score (or **standard score**) is a raw score expressed in terms of the number of standard deviation units it is away from the mean of the distribution from which it emanates. One way of writing the formula for the *z* score **transformation** is:

$$z = \frac{x}{s}$$ (6.2)

where: z = standard score (formula)
x = a deviation score, that is $X_i - \bar{X}$
s = standard deviation of distribution from which raw score is taken

Any raw score in any distribution can be transformed into a *z* score. The converted raw score represents the deviation of a specific score from the mean (of the distribution from which it has been taken) in standard deviation units. Some of the mathematical properties of *z* scores are (Runyon and Haber, 1976: 110–111):

1. The sum of z scores is equal to zero. Symbolically,

$$\Sigma z = 0$$

2. The z scores have a mean of zero, that is

$$\bar{z} = \frac{\Sigma z}{N} = 0$$

3. The sum of squared z scores equals N. This properly will be used for understanding one way of computing the Pearsonian correlation coefficient (Chapter 13). Thus, $\Sigma z^2 = N$. Mathematically,

$$\Sigma z^2 = \frac{\Sigma (X_i - \bar{X})^2}{s^2} = \left[\frac{1}{s^2} \, \Sigma (X_i - \bar{X})^2 \right]$$

$$= \frac{N}{\Sigma (X_i - X)^2} \left[\Sigma (X_i - \bar{X})^2 \right]$$

$$= N$$

4. The z scores have a standard deviation and variance equal to one. Symbolically, $\sigma_z = \sigma_z^2 = 1$. Mathematically,

$$\sigma_z^2 = \frac{\Sigma (z - \bar{z})^2}{N}$$

According to property 2 the mean of z scores is equal to zero so that

$$\sigma_z^2 = \frac{\Sigma z^2}{N}$$

According to property 3 the sum of the squared z scores equals N, therefore

$$\sigma_z^2 = \frac{N}{N} = 1$$

As we will see, the transformation of raw scores to z scores is important for at least two reasons: (1) since z scores are abstract numbers we can compare raw scores from different distributions when they have been converted into a common standard; (2) by referring the z score to the unit normal curve we may express the raw score as a percentile (the percentile of a raw score in relation to the normal curve only holds if the variable under examination is normally distributed).

THE RELATIONSHIP BETWEEN THE N.C. AND z SCORES

This relationship is frequently misunderstood so that elaborating upon its meaning is worthwhile. First of all, transforming raw scores to standard scores does *not* alter the shape of the original distribution. The change produced by the transformation only converts the mean of the distribution to zero and the standard deviation of the distribution to one. The distribution of z scores merely reflects the original distribution, that is, if the raw scores are normally distributed the z scores will be and if the raw scores are not normally distributed the z scores will not be. In brief, transforming raw scores to z scores will *not* convert a nonnormal distribution into a normal one.

There are affinities among raw scores, z scores, and percentiles of a *normally* distributed variable. This association is pictured in Figure 6.4 which has μ = 50 and σ = 10.

USES OF THE NORMAL CURVE AND STANDARD SCORES

The N.C. used in conjunction with standard scores is extremely important in statistics because measurements can be expressed using a common standard rather than in terms of their original units, for example, age, weight, height, and so forth. Consequently, the N.C. is one of the most practical as well as theoretical discoveries in statistical analysis. As the following example illustrates, it enables us to standardize or reduce to a common denominator measurements having different bases.

FIGURE 6.4

Relationships among Raw Scores, z Scores, and Percentiles of a Normally Distributed Variable

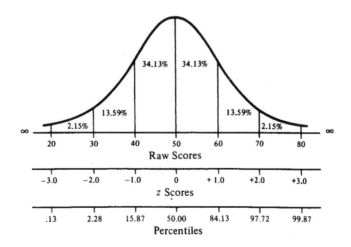

Let us say that three persons from different countries decide to exchange their currency among each other. A German has 1,000 marks, an Italian 1,000 lira, and an Indian 1,000 rupees. Would it be fair simply to exchange these monetary units as they stand? The answer to this query is "No!" assuming no one wants to be cheated. Why, then, can't a simple exchange of marks for lira, lira for rupees, and so forth, be sufficient? Each of these monies has been taken from a monetary distribution based on a different unit of measurement—the mark, the lira, and the rupee. Determining the comparability of the three requires us to reduce them to a common standard. With a common standard we can legitimately compare the value of the mark, lira, and rupee.

One way to compare the different monetary units (or any raw score distributions) would be to convert them to **standard scores** (sometimes called *z* **scores**) through a process known as the *z* **transformation.**[1] To transform any raw score to a *z* score, formula (6.3) is used (notice that this formula is mathematically identical to formula [6.2]):

$$z = \frac{X_i - \bar{X}}{s} \tag{6.3}$$

where: z = standard score
X_i = any raw score in a distribution
$\bar{X}$ = the mean of the distribution
s = the standard deviation of the distribution

To illustrate the computation and application of standard scores, let us assume that there are two students, designated S_1 and S_2, who have taken introductory sociology from different professors. On the final exam, S_1 received a raw score of 78 whereas S_2 received a raw score of 89. Without a standard for comparison, it looks as if S_2 did better than S_1. But is that true? To answer this question we need two additional pieces of information (see *z* score formula). We must know the mean ($\bar{X}$) and standard deviation (s) for each class. Let's say that the mean in class 1 is 75 ($\bar{X}_1 = 75$) and the standard deviation in class 1 is 6.5 ($s_1 = 6.5$), while the mean in class 2 is 88 ($\bar{X}_2 = 88$) and the standard deviation is 4 ($s_2 = 4$).

With these three pieces of information (three for each student, X_i, $\bar{X}$, and s), we can transform each student's raw score into its equivalent *z* score. When we convert each score in this fashion, we end up with a *standard score* or a *z score*. These standard scores are expressed in standard deviation units, and consequently, each raw score can be given a standard score equivalent. Let's perform this operation for S_1 and S_2 using formula (6.3):

$$S_1 = \frac{78 - 75}{6.5} = \frac{3}{6.5} = .46$$

$$S_2 = \frac{89 - 88}{4} = \frac{1}{4} = .25$$

Now it becomes clear which student did better *relative* to the other students in the

---

[1]This illustration is intended to be taken figuratively. It is used since this writer believes it facilitates grasping the logic behind z scores.

class. Figure 6.5 depicts this relationship. Since S_1's score falls to the right of S_2's score we can visually discern that there are fewer students above S_1 than is the case with S_2. A z score of .25 would be equivalent to a percentile of approximately 60 (.5000 of the N.C.'s area is to the left of the mean and .0987 of the area is between the mean and z = .25; hence, .5000 + .0987 = .5987).[2] On the other hand, a z score of .46 would be equivalent to a percentile of approximately 68 (.5000 of the N.C.'s area is to the left of the mean and .1772 of the curve's area is between the mean and z = .46; hence, .5000 + .1772 = .6772). Consequently, S_1 did better, relative to the class, than did S_2.

Additional Uses of Standard Scores and the Normal Curve

There are numerous generic applications of the z transformation. Since the N.C. is an important distribution used in both descriptive and inferential statistics, a table (Table B) of areas (proportions) under the curve has been placed in Appendix A of this book. Referring to this table, notice three columns labeled (A), (B), and (C). Column (A) represents the z score equivalent of a raw score; column (B) shows the area *between* the mean and respective z scores, and column (C) the area *beyond* particular z scores. *Since the N.C. is symmetrical only positive z scores are listed.* This means that regardless of the sign of the z score, the area between the mean and a particular z score and the area beyond a given z score is the same. Let us look at several illustrations.

FIGURE 6.5

Comparing Two Students' Exam Scores Using Standard Scores

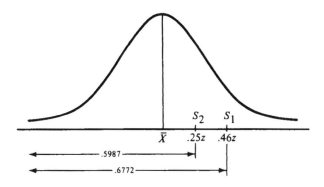

----

[2]The section entitled "Additional Uses of Standard Scores and the Normal Curve" will explain how a z score can be transformed into a percentile.

Finding the Area between z scores. Suppose we wish to know the area under the N.C. between .3z and 1.97z. The steps are these:

1. In the N.C. table (Table B) find the area between the mean and 1.97z. This value is .4756.
2. In the N.C. table find the area between the mean and .3z. This value is .1179.
3. Since we're interested in the area between .3z and 1.97z we simply *subtract* the two, or .4756 − .1179 = .3577. Therefore, about 36 percent of the area falls *between* these two points. Diagrammatically, the operation we've performed looks like Figure 6.6.

FIGURE 6.6

Scheme for Visualizing How to Find the Area between z Scores

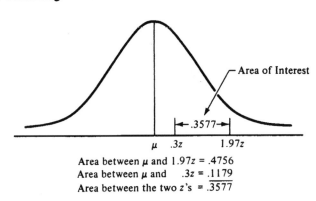

Area between μ and 1.97z = .4756
Area between μ and   .3z = .1179
Area between the two z's = .3577

Another illustration is this: suppose we wish to know the area (or percentage of cases) between −.75z and + 2.20z. These steps are necessary:

1. In the N.C. table find the area between the mean and .75z. This value is .2734.
2. In the N.C. table find the area between the mean and 2.20z. This value is .4861.
3. Since we're interested in the area between −.75z and 2.20z we simply *add* the two, or .2734 + .4861 = .7595. Therefore, approximately 76 percent of the area falls *between* these two points. Diagrammatically, this will look like Figure 6.7.

One important point to remember when finding the area between any two z scores is that when both z's are located on the *same* side of the curve, the area they encompass is determined by *subtracting* the two areas, and when the z's are located on *opposite* sides of the mean, the area they encompass is obtained by *adding* the two areas.

FIGURE 6.7

Scheme for Visualizing How to Find the Area between z Scores

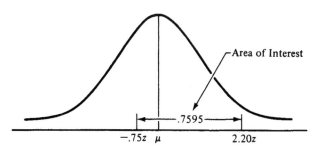

Area between μ and $-.75z$ = .2734
Area between μ and 2.20z = .4861
Area between the two z's = .7595

Determining the Number of Scores above or below a Given Raw Score. Another use of z scores is to determine the number of scores that fall above or below a given raw score. Suppose we have the following statistics: $\bar{X} = 100$, $s = 15$, and $N = 500$ and we want to know how many scores fall *above* a raw score of 120. We are assuming the variable is normally distributed. The following steps are recommended:

1. Convert the raw score (in this case $X_i = 120$) into a z score using the z transformation formula (6.3). Hence,

$$z = \frac{120 - 100}{15} = \frac{20}{15} = 1.33$$

2. The area between μ and 1.33z is .4082. Since we are interested in scores above 1.33z we must subtract .4082 from .5000 (.5000 because one-half the curve is above the mean and one-half below). Subtracting, .5000 − .4082 = .0918.

3. Multiply this proportion by the number of cases in the hypothetical example: .0918(500) = 45.90.

About 46 cases fall *above* a raw score of 120 and approximately 454 fall at and below that raw score.

Obtaining the Percentile Rank of a Raw Score. The percentile rank of a score of 120 is 91. Since the z score equivalent of a raw score of 120 is 1.33 we find the column which indicates that 9.18 percent of the cases fall beyond that z value. Since 50 percent of the cases fall below the mean we add that to the percent of cases between the mean and $z = 1.33$. The latter figure is .4082. Consequently, the percentile rank of 120 is 90.82 (50 + 40.82 percent = 90.82) or approximately 91.

Had the z score been -1.33 the percentile rank would have been 9, that is, about 91 percent of the scores would be beyond a z score of -1.33.

Finding a Raw Score from a z Score. Another use of z scores is in determining a person's raw score from his or her z score. To perform this operation formula (6.4) may be used:[3]

$$X_i = \bar{X} + z(s) \tag{6.4}$$

where: X_i = raw score

$\bar{X}$ = mean of the distribution

z = z score equivalent of raw score

s = standard deviation of the distribution

To illustrate, suppose a person has a z score of -1.24 in a distribution with a mean equal to 70 ($\bar{X} = 70$) and a standard deviation equal to 10 ($s = 10$). To determine the person's **raw score** substitute these values in formula (6.4):

$$\begin{aligned} X_i &= 70 + (-1.24)(10) \\ &= 70 + (-12.4) \\ &= 57.6 \end{aligned}$$

The person's raw score is equal to approximately 58.

SUMMARY

In this chapter we have discussed the properties of the normal curve and z scores. In addition, the relationship between the standardized N.C. and z scores was presented along with several generic applications of the z transformation. It should be mentioned that there are other kinds of **linear transformations** (like the t transformation). Although the emphasis in this chapter has been on the *descriptive functions* of the N.C. and z scores, in future chapters we will see their application in inferential statistics, that is, z scores are used in some tests of significance and the N.C. is used as a sampling distribution.

[3]Notice that formula (6.4) is derived from formula (6.2). Through transposing we are solving for X_i.

IMPORTANT CONCEPTS DISCUSSED IN THIS CHAPTER

Normal curve

Parameters

Statistics

Symmetrical

Ordinate

Asymptotic

Unit normal distribution (standardized
    normal curve)

Point of inflection

Chebyshev's Theorem (Tchebycheff's
    inequality)

z scores (standard score)

z transformation

Raw score

Linear transformation

REVIEW QUESTIONS

1. A high school student takes the SAT test and obtains a raw score of 550. If the mean of
    this test is 500 and the standard deviation is 100, what is the student's z score?
    a. Assuming the scores are normally distributed:
        (1) What is the student's percentile rank?
        (2) What percentage of students performed better?

2. Another high school student taking the SAT test obtains a z score of $-.37$. What is this
    student's raw score? (Use same $\overline{X}$ and s as in question 1.)
    a. What is the student's percentile rank?
    b. What percentage of students performed poorer than this student?

3. Assuming a normal distribution, what is the percentage of cases between:
    a. $+.61z$ and $+1.19z$
    b. $-.61z$ and $+.61z$
    c. $+.61z$ and $-1.19z$
    d. $+.57z$ and $+2.87z$
    e. $-1.92z$ and $+3.4z$

4. Discuss the nature and properties of the normal curve. In what way is it a bridge
    between descriptive and inferential statistics.

5. On an introductory sociology exam four students receive raw scores of 38 (S_1), 42
    (S_2), 55 (S_3), and 67 (S_4). If the mean and standard deviation of the exam is 42 and
    7.5, respectively, what are the four students' z scores?

6. On the introductory sociology exam (question 5 above) two students receive z scores of −1.87 and +.63.
   a. What are their raw scores?
   b. What are the percentile ranks of the two students?

7. Why are z scores (standard scores) useful in statistics?

3

INFERENTIAL STATISTICS

CHAPTER 7

INFERENTIAL STATISTICS: PARAMETER ESTIMATION

The branch of statistics known as **statistical inference** is concerned with two topics. One topic developed by Ronald Fisher and discussed in the next chapter is *hypothesis testing*. The second topic developed by Jerzy Neyman and discussed in this chapter, is known as **statistical or parameter estimation**. *The goal of this latter concern is to estimate population parameters on the basis of a sample selected from a larger universe of elements.* You will recall from Chapter 1 that the purpose of inferential statistics is to infer numerical characteristics (parameters) of a population (the complete set of elements of interest) from a sample (subset of elements) selected from that larger entity. In diagrammatic form, we are interested in the relationship between a population and a sample as depicted in Figure 7.1.

If the universe is large, as it often is in social research, it would be tremendously demanding in time, money, and effort to survey or obtain information from the entire set. Furthermore, there are instances when the population is infinite and/or conceptual. Interestingly, it is *not* necessary to obtain data from the complete set since by employing certain methodological/statistical procedures we may determine the accuracy of our sample by using some basic probability principles.

Since we rarely study populations exhaustively, we rely on the outcomes of carefully selected samples (statistics) for understanding the universe. Keep in mind that the statistics calculated on the basis of sample data are not of intrinsic interest; instead, they are a means to an end, the end being an understanding of the universe. In order to understand the nature of the inference process we must discuss what is probably the single most important concept in inductive statistics, that of *sampling distribution.* Before we dwell on this concept let us continue the logical scheme relating the level of measurement to the appropriate statistical techniques discussed in this chapter. Figure 7.2 is presented for this purpose. Notice that with interval/ratio level data constructing a confidence interval for a mean is recommended whereas with nominal and ordinal data we construct confidence intervals for proportions or percentages.

FIGURE 7.1

A Scheme for Visualizing the Nature of Parameter Estimation

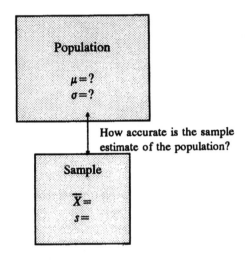

FIGURE 7.2

Parameter Estimation Techniques by Levels of Measurement

Appropriate Statistical Technique	Levels of Measurement		
	Nominal	Ordinal	Interval/Ratio
Parameter estimation techniques	Confidence interval for a proportion* (or percentage*)	Confidence interval for a proportion* (or percentage*)	Confidence interval for a mean

*Variable must be dichotomized.

SAMPLING DISTRIBUTION

By definition, a **sampling distribution** *is a theoretical probability distribution indicating the different occurrences of a sample statistic if one were to select all possible samples of a fixed size from a given population.* Admittedly, this definition is not easily comprehended without a concrete illustration. Consequently, let us take a specific example.

Suppose our population consisted of 20,000 students and we were interested in the average age of the student body. The average age would be a parameter that is *fixed* and *unknown* and is what we wish to estimate through the selection of a sample. How we select the sample from the larger universe is of major importance. Generally, we assume some form of random sampling in which the probability of selecting different elements in the universe is equal. In other words, each element has an equal (or known) chance of being selected.

If we selected a single random sample of 100 students, asked these students their ages, and then computed the arithmetic mean for the ages of those selected, it is unlikely that our sample mean would exactly equal the population mean. In fact, were we to select a second, third, fourth, ad infinitum random sample it is probable that there would be very few, if any, *sample means* that would yield values exactly equal to the *population mean*. In brief, in statistical inference we assume that a sample estimate is somewhat discrepant with the universe parameter. Any discrepancy between the sample statistic and universe parameter which is the result of random sampling is termed **random sampling error.** Fortunately, the statistician has found that sampling errors behave systematically; that is, sampling errors have a known pattern or shape to them. It is this overall pattern or shape of sampling errors that gives rise to the concept of sampling distribution. There are a variety of statistical techniques that are used to estimate the amount of sampling error, and these procedures vary in accordance with the sample statistic (for example, whether it is a mean, proportion, percentage, or variance, etc.) and according to the characteristics of the sample (whether it is large, small, simple, stratified, or cluster, etc.). Here we will illustrate two generic types: one for *means* and the other for *proportions for large random samples*.

Since a sampling distribution is a *univariate* distribution we may use measures of central tendency, for example, mean; measures of dispersion, for example, standard deviation or variance; and measures of form, for example, kurtosis or skewness, to describe the sampling distribution.

Let us generate an *empirical sampling distribution*. Of course, by definition a sampling distribution is theoretical or conceptual in nature and rarely empirically generated. However, this exercise seems to be necessary if this pivotal concept is to be adequately grasped. The following paragraph with an example to succeed it should be helpful in visualizing what is involved. There are different sampling distributions depending upon the statistic involved. For heuristic purposes we will focus exclusively upon the **sampling distribution of means and sampling errors.**

A random sample of a given size is selected from the universe. The statistic, for example, mean or proportion, computed from this sample is considered a single observation. The population consists of all possible samples that can be selected from the original universe using the same random sampling procedure and the same sample size. We compute a statistic for all possible samples. The computed statistics become the variable being studied, and we construct a frequency distribution of that variable. This distribution is a sampling distribution, and we ultimately compute the mean and standard deviation of the sampling distribution to understand its nature.

Let us demonstrate the relationships among these ideas with a hypothetical experiment. Assume we have the following population of four elements:

$$X_i$$

1(a)
2(b)
3(c)
4(d)

Imagine randomly selecting all possible X_i's using a sample size of two with *replacement* (replacement is when the elements selected are replaced before successive samples are drawn). When the population is relatively small, as it is here ($N = 4$), it is desirable to sample *with* replacement. On the other hand, when the universe is infinitely large, one may employ sampling *without* replacement. The number of possible samples that could be drawn from a population with four elements (1, 2, 3, and 4 in our example), taking two at a time, is:

$$N^n$$

where: N = number of elements in the population
        n = sample size

In the present case, $N^n = 4^2 = 16$ possible samples.[1] Suppose we label each population value with a lowercase letter, for example, $a = 1$, $b = 2$, $c = 3$, and $d = 4$. If we selected samples two at a time, *all the possible arrangements we could select* appear in Table 7.1.

If we then treat each statistic (sample mean), for example, 1.0, 1.5, 2.0, . . . , 4.0 in Table 7.1, as a raw score (single observation), we may construct a *frequency (sampling) distribution* for these sample means as appears in Table 7.2. Note the probabilistic nature of this distribution. Some means, for example, 2.5, 3.0, and 2.0, occur more often than others, for example, 4.0 and 1.0. For these data a mean of 2.5 is likely to occur about 25 percent of the time whereas means of 4.0 and 1.0 are likely to occur about 6 percent of the time.

---

[1]Technically speaking, this procedure—N^n—only applies to sampling *with* replacement. When sampling *without* replacement we do not permit the same case to reappear more than once and, as a consquence, the number of possible samples is determined as follows:

$$\frac{N}{n} = \frac{N!}{(N-n)!\,n!} = \frac{4!}{(4-2)!\,2!} = 6$$

This latter formula is used to determine the number of combinations of N elements taken n at a time. Notice the exclamation mark (!). This is called a *factorial sign* and instructs us to multiply the number by all values less than it but larger than zero. For example, $4! = (4)(3)(2)(1) = 24$. In general $N! = N(N-1)(N-2)(N-3) \ldots$.

TABLE 7.1

Sampling Distribution of $\bar{X}$'s and Sampling Errors

Possible Samples (N^2)				
No.	Letter Designation	Sample Values	Sample Means ($\bar{X}$)	Sampling Errors $(\bar{X} - \mu_{\bar{X}})^2$
1	aa	1 + 1	1.0	$1.0 - 2.5 = -1.5^2 = 2.25$
2	ab	1 + 2	1.5	$1.5 - 2.5 = -1^2 = 1.00$
3	ac	1 + 3	2.0	$2.0 - 2.5 = -.5^2 = .25$
4	ad	1 + 4	2.5	$2.5 - 2.5 = 0^2 = .00$
5	ba	2 + 1	1.5	$1.5 - 2.5 = -1^2 = 1.00$
6	bb	2 + 2	2.0	$2.0 - 2.5 = -.5^2 = .25$
7	bc	2 + 3	2.5	$2.5 - 2.5 = 0^2 = .00$
8	bd	2 + 4	3.0	$3.0 - 2.5 = .5^2 = .25$
9	ca	3 + 1	2.0	$2.0 - 2.5 = -.5^2 = .25$
10	cb	3 + 2	2.5	$2.5 - 2.5 = 0^2 = .00$
11	cc	3 + 3	3.0	$3.0 - 2.5 = .5^2 = .25$
12	cd	3 + 4	3.5	$3.5 - 2.5 = 1^2 = 1.00$
13	da	4 + 1	2.5	$2.5 - 2.5 = 0^2 = .00$
14	db	4 + 2	3.0	$3.0 - 2.5 = .5^2 = .25$
15	dc	4 + 3	3.5	$3.5 - 2.5 = 1^2 = 1.00$
16	dd	4 + 4	4.0	$4.0 - 2.5 = 1.5^2 = 2.25$
$N = 16$			$\Sigma = 40$	$\Sigma = 10$

$$\mu_{\bar{X}} = \frac{\Sigma \bar{X}}{N} \qquad \sigma_{\bar{X}} = \sqrt{\frac{\Sigma(\bar{X} - \mu_{\bar{X}})^2}{N}}$$

$$= \frac{40}{16} \qquad\qquad = \sqrt{\frac{10}{16}}$$

$$= 2.5 \qquad\qquad = .79$$

TABLE 7.2

Sampling Distribution of $\bar{X}$'s for Samples of Size Two Selected from a Population of Four

$\bar{X}$'s	f	Fraction	Proportion	Percentage
4.0	1	1/16	.0625	6.25
3.5	2	2/16	.1250	12.50
3.0	3	3/16	.1875	18.75
2.5	4	4/16	.2500	25.00
2.0	3	3/16	.1875	18.75
1.5	2	2/16	.1250	12.50
1.0	1	1/16	.0625	6.25
	$\Sigma = 16$	16/16	1.0000	100.00

Taking the data in Table 7.2 let us construct a *frequency bar graph* using the procedure outlined in Chapter 3. We will locate frequencies along the ordinate and the sample means along the abscissa. This has been done in Figure 7.3.

FIGURE 7.3

Bar Graph Representing a Sampling Distribution of Means for Samples of Size Two Selected from a Population of Four

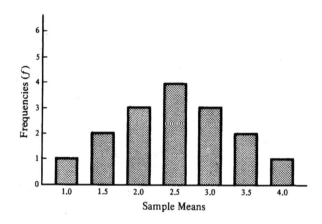

Notice that this distribution of sample means is already taking on the form of the normal curve. If we were to repeat the above procedures using a sample size of three rather than two, what would happen? To do this empirically would be laborious but, mathematically, it can be shown that as sample size increases the dispersion of sample means becomes more compact. It is also known that sample means from randomly selected samples will gravitate toward the universe mean which is at the center of the distribution.

Finally, let us construct a *sampling distribution of sampling errors* and then a bar graph visually displaying their distribution. To do this we work with the last column $(\bar{X} - \mu_{\bar{x}})^2$ in Table 7.1. (Note, however, that the squared differences will *not* be used.) Table 7.3 contains the distribution of sampling errors. Again, your attention is called to the patterned nature of this distribution. Furthermore, notice that small divergencies (e.g., ±.5) are common and large divergencies (e.g., ±1.5) are less common. Let us construct a *frequency bar graph* using the data in Table 7.3. We follow standard procedure and locate frequencies along the ordinate and, in this case, sampling errors along the abscissa. The completed graph appears in Figure 7.4.

In both illustrations—sampling distribution of means and sampling distribution of sampling errors—the distribution of the statistic is not haphazard but remarkably orderly and patterned. It is this orderly and predictable pattern to sampling distributions that permits the statistician to make meaningful and intelligible inferences from the sample to the larger population.

TABLE 7.3

Sampling Distribution of Sampling Errors for Samples of Size Two Selected from a Population of Four

Sampling Errors	f	Fraction	Proportion	Percentage
1.5	1	1/16	.0625	6.25
1.0	2	2/16	.1250	12.50
.5	3	3/16	.1875	18.75
.0	4	4/16	.2500	25.00
− .5	3	3/16	.1875	18.75
−1.0	2	2/16	.1250	12.50
−1.5	1	1/16	.0625	6.25
	$\Sigma = 16$	16/16	1.0000	100.00

FIGURE 7.4

Bar Graph Representing a Sampling Distribution of Sampling Errors for Samples of Size Two Selected from a Population of Four

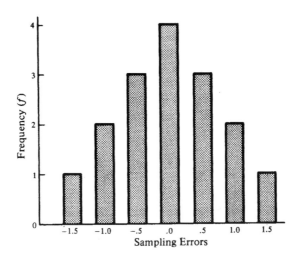

The Central Tendency, Dispersion, and
Form of a Sampling Distribution

Central Tendency. The mean of a sampling distribution (symbolized $\mu_{\bar{X}}$) is obtained with formula (7.1):

$$\mu_{\bar{X}} = \frac{\Sigma \bar{X}}{N} \tag{7.1}$$

where: $\mu_{\bar{X}}$ = mean of a sampling distribution
$\bar{X}$ = sample mean
N = number of samples

For the data in Table 7.1 here is what we do. For each of our 16 samples we compute the mean, for example, $1(a) + 1(a) = 2 \div 2 = 1, \ldots, 1(a) + 4(d) = 5 \div 2 = 2.5, \ldots, 4(d) + 4(d) = 8 \div 2 = 4$. The mean is a statistic, of course, and is treated as a single observation. The mean of the sampling distribution is obtained by summing these means and dividing by the number of samples. Doing this, $\mu_{\bar{X}} = 40/16 = 2.5$.

Dispersion. On the other hand, the standard deviation of a sampling distribution of means, called the **standard error of the mean** (symbolized $\sigma_{\bar{X}}$) is obtained with formula (7.2):

$$\sigma_{\bar{X}} = \sqrt{\frac{\Sigma(\bar{X} - \mu_{\bar{X}})^2}{N}} \tag{7.2}$$

where: $\sigma_{\bar{X}}$ = standard error of the mean
$\bar{X}$ = sample mean
$\mu_{\bar{X}}$ = mean of the sampling distribution
N = number of samples

For the data in Table 7.1 we treat each sample mean as a raw score (single observation), find the difference between the mean of the sampling distribution ($\mu_{\bar{X}}$) and each sample mean ($\bar{X}$) and square that difference. After summing these squared differences and dividing by N the square root is extracted. This operation produces the standard error of the mean. For example, $1 - 2.5 = -1.5^2 = 2.25, 1.5 - 2.5 = -1.0^2 = 1.00, \ldots, 4.0 - 2.5 = 1.5^2 = 2.25$. This operation has been performed in the column labeled $(\bar{X} - \mu_{\bar{X}})^2$ in Table 7.1. Plugging our values into formula (7.2), the standard deviation of the sampling distribution (standard error of the mean) would be .79, that is:

$$\sigma_{\bar{X}} = \sqrt{\frac{\Sigma(\bar{X} - \mu_{\bar{X}})^2}{N}} = \sqrt{\frac{10}{16}} = \sqrt{.625} = .79$$

The standard error of the mean measures the variability of sample means around the population mean. The difference between the standard error and the standard deviation is that the latter measures variability of *scores* around their mean whereas the former measures variability of *sample means* around the universe mean.

Form. In order to extrapolate from a sample to a universe it is vitally important to know the specific form of the sampling distribution. Here we are introduced to one of the most important statistical theorems, the **central limit theorem**. It states that if repeated random samples of size n are selected from a normally distributed population with mean $= \mu$ and standard deviation $= \sigma$, the means of our samples will be normally distributed with mean $= \mu$ and standard error $= \sigma/\sqrt{n}$. Furthermore, if n (sample size) is large, the distribution of sample means will approximate normality with mean $= \mu$ and standard error $= \sigma/\sqrt{n}$ *regardless of the shape* of the population from which the samples were selected. This theorem tells us that even with a small n, the distribution of simple random samples selected from a normal universe will produce a normal sampling distribution. It also says that as long as n is large (100 to be conservative) the sampling distribution of means will tend to be normal even if the population is skewed. (This latter statement is sometimes referred to as the **law of large numbers** to distinguish it from the central limit theorem).

In summary, the central tendency and dispersion of the sampling distribution of means are obtained using formulae (7.1) ($\mu_{\bar{x}}$) and (7.2) ($\sigma_{\bar{x}}$). The form or shape of this sampling distribution is known via the central limit theorem.

PROBLEMS IN PARAMETER ESTIMATION

If one wants to estimate the population average, that is, μ, why not simply use the sample mean, that is, $\bar{X}$? As we said earlier, if one wants to know the average of a particular population parameter there are *several* measures of central tendency that could be used. In short, in addition to the sample mean, the sample median or sample mode could be employed to estimate the population average.

Since it is possible to use different averages to estimate the population para-meter(s), we need some guidelines for making our selection. Mathematicians have developed several sound criteria for helping us determine the true population values. One of these criteria is *bias*. The ideal in statistical estimation is to select a statistic that is an **unbiased estimate** of its parameter counterpart. More specifically, a *sample estimate is an unbiased estimate of a population parameter if the mean of its sampling distribution is exactly equal to the value of the parameter being esti-mated.* It so happens that the sample mean ($\bar{X}$) is an unbiased estimate of the population mean (μ) since the mean of the sampling distribution, designated $\mu_{\bar{x}}$, has μ as its mean. In a practical sense, this suggests that using the sample mean to estimate the population mean is mathematically adequate. In other words, if the *expected value* of a statistic, $\bar{X}$ in this case, *is* the parameter which it is attempting to estimate, the statistic is said to be an unbiased estimator of the parameter. Bear in mind that the expected value is *not* a single sample value but the average value it takes on for its sampling distribution.

Statisticians use a capital E to designate the expected value of a statistic. The value expected of the sample mean would be expressed $E(\bar{X})$. We will now illustrate why the sample mean is an unbiased estimator of the population mean or, to express this relationship symbolically, $E(\bar{X}) = \mu$.

Recall that an unbiased estimate is defined as one in which the mean of the sampling distribution of means ($\mu_{\bar{X}}$) is equal to μ. In our previous example we said the universe contained four elements with the values of 1, 2, 3, and 4. The μ for this set is easily calculated to be 2.5 ($\mu = \Sigma X_i / N = 10/4 = 2.5$). Imagine, as we have done in Table 7.1, selecting all possible samples of size two, adding together each of the selected values and calculating a mean for each sample of size two. In the column labeled Sample Means ($\bar{X}$) (Table 7.1) this has been done. If each of these sample means is then treated as a raw score (X_i) and all sample means are summed and this sum is divided by the number of samples, the mean of the sampling distribution of means is calculated to be 2.5 ($\mu_{\bar{X}} = \Sigma \bar{X}/N = 40/16 = 2.5$). We have demonstrated the unbiased nature of the mean by showing that $\mu_{\bar{X}} = \mu$, that is, $E(\bar{X}) = \mu$.

Although $\bar{X}$ is an unbiased estimator, the sample standard deviation (s) is a **biased estimator** of the population standard deviation (σ), since the standard error of the mean ($\sigma_{\bar{X}}$), which is defined as *the standard deviation of a sampling distribution of means* is *not* equal to the population standard deviation. Specifically, the sample standard deviation *underestimates* the population standard deviation. In short, $E(s) \neq \sigma$; in fact, $E(s) < \sigma$. Let us prove this.

The sample standard deviation is a *biased* estimate of σ since it tends to systematically underestimate σ. Knowing the values in the population (1, 2, 3, and 4) σ could easily be computed to be 1.12 using formula (5.11):

$$\sigma = \sqrt{\frac{\Sigma X_i^2 - \frac{(\Sigma X_i)^2}{N}}{N}}$$

$$= \sqrt{\frac{30 - \frac{(10)^2}{4}}{4}}$$

$$= \sqrt{\frac{30 - \frac{100}{4}}{4}}$$

$$= \sqrt{\frac{30 - 25}{4}}$$

$$= \sqrt{\frac{5}{4}}$$

$$= \sqrt{1.25}$$

$$= 1.12$$

Table 7.4 illustrates this operation using the formula (5.10):

$$\sigma = \sqrt{\frac{\Sigma (X_i - \mu)^2}{N}}$$

TABLE 7.4

Calculation of σ from a Known Universe

X_i	μ	$X_i - \mu$	$(X_i - \mu)^2$
1	2.5	−1.5	2.25
2	2.5	−.5	.25
3	2.5	.5	.25
4	2.5	1.5	2.25
			$\Sigma = 5.00$

$$\sigma = \sqrt{\frac{\Sigma(X_i - \mu)^2}{N}} = \sqrt{\frac{5}{4}} = \sqrt{1.25} = 1.12$$

To calculate the standard deviation of a sampling distribution ($\sigma_{\bar{X}}$) we treat each sample mean as a raw score, subtract $\mu_{\bar{X}}$ (mean of the sampling distribution) from each sample mean, square these differences and sum them, divide by N and take the square root. This operation has been performed in the column labeled ($\bar{X} - \mu_{\bar{X}})^2$ in Table 7.1. If we used the conventional formula for computing $\sigma_{\bar{X}}$ (the standard deviation of a sampling distribution) the value produced would be .79:

$$\sigma_{\bar{X}} = \sqrt{\frac{\Sigma(\bar{X} - \mu_{\bar{X}})^2}{N}} = \sqrt{\frac{10}{16}} = \sqrt{.625} = .79$$

Obviously, .79 $<$ 1.12. Since $\sigma_{\bar{X}} < \sigma$ it is said to be a biased estimate. To inflate this value we reduce the denominator by unity, that is, we use $n - 1$ rather than n. If we knew σ, the standard error of the mean could be computed by using formula (7.3):

$$\sigma_{\bar{X}} = \frac{\sigma}{\sqrt{n}} \qquad (7.3)$$

where: $\sigma_{\bar{X}} =$ standard error of the mean
  $\sigma =$ population standard deviation
  $n =$ number of observations

However, when we don't know σ, we must estimate it from the sample standard deviation by employing formula (7.4):

$$s_{\bar{X}} = \frac{s}{\sqrt{n-1}} \qquad (7.4)$$

where: $s_{\bar{X}}$ = estimated standard error of the mean
s = sample standard deviation
$n-1$ = correction factor used to bring the sample estimate more in line with the known values of σ.[2]

A second mathematical criterion in estimation is **efficiency.** The efficiency of an estimate refers to the degree to which the sampling distribution is clustered about the true value of the mean of the universe. Some statisticians believe this is more important than bias since a particular sample's value ($\bar{X}$) doesn't always *exactly* equal the sampling distribution's value ($\mu_{\bar{X}}$). A third criterion, beyond the scope of this text, is termed the *principle of maximum likelihood.* Some of the more advanced statistics books present a discussion of this concept.

TWO KINDS OF PARAMETER ESTIMATES

Point Estimation

The first type of estimator is called a **point estimation.** Here interest is in the best *single* value which can be used to estimate a parameter. If we've selected a single random sample we may estimate the mean of the population (μ) to be the mean of the sample ($\bar{X}$). Obviously, sample means can vary, but the unbiased nature of the sample mean permits us to employ it as an estimator of μ. This estimate is in some ways analogous to guessing that your instructor weighs 175 pounds. In other words, you've used a single value, 175 pounds, to estimate the instructor's actual weight (the parameter). Most of you would agree that such an estimate is prone to vary from one day to the next and from student to student, and few would be willing to bet their last dollar on the precision of the guess (or estimator). In brief, the major disadvantage of a point estimate is that it provides no indication of sampling error. These reservations lead us into another type of estimator.

nterval Estimation: Confidence Intervals

The second type of estimator is called an *interval estimate* or **interval estimation.** Here we are interested in a *range* of values (interval of values) as an estimate of a

---

[2] Even with the correction factor the sample standard deviation is *not* an unbiased estimate. However, the computation of the *sample variance* in conjunction with the use of the correction factor does produce an unbiased estimate of the population variance since $E(s^2) = [(n-1)/n]\,\sigma^2$. Because of this the sample variance is used more often in inferential statistics than is the sample standard deviation.

population parameter. Let us return to the example of estimating your instructor's weight. How confident are you that your instructor weighs exactly 175 pounds? Probably, not very! However, if you guessed the weight to be somewhere between 165 and 185 pounds you undoubtedly would be more certain. Moreover, you may be willing to bet your bottom dollar that your instructor weighs between 150 and 200 pounds. Note that as the interval becomes wider, for example, 165–185 and 150–200, your confidence increases that the true value (weight of the instructor) is contained within those limits. In an analogous fashion this is what we do in constructing **confidence intervals**.

To employ interval estimation for a mean we use the following generic formula (7.5):

$$\text{interval estimate for a mean} = \overline{X} \pm z\, (\sigma_{\overline{X}}) \qquad (7.5)$$

where: $\overline{X}$ = sample mean
z = z value appropriate to confidence interval selected
$\sigma_{\overline{X}}$ = standard error of the mean obtained by $\sigma/\sqrt{N}$

When the population standard deviation is *known*, formula (7.5) becomes: $\overline{X} \pm z$ $(\sigma/\sqrt{N})$. When it is *not known* and must be estimated from the sample standard deviation it must be modified; hence, it becomes:

$$\text{interval estimate for a mean} = \overline{X} \pm z \left[\frac{s}{\sqrt{n-1}} \right] \qquad (7.6)$$

STEPS IN CONSTRUCTING CONFIDENCE INTERVALS

The first decision that must be made is how much risk you are willing to take in making an error in stating that the parameter is somewhere in the confidence interval when, in fact, it may not be. Let's assume you would be willing to make this error 5 percent of the time. In this case you would employ what statisticians call the **95 percent confidence interval (limits)**. On the other hand, say you would be willing to make this miscue 1 percent of the time. This is technically called the **99 percent confidence interval (limits)**. Other confidence intervals may be chosen, but these are the most customary ones.

The interval is obtained by going out in both directions (+ and −) from the sample mean (which may be thought of as a point estimate) a certain multiple of standard error units corresponding to the confidence interval selected.[3] The z values for the 95 percent and 99 percent confidence intervals are 1.96 and 2.58, respectively. The confidence level one decides to use is converted into a z *score* or the number of standard errors to be included in the interval. This is done by turning

---

[3]One might legitimately argue that the sampling error of a single sample cannot be measured since we never really know the universe mean. But, the single sample does provide us with a single value (point estimate) that is an unbiased estimate of the parameter since $E(\overline{X}) = \mu$. Combining this observation with our knowledge of the sampling distribution it becomes possible to construct a meaningful band within which the parameter should lie.

to the N.C. table, B in Appendix A of this book. Since the central limit theorem enables us to use the N.C. table, we want to find how many standard errors from the mean we must go to include the desired percent (95 percent or 99 percent usually) of the sample means. Since the N.C. is symmetrical only the positive z scores are listed. To include 95 percent or 99 percent of the area under the curve we look for one-half of these percents, or 47.5 and 49.5, respectively. Then we find the z values that have 2.5 and .5 percent of the area beyond them or 47.5 and 49.5 percent between the z score and the mean. The z scores for the 95 percent and 99 percent confidence levels are 1.96 and 2.58, respectively. These values (1.96 and 2.58) are identical to the critical values in two-tailed hypothesis testing illustrations to be discussed in the next chapter. Thus, to determine the 95 percent confidence level (to estimate the population mean, μ), formula (7.7) is used:

$$95 \text{ percent confidence interval} = \bar{X} \pm 1.96(\sigma_{\bar{X}}) \qquad (7.7)$$

Given: $\bar{X} = 12$, $\sigma = 3$, and $N = 81$, let us construct the 95 percent confidence interval. Since the population standard deviation is known, formula (7.7) is appropriate with $\sigma_{\bar{X}}$ computed using formula (7.3):

$$95 \text{ percent confidence interval} = \bar{X} \pm 1.96\left(\frac{\sigma}{\sqrt{N}}\right)$$

Substituting our values:

$$95 \text{ percent confidence interval} = 12 \pm 1.96\left(\frac{3}{\sqrt{81}}\right)$$

$$= 12 \pm 1.96\left(\frac{3}{9}\right)$$

$$= 12 \pm 1.96(.333)$$

$$= 12 \pm .65$$

The 95 percent confidence interval runs from 11.35 to 12.65. These two end values are called the **confidence, fiducial, or credibility limits.** Sometimes the interval is expressed in this form and means we are 95% confident that μ is equal to or greater than 11.35 and equal to or less than 12.65.

$$C(11.35 \leq \mu \leq 12.65) = .95$$

INTERPRETATION OF CONFIDENCE INTERVALS

The interpretation of confidence intervals is in terms of *long-run* results. In other words, if we continued to select random samples indefinitely from the same population, and constructed confidence intervals for each, *95 of the 100 confidence intervals would include the parameter and 5 of the 100 would miss it.* In our illustration, if we continued this procedure over and over again we'd expect the true μ to be trapped by 95 percent of the confidence intervals.

The interpretation of confidence intervals is a bit tricky and needs to be elaborated. Let us assume that in constructing the 95 percent confidence interval we compute the *fiducial limits* to be 11.35 and 12.65. A common *error* is to say that 95 percent of the time μ is between 11.35 and 12.65. At any point in time the parameter μ is *fixed* and *unknown* and our goal is to estimate its value. Actually μ is or is not within the confidence limits and the probability is 0 if it isn't and 1.0 if it is. It is actually the computed $\bar{X}$ that varies from one random sample to the next, and of course $\bar{X}$ is used in constructing the confidence interval. From our knowledge of the sampling distribution we know that 95 percent of the $\bar{X}$'s will lie within 1.96 standard error units and 5 percent will lie outside this band of values. Therefore we say that in the long run 95 percent of the *confidence intervals* we construct will include the parameter we are attempting to estimate. In diagrammatic form this logic can be understood by examining Figure 7.5.

FIGURE 7.5

Sampling Distribution of Means Illustrating Distribution of Confidence Intervals of Hypothetical Sample $\bar{X}$'s Around μ

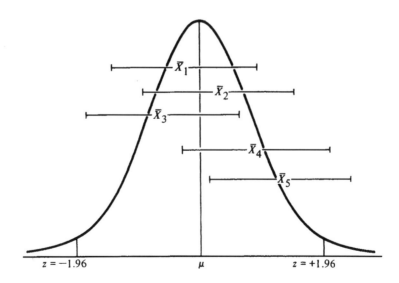

Notice that in (hypothetical) random samples 1 through 4 that the interval has *trapped* the parameter but in sample 5 it has not. To reiterate, the parameter μ is fixed and the confidence intervals are constructed around the mean; and with our knowledge of the probabilistic nature of the normal curve, 95 percent of the intervals will catch the parameter and 5 percent will not.

Let us construct the 99 percent confidence interval for the same data. The only change that must be made is to substitute the z value of 2.58 for 1.96. Thus:

$$99 \text{ percent confidence interval} = 12 \pm 2.58 \left(\frac{3}{\sqrt{81}} \right)$$

$$= 12 \pm 2.58 \left(\frac{3}{9} \right)$$

$$= 12 \pm 2.58(.333)$$

$$= 12 \pm .86$$

Using statistical notation this confidence interval may be expressed as:

$$C \ (11.14 \leq \mu \leq 12.86) = .99$$

The 99 percent confidence interval extends from 11.14 to 12.86. Once again, this is interpreted in long-run terms. If we continued this procedure indefinitely, 99 of the 100 confidence intervals should contain μ and only 1 of the 100 should not.

In actual research the 95 percent and 99 percent confidence intervals are the ones most frequently used. Despite these conventional levels, it is possible to construct any confidence interval, for example, 90 percent, 85 percent, 80 percent, and so forth, by employing the appropriate z score. For illustrative purposes let us construct the **90 percent confidence interval (limits)** for the data above. The only change that is necessary is to locate the z value appropriate to this level. In the N.C. table you will find a z value of 1.645 (actually this value is the result of inter-polating between a $z = 1.64$ and a $z = 1.65$) divides the curve in such a fashion that about 10 percent of the area exceeds that value. Hence,

$$90 \text{ percent confidence interval} = \bar{X} \pm 1.645 \left(\frac{\sigma}{\sqrt{N}} \right)$$

$$= 12 \pm 1.645 \left(\frac{3}{\sqrt{81}} \right)$$

$$= 12 \pm 1.645 \left(\frac{3}{9} \right)$$

$$= 12 \pm 1.645(.333)$$

$$= 12 \pm .55$$

Consequently, the 90 percent confidence interval extends from 11.45 to 12.55. It is interpreted in a similar fashion as above, that is, in the long run we would expect the true population mean to be contained within 90 percent of the confidence intervals. In symbolic form,

$$C \ (11.45 \leq \mu \leq 12.55) = .90$$

In the three examples above, the construction of the 95 percent, 99 percent, and 90 percent confidence intervals was demonstrated. In all cases we assumed that the *population* standard deviation (σ) was known. Most frequently, this is not the case. When σ is not known, it must be estimated from the *sample* standard deviation, and this estimate requires a modification in the formula. Instead of employing the formula $\overline{X} \pm z\,(\sigma/\sqrt{N})$, we must use formula (7.6), which may be written:

$$\text{interval estimate for a mean} = \overline{X} \pm z \left(\frac{s}{\sqrt{n-1}} \right)$$

If we had the following information: $n = 100$, $\overline{X} = 120$, and $s = 10$, and wished to construct the 99 percent confidence limits we would simply substitute these values into formula (7.6). Doing this according to the formula above:

$$\text{interval estimate for a mean} = 120 \pm 2.58 \left(\frac{10}{\sqrt{100-1}} \right)$$

$$= 120 \pm 2.58 \left(\frac{10}{9.95} \right)$$

$$= 120 \pm 2.58 \,(1.01)$$

$$= 120 \pm 2.61$$

The credibility limits are 117.39 and 122.61. Ninety-nine percent of the confidence intervals should trap μ. In standard notation,

$$C\,(117.39 \leq \mu \leq 122.61) = .99$$

OBSERVATIONS ON CONSTRUCTING CONFIDENCE INTERVALS

Confidence intervals, unlike point estimates, permit the investigator to indicate the degree of accuracy of the sample estimate. In other words, one can state that 90 percent, 95 percent, or 99 percent, and so forth, of the intervals will catch the true population parameter (μ). Note that one *cannot* say that 90 percent, 95 percent, or 99 percent of the time that μ will *exactly* equal a specific value (for example, the sample mean). Our statements, in other words, are made with respect to the constructed *intervals* and not for a *particular value*.

A confidence interval for a population parameter is obtained by taking the point estimate (sample mean) of the parameter and encasing it within an interval the width of which is a function of the standard error of the mean.

Notice what happens to the interval's width as the confidence interval is increased. For example, the credibility limits for the 90 percent confidence interval were 11.45 and 12.55; for the 95 percent confidence interval they were 11.35 and 12.65; and for the 99 percent confidence interval they were 11.14 and 12.86. As we increased the confidence levels we increased the chances of including the population parameter by increasing the band (or width) of the interval.

Note, too, that the size of the confidence interval is a function of the magnitude of the standard error. And, the standard error is a function of the sample size (*n*) and the standard deviation (*s*) of the sample. In fact, it is the **law of large numbers,** an important statistical theorem, that asserts that as the sample size increases the standard error decreases.

CONFIDENCE INTERVALS FOR A PROPORTION (PERCENTAGE)[4]

The procedure for computing a confidence interval for a proportion (or percent) is the same as that for a mean. After obtaining the proportion of interest in the sample, we attach to it a multiple of standard errors appropriate to the confidence level desired. As with any statistic, it is important to know the nature of its distribution. The *binomial sampling distribution* is the appropriate one for a proportion (See addendum at the end of this chapter).

The Binomial Sampling Distribution

This writer conducted a poll of student attitudes toward the impeachment of a former President. To exemplify the binomial sampling distribution let us consider one of the items, modified for our purposes, asked of 410 randomly selected students at Illinois State University. Do you believe the President should be impeached? Yes _____ or No _____ . The binomial probability distribution is appropriate for analyzing *dichotomized nominal level data* such as these.

Central Tendency. The mean of a binomial distribution is obtained by formula (7.8):

$$\mu_b = np \tag{7.8}$$

where: μ_b = mean of the binomial distribution
          n = sample size
          p = proportion of outcome of interest, for example, proportion of students favoring impeachment

---

[4]Frequencies, proportions, and percentages are different ways of presenting the same information. Notice in the text that any one can be easily derived from any other.

Actually, formula (7.8) is the mean of a *frequency* count and by dividing the mean of the binomial by n we obtain the mean proportion. Hence, the mean of a proportion ($\bar{p}$) becomes:

$$\bar{p} = \frac{np}{n} \tag{7.9}$$

Dispersion. The standard error of the binomial can be expressed as:

$$\sigma_b = \sqrt{npq} \tag{7.10}$$

where: σ_b = standard error of the binomial distribution
n = sample size
p = proportion of interest
q = $1 - p$

Again, formula (7.10) is the standard error of a *frequency* and to convert it into a **standard error of a proportion** (s_p) we divide pq by n as in formula (7.11). Hence,

$$s_p = \sqrt{\frac{pq}{n}} \tag{7.11}$$

where: s_p = standard error of a proportion
p = proportion of characteristic of interest
q = $1 - p$
n = sample size

Form. The shape of the binomial distribution is a function of n and p. When p = .5 a symmetrical distribution describes the form of the statistic. Furthermore, as n becomes larger the binomial distribution approximates that of the normal curve (distribution). To illustrate this consider the following logic describing the poll of student attributes toward impeachment.

The official student roster was used to select the sample. For the moment let us digress from the actual outcome that will be reported shortly and assume that 55 percent of those chosen said yes to the query and 45 percent said no. Figure 7.6, called a *dotplot,* presents an X axis that represents all possible values of this parameter in the universe of students. We locate a horizontal line (X axis) with selected proportions (or percents) indicated and place a dot corresponding to the outcome of this sample.

Let us further assume that we continue to select five more random samples of the same size with the percent favoring impeachment being 48 percent, 49 percent, 54 percent, 50 percent, and 52 percent, respectively. Let us place dots corresponding to the proportion of the students favoring impeachment for samples two through six.

Notice that each of the random samples gives a different estimate of the parameter. Although we have increased the variability of our sample estimates, if we were to continue to select random samples indefinitely and compute the proportion favoring impeachment and place a dot at the appropriate point along the axis above, the distribution of sample proportions would come to take on a familiar appearance. If we add a Y axis to Figure 7.6 these random samples would look like Figure 7.7 (see Babbie, 1992: 202–205 for a similar discussion). The familiar appearance is that of the normal curve. The form or shape of the binomial distribution approximates that of the normal curve, particularly when the sample size is large and $p = .5$. Moreover, it can be demonstrated mathematically that as long as both np and nq are ≥ 5, the N.C. is a reasonably good approximation to the binomial probability distribution.[5]

FIGURE 7.6

**Hypothetical Dotplot of the Proportion of Students
Favoring Impeachment**

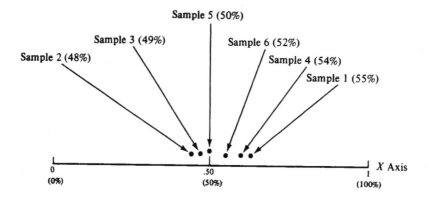

Given this rationale, the formula for a confidence interval for a proportion becomes:

$$\text{confidence interval for a proportion} = p \pm z \sqrt{\frac{pq}{n}} \qquad (7.12)$$

---

[5] The *Poisson distribution*, named after the French mathematician Siméon Denis Poisson (1781–1840), may be used when n is large but p is extremely large or small. Under those circumstances where $p < q$ and $np < 5$, the Poisson distributions is a reasonably good approximation to the binomial distribution with the formula:

$$P(r) = \frac{\lambda^r e^{-\lambda}}{r!}$$

where: r refers to the number of successes in n trials, $\lambda = np$, and e is the natural constant approximately equal to 2.7183.

where: p = proportion of characteristic of interest

q = $1 - p$

z = z score corresponding to confidence interval selected

$\sqrt{\dfrac{pq}{n}}$ = standard error of a proportion

Because the binomial sampling distribution approximates the normal distribution, particularly when n is large, we may use the familiar z scores for constructing the confidence interval. In such instances the standard error of a proportion has a similar meaning to that of the standard deviation.

FIGURE 7.7

A Dotplot Depicting the Sampling Distribution of Proportions

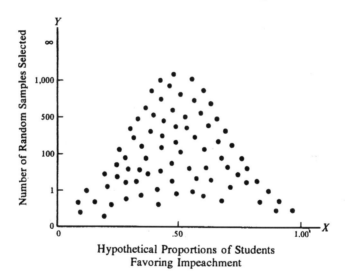

Hypothetical Proportions of Students
Favoring Impeachment

The 95 percent and 99 percent confidence intervals for the impeachment query are computed using formula (7.12) and substituting the appropriate values. The actual outcome of the survey of 410 randomly selected students indicated 55 percent favoring impeachment.

$$95 \text{ percent confidence interval} = .55 \pm 1.96 \sqrt{\frac{(.55)(.45)}{410}}$$

$$= .502 \text{ to } .598$$

$$99 \text{ percent confidence interval} = .55 \pm 2.58 \sqrt{\frac{(.55)(.45)}{410}}$$

$$= .487 \text{ to } .613$$

Our interpretation is that 95 percent (or 99 percent) of the confidence intervals will contain the true proportion of students favoring impeachment. We are able to make such statements because of our knowledge of the sampling distribution of proportions. Written in standard notation,

$$C\,(.509 \leq \pi \leq .590) = .90$$
$$C\,(.502 \leq \pi \leq .598) = .95$$
$$C\,(.487 \leq \pi \leq .613) = .99$$

SUMMARY

Parameter estimation, one branch of inferential statistics, is concerned with the correspondence between a sample and the population from which the sample is selected. To understand this relationship a discussion of the concepts sampling distribution and sampling error was presented along with a consideration of the nature of biased and unbiased estimates. To understand the logic it is useful to be clear that three different distributions are involved: one of samples ($\overline{X}$ and s), one of populations (μ and σ), and one of sampling distributions ($\mu_{\overline{x}}$ and $\sigma_{\overline{x}}$). If these are not clear they should be reexamined and studied.

Since a point estimate fails to indicate the amount of sampling error, most statisticians prefer interval estimates which enable use to estimate the probable amount of error. To construct an interval estimate (mean or proportion) we enclose the point estimate in a range of values corresponding to the standard error of the statistic and the z score corresponding to the chosen confidence level.

Finally, the interpretation of confidence intervals is in terms of long-run expectancies; that is, given our knowledge of certain statistical principles and their interrelationships, we expect the true population parameter to be trapped by the intervals a certain percentage of the time. It is the procedure rather than the particular interval in which our faith or confidence lies.

IMPORTANT CONCEPTS DISCUSSED IN THIS CHAPTER

Statistical inference

Statistical estimation

Sampling distribution

Random sampling error

Sampling distribution of means and sampling errors

Mean of a sampling distribution ($\mu_{\overline{x}}$)

Standard error of the mean ($\sigma_{\overline{x}}$)

Central limit theorem

Law of large numbers

Unbiased estimate

Biased estimate

Efficiency (of an estimate)

Point estimation

Interval estimation

Confidence intervals

95 percent confidence interval (limits)

99 percent confidence interval (limits)

Confidence, fiducial, and/or credibility limits

90 percent confidence interval (limits)

Standard error of a proportion (s_p)

Dotplot

REVIEW QUESTIONS

1. What is the purpose of inferential statistics? How are the concepts of population, sample, and sampling distribution related to this goal?

2. What is the difference between a standard deviation and a standard error, and the population (or sample) mean and the mean of a sampling distribution? Why is it necessary to make these distinctions?

3. In what ways are interval estimates *superior* to point estimates?

4. Two important statistical theorems are the central limit theorem and the law of large numbers. Define each of these and discuss their statistical importance.

5. Suppose you are a sociologist working with a state's bureau of vocational guidance. Your clientele is, by definition, a group with below normal IQs. You wish to know the range of IQs of those being served and to do this you draw a random sample of the clientele from a list of all persons being handled by the agency. You compute the mean to be 93 and the standard deviation to be 14 from a sample of 100.
   a. Construct the 90 percent, 95 percent, and 99 percent confidence intervals.
   b. Interpret the meaning of these intervals.

6. Given: $n = 225$; $\overline{X} = 76$; and $\sigma = 9$.
   a. Construct the 95 percent and 99 percent confidence intervals.

7. Given: $n = 75$; $\overline{X} = 82$; and $s = 8$.
   a. Construct the 90 percent, 95 percent, and 99 percent confidence intervals.

8. Given: $n = 50$; $\overline{X} = 165$; and $s^2 = 64$.
   a. Construct the 90 percent, 95 percent, and 99 percent confidence intervals.

9. Suppose you draw a random sample of 10 grade school children and ask each of them their age. Their ages are 10, 12, 8, 8, 9, 7, 6, 8, 9, 10. Construct the 90 percent, 95 percent, and 99 percent confidence intervals for these data.

10. One Harris poll taken during the O.J. Simpson trial found 57% of the 1,005 adults surveyed believing he was guilty.
    a. Construct the 99, 95, and 90 percent confidence intervals.

Addendum

The *binomial probability distribution* is an important one in inferential statistics and facilitates our understanding of discrete random variables. It has relevance for both parameter estimation and hypothesis testing. In hypothesis testing we compare obtained results with chance expectation in deciding on the "truth" or "falsity" of hypotheses. Suppose we flip a coin twenty times and obtain fifteen heads. Assuming the coin is "fair", what is the probability of that particular outcome occurring? The likelihood of obtaining 15 heads in 20 tosses can be determined by the binomial probability algorithm:

$$p(n) = [N! \, (p^n) \, (q^{N-n})]/n! \, (N - n)!$$

where:

n = the number of "successes"
N = the total number of trials
p = the probability of a "success" on a single trial
$q = (1 - p)$

Hence, the probability of 15 heads, i.e., "successes", in 15 trials (or flips) is computed to be:

$$p \, (15) = [20! \, (.5^{15}) \, (.5^5)]/15! \, (5!) = .015$$

The binomial probability algorithm can be used to generate the number of "successes" in N trials. More generally, the formula can be used in a binomial situation, one in which: (1) there are only two possible outcomes, (2) the trials are independent of each other, and (3) each trial is the same as each other. The form, with associated probabilities, of obtaining 0 thru 20 heads in twenty coin tosses is (Malec, 1993):

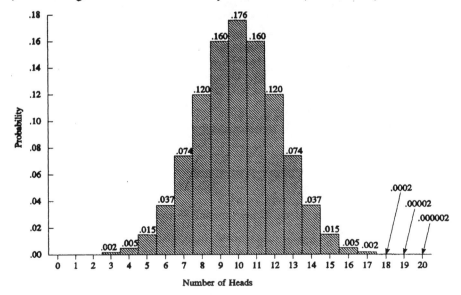

CHAPTER 8

INFERENTIAL STATISTICS: MEASURES OF SIGNIFICANCE

The purpose of **inferential statistics,** as we saw in Chapter 7, is to enable the investigator to say something about the numerical characteristics of the population on the basis of a sample drawn from this larger entity. In short, the sample is instrumental in helping to reach the goal of arriving at accurate and precise statements about the salient statistical dimensions of the parent population.

Statistical estimation and **hypothesis testing** are similar in that both rely heavily upon our knowledge of a statistic's sampling distribution. It is the distribution of a sample statistic that we depend upon for inferring properties of a population from a sample drawn from it. Although affinities exist between these two branches of inferential statistics, each branch involves a fundamentally different rationale. For example, in interval estimation of population parameters we collect sample data and end up with a range of values within which it is probable that the parameter lies. In this chapter we will see that hypothesis testing begins with an assumption or hypothesis about the population and then sample data are gathered and examined statistically to determine whether or not the initial assumption is acceptable. Notice that with interval estimation no a priori position is taken with respect to the parameter value whereas with hypothesis testing a position is taken or a prediction made (Mueller, Schuessler, and Costner, 1970: 394–395). In this chapter we concentrate upon the *logic* of hypothesis testing.

Since sampling is so important in inductive statistics, the question "Why sample?" needs answering. Let us say we are interested in students' attitudes toward abortion at a Midwestern university that enrolls 20,000 students. Imagine the time, energy, and money that would be needed to locate and survey 20,000 students (when every element in a population has been considered, the technique is called a *census* as distinguished from a **sample**). One reason for sampling is that it is virtually impossible to study the entire set. In other words, sampling has a very practical dimension to it. Another reason sampling looms important is theoretical. One aspect of probability statistics is known as statistical estimation whereby we estimate the key characteristics of the universe on the basis of a sample selected from it (within a certain margin of error). In short, there is really no need to survey every case since, statistically, it's possible to determine how closely, with a certain degree of error, our sample results correspond to the population. Another reason for sampling is that the population sometimes remains elusive. For example, it would be difficult to determine the population of pimps, prostitutes, and white-collar criminals. Sometimes we must study an ambiguous subset of elements or nothing at all. The selection of a sample is not, or should not be, left to chance. Since the researcher wants the sample's characteristics to be as close as possible to the population's, how the former is selected should be meticulously considered. A good sample is one that is *representative* of the universe. Representative means that it provides an accurate miniature picture of the larger entity. How does one maximize the probability of choosing a representative sample? The answer to this query leads us to a consideration of the different types of samples.

There are two general categories of sampling designs: (1) **probability sampling,** and (2) **nonprobability sampling.** In each category there are several subtypes. There are four common subtypes of probability samples. The first is known as **simple random sampling.**[1] A simple random sample (SRS) is one that gives each element in the population an *equal or known* chance of being selected. To select a random sample the researcher must first locate or construct a list (technically known as the *sampling frame*) for all elements in the **population.** A SRS may be selected by giving each component of the population a unique number and then selecting the actual cases by using a table of random digits, Table I in Appendix A of this book, or through some mechanical process, for example, the "fishbowl" technique. *Systematic, stratified* and *cluster sampling* are modifications of the SRS approach. One important statistical feature of probability samples is that they facilitate representativeness, that is, *probability samples are more likely to produce a "good" (representative) sample than are nonprobability samples.* A second important property of these samples is that they help to control the researcher's biases, both conscious and unconscious. They do this by removing the decision of which particular elements to select from the researcher's purview. A third advantage is that they permit the investigator to indicate the degree of confidence in the sample selection and measure the margin of error (See Table 8.3 at the end of the chapter.).

Nonprobability sampling, like probability sampling, has several subtypes. Some of these subtypes are technically called *accidental, quota, purposive,* and *snowball samples.* The common threads that tie these nonprobability samples together are: (1) they are less likely to yield a representative sample, (2) they are less

---

[1]Simple random sampling is the backbone of inferential statistics since most statistical theories and techniques were derived on the assumption of this sampling procedure. In generalizing from a sample to a universe one must be cautious if this assumption has been violated.

likely to control the researcher's biases, and (3) they do not enable the investigator to indicate the degree of accuracy of the sample or measure the margin of error.

A good sample has two criteria to meet. The first, just discussed, is **representativeness** and the second is **adequacy**. Adequacy concerns the size of the sample in relation to the universe. Adequacy considerations relate to the concept of the **sampling fraction** symbolized by n/N where $n =$ sample size and $N =$ population size. There is no all-purpose recommended sample size. The desired size varies according to the subtype of probability sample used in the study and is to be taken only as a guide. Sometimes less than 10 percent, sometimes more than 10 percent is necessary. *Why is the size of the sample important?* Theoretically, the odds of a small sample fluctuating or vacillating are greater than those of a large sample. In statistical vernacular, a small sample is more likely to be unstable than is a large one because with fewer elements selected a more atypical outcome becomes increasingly probable.

STATISTICS AND PARAMETERS

It is necessary once again to distinguish between the characteristics of the population and the characteristics of the sample. The former are called **parameters** while the latter are termed **statistics**. It will become obvious why this distinction is important when hypothesis testing is discussed. Greek letters, μ and σ, are used in referring to population characteristics, mean and standard deviation, respectively; Roman (or Latin) letters, $\overline{X}$ and s, are used when referring to sample characteristics, mean and standard deviation, respectively. Whereas parameters are assumed to be *fixed* and *unknown,* statistics are assumed to be known, that is, the values of a particular sample are known, and not fixed, that is, likely to vary from sample to sample.

HYPOTHESIS TESTING

There are two generic types of hypothesis testing models. One is labeled **classical statistical inference** and entered the social science arena during the 1920s. The second type, known as *Bayesian statistical analysis,* is of more recent vintage (circa 1950) even though it has been informally around for a much longer period. Although this writer expects more will be seen of the eponymous Bayesian approach, the discussion here will focus upon the classical design, the more commonly found one in the behavioral sciences.

In Chapter 2 we indicated that one dominant analytical mode in the social sciences is termed the *hypothetico-deductive method.* In this approach, research is conducted to determine the acceptability of stochastic hypotheses derived from various theories of behavior. When hypotheses are derived from fruitful theoretical schemes, empirical data are collected which should enable us to judge the acceptability of the hypotheses. The decision the investigator makes about the data's meaning may lead him or her to retain, reject, retest, or reframe the hypotheses and the theory. In testing hypotheses we are basically interested in whether or not the difference between two or more statistics is a real difference or whether it is merely a chance variation. Accordingly, *the basic principle behind statistical tests is to compare obtained results with chance expectations.* The sampling distribution of the appropriate statistic provides the researcher with the expected or probabilistic results. It is from this idea that *probability statistics* or *probabilistic interpretation* gets its name. These tests are called *tests of the significance of differences* or, more parsimoniously, *significance tests* or **tests of significance.**

The systematic nature of science implies that the research process is a logical one. This logical scheme, often modified in actual research, will be presented in a step-by-step sequence in this section.[2] It should be reiterated that the steps are *ideal-typical* and not irrevocable.

Hypotheses

There are several different types of hypotheses of which the researcher must be cognizant. A persistent issue, particularly since the advent of the Women's Movement, is the relationship between IQ and gender. The sexism that pervades our social system has often led to the conclusion that males are smarter than females. Leaving aside the social problems aspect of this polemic, assume you want to test this proposition. To test it, you must recognize three different types of hypotheses.

As it stands, you have a **research hypothesis.** This hypothesis is not directly testable for at least two reasons. First of all, it must be *operationalized* (see Chapter 2 for a review of this concept). Gender, or sex, is relatively easy since there are anatomical as well as other less obvious differences between males and females. IQ, however, is more elusive. As the researcher you must be explicit about what IQ is conceptually and how you will measure it. As you may surmise, there are many different ways of defining and measuring intelligence. A second reason this hypothesis cannot be directly tested involves the notion of **causality.** Cause-effect connections are frequently implicit in our research designs, although philosophically and scientifically difficult to establish.

Sometimes the research hypothesis is called a *substantive hypothesis* and it must be translated into a *statistical hypothesis* before it can be confirmed or disconfirmed. There are two generic statistical hypotheses: (1) the *null hypothesis* and (2) the *alternative hypothesis.*

[2]Siegel (1956: chap. 2) was most influential in this step-by-step approach to hypothesis testing.

The **null hypothesis,** symbolized H_0, ordinarily states that there is no difference in the *population(s)* from which the sample(s) was/were selected. Substantively speaking, this amounts to saying that there is no IQ difference in the male (μ_1) and female (μ_2) populations from which the samples were selected. Symbolically, H_0: $\mu_1 = \mu_2$ or $\mu_1 - \mu_2 = 0$. Substantively speaking once again, this reasoning indicates that the mean score of all males (μ_1) is equal to the mean score of all females (μ_2) or that the difference between the mean IQ scores of males and the mean IQ scores of females is equal to zero, $\mu_1 - \mu_2 = 0$. It should be noted that the null hypothesis is frequently the hypothesis we hope to disprove. However, due to the elusive nature of causality we must find support for our hypotheses indirectly.

The **alternative hypothesis,** symbolized H_1, is tentatively retained or accepted (the terminology varies from one statistician to the next) when the null hypothesis is rejected. In substantive terms this would amount to concluding that there is a significant difference between male and female IQ scores. Symbolically, H_1: $\mu_1 \neq \mu_2$ or $\mu_1 - \mu_2 \neq 0$.[3] This means that the mean IQ score of males (μ_1) is not equal to the mean IQ score of females (μ_2) or that the difference between the mean IQ scores of males and the mean IQ scores of females is not equal to zero, $\mu_1 - \mu_2 \neq 0$.

The rationale for beginning with a null hypothesis when interest usually lies in an alternative one is often confusing to the student. There are several reasons for beginning with the null. Since its inception by Sir Ronald A. Fisher, the logic of statistical inference has revealed that the null hypothesis (as well as the alternative) can never be directly proved. In other words, proof is indirect.

To illustrate this indirect proof imagine tossing a die six times. Assume a 1, 2, 3, 4, 5, and 6 came up on the respective tosses. Does this prove that the die is "honest" (not loaded)? The answer is "No" since no matter how many times we toss the die we could never exhaust the universe of outcomes. The best statement we could make is that there is no reason to suspect that the die is loaded. How could we establish that a die is loaded? The only way this could be done would be to claim that it is improbable that the die is honest given certain types of outcomes. This type of reasoning is what underlies hypothesis testing, that is, by rejecting equality we claim a difference.

The point is that we cannot prove the absolute truth of either the null or alternative hypothesis. We say that the alternative is probably true if we can reject the null. But we can never prove the null by failing to reject the alternative hypothesis since such an outcome could be due to sampling error. It really appears that the social researcher is on the horns of a dilemma. What this highlights more than anything else is the *probabilistic* world in which statistical inference resides.

Statisticians maintain that, logically, the strongest statement that can be made under those circumstances where the alternative does not appear plausible is, "We fail to reject the null hypothesis," rather than "We accept the null." If we were

---

[3]For the present discussion the alternative hypothesis has been considered *nondirectional* in nature. This is technically referred to as a *two-tailed test*. The one-tailed or directional hypothesis will be discussed in the next sections.

to say that we accept the null it would suggest that it is true. Logically it is not the case that by failing to reject the null we can establish its truth. Fisher's (1935: 16) statement regarding this discussion is instructive:

> ... it should be noted that the null hypothesis is never proved or established, but is possibly disproved, . . . Every experiment may be said to exist only in order to give the facts a chance of disproving the null hypothesis.

Granted that the proof of the null and alternative is indirect, why do we commence research with the null? The answer is that we choose a test statistic's sampling distribution assuming the truth of the null hypothesis. In other words, assuming the null is true, the sampling distribution provides us with the probability of different outcomes, those that occur relatively frequently as well as those that occur infrequently. If our sample statistic produces a value that would occur infrequently under the null, doubt is cast upon the null hypothesis. On the other hand, if the statistic is one that would occur frequently under the null, it is probable that the null is true.

In this section a discussion of the research, null, and alternative hypotheses was presented. It is important to keep in mind the differences among them as well as the logical relationships they have with each other. Once the research hypothesis has been operationalized, a statement is made about a future outcome, set forth in such a way that the statement can be accepted or rejected. This statement is contained within the null hypothesis conceptualization.

Choosing a Statistical Test

The field of statistics has developed to the point where alternative analytic techniques are available for practically any data analysis. Just the same, there are several useful criteria for deciding upon the particular test to use. Answering the following questions will be helpful in this decision-making process.

1. *What level of measurement is/are the variable(s)?* Here our concern is with whether our data best conform to the nominal, ordinal, or interval/ratio measurement assumptions. As we have seen in previous chapters, each level of measurement has appropriate measures of central tendency and dispersion; the same is true of measures of association and, as we will shortly see, tests of significance. Since the theory of measurement has a cumulative property to it, it is legitimate to drop down a level if the researcher has some doubts about the actual measurement level of the relevant variables. However, all things being equal, one should use the highest level statistics available since they are more powerful than lower level techniques. This consideration is consistent with the frequently made assertion that parametric measures, that is, interval/ratio statistics, are often better to use than nonparametric measures, that is, nominal and ordinal statistics, since the former use the *stronger* mathematical properties of the numbers assigned to the variables.

2. *How many samples are there?* There are three categories of significance tests, based upon the number of samples, that are important to understand in choosing an appropriate statistical technique: (a) **one-sample tests**—these tests call for drawing a single, usually random, sample and the techniques enable us to tell whether or not the particular sample selected could have come from a specific population (with a specified distribution); (b) **two-sample tests**—these tests involve selecting two (usually random) samples and the techniques enable us to determine whether the two samples could have been drawn from the same population; and (c) **k-sample tests**—k is the symbol which designates three or more samples; these tests involve the selection of three or more random samples and they permit us to determine whether the k samples could have been drawn from the same universe. (Notice that although "k" has been used differently in previous chapters, in the context of significance tests it will be used as defined here.)

3. *Are the samples related or independent?* A **related sample** (sometimes called a **matched** or **correlated sample**) is one in which the subjects act as their own controls in a *before/after* research design or in a research design in which the subjects are matched (*matched group design*) on relevant characteristic(s). There are two generic matching techniques: (1) *precision matching*—for each person in the one group there is a person in the second group who is identical or as nearly identical as possible on the salient characteristic(s), and (2) *frequency distribution matching*—instead of matching on a one-to-one basis, the overall or average relevant characteristic(s) are similar in the groups being compared.[4]

Independent samples are samples that contain elements (persons, objects, and things) that are, by design, mutually exclusive. There are two ways for arriving at independent samples: (1) the elements may be drawn at random from different universes, or (2) the different treatments, that is, independent variables, may be assigned randomly to the elements of the same sample.

When these queries have been correctly answered the investigator will have eliminated inappropriate measures and arrived at the point where the selection of the most appropriate test(s) is/are facilitated.

The Level of Significance and Sample Size

When the two previously mentioned steps have been completed, the next step is to specify the level at which you want to test your hypothesis. At this juncture, the probabilistic nature of statistics becomes explicit again. The choice of a **level of significance,** designated alpha ("α"), amounts to deciding how many times you can tolerate incorrectly rejecting the null hypothesis. Traditionally, this decision

---

[4] The purpose of matching is to statistically remove a (usually) significant source of variability in the data. In an experiment there are at least three factors that are influential: (1) individual differences, (2) effects of experimental variable, and (3) random errors. By employing correlated samples we remove a source of variability and obtain a clearer picture of the role of the experimental (independent) variable.

was made *before* the data were collected; today's opinions are less rigid. Today statisticians are increasingly prone to determine at what level the data are significant. This probability is called the *p-value*. To help us select a level of significance, convention is at our disposal. While any level may be selected, it is common to decide on the *.05* (5 percent) level, or *.01* (1 percent) level, or *.001* (.1 percent) level of significance. These three are the most common values of alpha. There is nothing sacred about these levels of significance other than the fact that they represent reasonably rare, chance, improbable outcomes. For an interesting and informative exposition of levels of significance see Skipper, et al. (1967) and Labovitz (1968).

What does the .05 (or .01 or .001) level of significance mean? It is a decision that involves the probability of rejecting the null hypothesis when it should have been accepted 5 times out of 100 (or 1 time out of 100 or 1 time out of 1,000). To say it a different way, if the probability of the occurrence of H_0 is equal to or less than the stated alpha value, the researcher is obliged to reject H_0 and tentatively accept H_1 (the alternative hypothesis).

To illustrate the manner in which levels of significance operate let us consider the now-familiar normal curve and its properties. In some tests of significance z scores are employed. The z statistic uses the normal curve as its sampling distribution. A z score of what magnitude cuts off 5 percent of the area under the normal curve? To answer this we need to consult the N.C. table, B in Appendix A, and find the z value that divides the curve so that 5 percent is at the extreme ends of the curve. That z value is 1.96. A z of 1.96 places .0250 (2½ percent) of the normal curve's area at *each* end. Consequently, 2½ percent on the extreme right plus 2½ percent on the extreme left adds up to 5 percent, which is the significance level selected.

What if we had decided to use the .01 level rather than the .05? A z score of what magnitude cuts off 1 percent of the area under the N.C.? Once again, we consult the N.C. table. A z score of 2.58 (approximately) places .0049 (.5 percent) of the normal curve's area at each end. Adding .5 percent on the one extreme to .5 percent on the other extreme yields our selected alpha value of .01.

Notice that the selected level of significance is translated into an area of the sampling distribution. Using the normal curve as a sampling distribution we know that the area *beyond* a z value of ±1.96 includes approximately 5 percent of the cases and a z value of ±2.58 includes about 1 percent of the cases. The shape of different sampling distributions is variable but *conceptually* you should imagine doing the same thing, that is, selecting an area that includes values of a sample within which a predetermined percent of the sample statistics should and should not fall.

If the level of significance involves the probability of rejecting the null hypothesis, how do we decide whether to reject the null or fail to reject it? From our knowledge of a statistic's sampling distribution we know that some outcomes would occur often while others would occur infrequently if the null hypothesis were true. As with the normal curve where the probability of occurrence becomes less and less as we move into the tails of the curve, any outcome of a statistic's sampling distribution can occur but some outcomes are more probable and others less probable. The level of significance is the probability value that we select and decide to use as the cutting off point for rejecting the null statement. Bear in mind, though, that the probabilistic nature of a sampling distribution implies that we may incorrectly reject the null, but we reason that extreme outcomes suggest that the correctness of the null hypothesis is questionable.

Diagrammatically, the .05 and .01 levels of significance are depicted in Figures 8.1 and 8.2. To determine the z value appropriate to the .001 level one would consult the N.C. table in an analogous manner.

FIGURE 8.1

Areas under N.C. When Alpha Equals .05 (Two-Tailed Test)

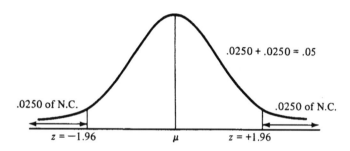

FIGURE 8.2

Areas under N.C. When Alpha Equals .01 (Two-Tailed Test)

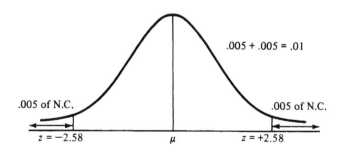

The **sample size**, designated n or N,[5] is simply the number of cases studied or the number of observations made. Shortly we will see why a large sample size is generally better than a small one.

[5] In this text the symbol N rather than n is sometimes used to designate the sample size.

In short, the level of significance is a decision rule we make for erroneously rejecting H_0 and the sample size is the number of cases studied.

Types of Errors

There are two types of **decision errors** that are necessary to discuss in hypothesis testing. The meaning of the word "error" in this context does not so much imply a mistake as an acknowledgement that the inferential statistical world is a probabilistic one in which decisions are made in the face of uncertainty. The first type is called a **type I error** or **alpha error**. When we set alpha equal to .05 ($\alpha = .05$), and we reject H_0, there is the potential probability that 5 times in 100 we will be wrong; in other words, we may have rejected the null hypothesis when it was actually true. A formal definition of the error of the first type is: *if the null hypothesis (H_0) is true and we reject it, our decision is in error and this rejection of a true H_0 is referred to as a type I error.* We've rejected the null hypothesis when it should have been accepted.

The probability of making an alpha error is equal to the sum of the probabilities of each of the outcomes within the critical region. The **critical region (region of rejection)** is the entire zone that is equal to and greater than the critical value. The **critical value** is the minimum value sufficient to reject the null hypothesis. To illustrate refer to Figure 8.1. The 5 percent level of significance was chosen. The critical value was $z = \pm 1.96$. The critical region encompasses all values equal to ± 1.96 and beyond, for example, $\pm 1.97, \pm 1.98, \pm 2.87$, ad infinitum. The probability of making a type I error is referred to as, and is identical to, the level of significance chosen. Furthermore, it may be set at any desired level, but most commonly, the level chosen is either .05, .01, or .001.

Intuitively, one may suspect that type I errors, as well as any other errors, should be minimized. This can be done by decreasing the alpha value, for example, with alpha equal to .05 there are 5 chances in 100 of being wrong, with alpha equal to .01 there is 1 chance in 100 of being wrong, and with alpha equal to .001 there is 1 chance in 1,000 of being wrong.

You might ask, *"If you are aware of making an error why can't it be completely eliminated?"* First of all, the probability of a type I error refers to the probability of a sample statistic's distribution in a large number of trials, for example, 100 or 1,000. Of course, one does not usually replicate a study that many times to check on the relationship between the actual sample outcomes and those specified in the sampling distribution. Secondly, 5 percent or 1 percent levels of significance indicate the maximum possible errors of the first type. In a single experiment or study the probability of making this error is not necessarily .05 or .01. Again, our logic is in terms of a large number of outcomes. Unfortunately, alpha errors are not the only consideration.

The second type of error, called a **type II error** or **beta error**, occurs when we accept H_0 but should have rejected it. In short, a type II error is committed when we incorrectly accept or retain the null hypothesis. Alpha errors and beta errors are *inversely* related. What this means, practically speaking, is that as you reduce the probability of making an error of the first type, you increase the probability of making an error of the second type. In other words, the more stringently we set the rejection level (.01 versus .05), the less the probability of a type I error and the greater the likelihood of a type II error. The converse is also true: the less rigorously we set the level of significance (.05 versus .01), the greater the probability of an error of the first type and the smaller the likelihood of an error of the second type.

Type II errors are considerably more complicated than may appear on the surface. Although the maximum probability of a type I error is equal to the critical area in the sampling distribution, the maximum probability of a type II error is *not* equal to the area excluded by the critical region. Specifically, if alpha is set at .01 the probability of a type I error is 1 percent but the probability of a type II error is not 99 percent. While it is sometimes possible to compute the probability of a type II error, usually the necessary information, the value of the parameter being studied, is not available.

What is the social researcher to do to minimize these decision-making errors? Let us first answer this query for type I errors. We already know that by making the critical region smaller and smaller, as in successively selecting .05, .01, .001 levels of significance, the probability of this error is reduced. However, this has the discouraging side-effect of increasing type II error probabilities. But we can reduce errors of the first type *without* increasing errors of the second type. One way to achieve this is to increase the sample size since sampling error is inversely associated with n. In short, as the sample size increases, sampling error decreases.

A second way to reduce type I error probabilities is to replicate the investigation. It is known that independent replications of a study decrease type I error probabilities. The probability of a type I error in two successive studies is $(.05)^2$ or .0025. In three successive studies it is $(.05)^3$ or .000125, and in four successive studies it is $(.05)^4$ or .000006, etc.

To reduce the probability of making an error of the second type one may: (1) increase the size of the critical region, for example, use the .05 rather than .01 level of significance, (2) increase the sample size, (3) replicate the investigation, and (4) use a one-tailed test. In the next section we will discuss one- and two-tailed tests and see why type II errors are reduced in the former situation. Note that both type I and type II errors may be reduced by increasing n and replicating the study.

Let us summarize the nature of type I and type II errors. A type I error is possible when we reject the null hypothesis and a type II error is possible when we fail to reject the null hypothesis. This means that we must be attuned to a decision error of the first type when H_0 is rejected and a decision error of the second type when we fail to reject the null hypothesis. Of course, we want to reject the null when it's false and fail to reject it when it's true. Table 8.1 illustrates the relationships between the null hypothesis, the decision made, and the potential decision errors.

Let us reiterate some of the key points discussed in this section. The relationship between alpha (α) and beta (β) errors is an *inverse* one, that is, as alpha increases, beta decreases and vice versa. Given this state of affairs, what can be done? Since there is always some chance of error (given the probabilistic foundation of statistics) and since type II errors are more elusive and difficult to deal with, statisticians prefer to limit the probability of making a type I error. Furthermore, by selecting a low level of significance the researcher is, in effect, more willing to say that there is no difference when there is one than to say there is a difference when there isn't one. This feature surely attests to the conservative nature of the scientific enterprise. Both errors can be reduced by increasing sample size (this is one reason why a large n is better than a small n) and by replicating the study. Practically speaking, the researcher must strike a balance that optimizes the outcome or use to which his or her analysis will be put. This balancing approach is sometimes referred to as the *minimax principle:* minimizing the maximum error(s) made or anticipated. Toward this goal, the notion of power becomes relevant.

TABLE 8.1

The Relationships between the Null Hypothesis, the Decision Made, and Decision Errors

Null Hypothesis Is –	Decision to –	
	Reject H_0	Fail to Reject H_0
True	Type I error (α)	Correct decision $(1 - \alpha)$
False	Correct decision $(1 - \beta)$ (power)	Type II error (β)

Power

Technically speaking, the **power** *of a statistical test is defined as the probability of rejecting the null hypothesis when it is, in fact, false.* Obviously, power is a great aid to investigators since it helps them make the correct decision. The lower left cell in Table 8.1 represents power. The relationship between power and beta is depicted below:

$$\text{power} = 1 - \text{probability of a type II error}$$

or

$$\text{power} = 1 - \beta$$

The power of a test is also related to the sample size. More succinctly, the probability of committing a type II error decreases as sample size increases, and thus power increases as n increases. No attempt will be made here to elaborate on the nuances of this important although difficult concept. Numerous texts present the power functions of statistical tests for samples of varying sizes.

Before moving on, let's reiterate several key themes. First of all, the level of significance (designated α) is the probability that H_0 will be falsely rejected. In short, the significance level denotes the probability of committing a type I error. Secondly, beta is the probability that H_0 will be falsely accepted. In short, β is the probability of committing a type II error. Thirdly, the power of a test, $1 - \text{beta}$, denotes the probability of rejecting H_0 when it is false and should be rejected. Fourthly, and what remains to be discussed, is the relationship between the nature of the statistical test, one- or two-tailed hypotheses, and power.

One-Tailed Test

In social research that is guided by some broader theoretical scheme, the theory often suggests plausible alternatives to the null hypothesis. Under such circumstances one would ordinarily employ a *one-tailed* or *directional hypothesis*. When a directional hypothesis is used, the investigator is not only claiming that the population parameter is different from the one hypothesized in the H_0, but is also asserting the *direction* of the difference. The effect of a one-tailed vis-à-vis a two-tailed test is that the location of the region of rejection or the critical area of the test statistic's sampling distribution will be altered. With a one-tailed test the entire critical area will be located in a *single* tail of the sampling distribution, whereas with a two-tailed hypothesis the critical area will be evenly divided between the two extreme ends of the curve. An example dealing with population means should make this clear.

A **one-tailed test**, sometimes called a *directional* or *delta test* (or hypothesis), asserts that one mean (e.g., μ_1) is either greater than or less than another mean (e.g., μ_2), that is, $\mu_1 > \mu_2$ or $\mu_1 < \mu_2$ or vice versa. When the researcher has sound reasons (or evidence), perhaps a theory suggesting that one group, for example, experimental group, will score higher than another group, for example, control group, then the directional test is warranted. To illustrate, assume a revolutionary method has been developed that supposedly increases a person's reading speed fourfold. In other words, early studies of this new approach are convincing enough to hypothesize that the mean number of words read, call it μ_1, is greater than the mean number of words read under the old system, call it μ_2. On this basis the researcher would probably prefer to hypothesize that μ_1 (new reading method) $> \mu_2$ (old reading method); hence, a one-tailed test would be called for. It would have been permissible to specify the alternative hypothesis a different way: $\mu_2 < \mu_1$. These latter symbols are an alternate way of expressing the same thing, for testing purposes, as $\mu_1 > \mu_2$. Notice that *it is the expression of the alternative hypothesis that determines the nature of the test*.

Heretofore the level of significance and critical region were discussed with a two-tailed situation in mind. The important query becomes: *What difference does the nature of the test, that is, whether it's one or two-tailed, make in hypothesis testing?* First of all, in a one-tailed test the investigator is concerned with only one end of the appropriate curve or sampling distribution of the statistic. With a one-tailed test, alpha set at .05, the 5 percent area is located in one tail rather than divided equally between the two tails. You will recall in the previous examples that when the .05 level of significance was chosen, 2½ percent of the curve's area was placed in the extreme left tail and 2½ percent of the curve's area was placed in the extreme right tail. In a one-tailed test the entire area is placed in one of the tails. To determine which tail requires one to scrutinize the manner in which the alternative hypothesis is phrased.

Using the z statistic and the N.C. as a sampling distribution let us determine the critical value for a one-tailed test in which α = .05. In the N.C. table locate the z value that divides the curve in such a way that 5 percent of the area falls beyond the selected z. This z value is 1.64 or 1.65. Since there is no area *exactly* equal to .4500, ideally, we should interpolate. If we did this the appropriate z would be 1.645. At the .05 level of significance for a one-tailed test the zone of rejection would consist of all values equal to or greater than 1.645 standard errors away from the mean in the direction of the alternative hypothesis. Approximately 45 percent of the curve's area, then, falls between the mean and z = 1.645 and 5 percent of the curve's area falls beyond z = 1.645. Remember that the curve is symmetrical; consequently, the same relationship holds for a z = −1.645 as for a z = +1.645.

In a similar vein we would determine the critical value for a one-tailed test in which alpha = .01. Again, we locate the value in the N.C. table that divides the curve in such a manner that 1 percent of the area falls beyond the selected z. Although z values of 2.32 and 2.33 are about equally close, it is conventional to use the latter figure. For a one-tailed test in which the .01 level of significance is used, the critical region would consist of all points equal to or greater than 2.33 standard errors away from the mean in the direction of the alternative hypothesis. Figures

FIGURE 8.3

Critical Regions of a One-Tailed Test When Alpha (α) = .05 and .01

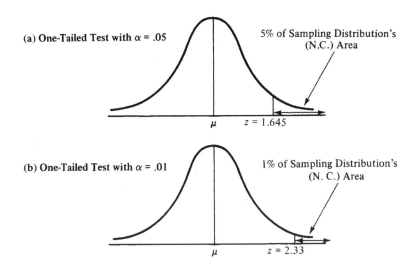

8.3 and 8.4 diagram the relationships between the z values, critical regions, and one- and two-tailed tests with alpha equal to .05 and .01.

FIGURE 8.4

Critical Regions of a Two-Tailed Test When Alpha (α) = .05 and .01

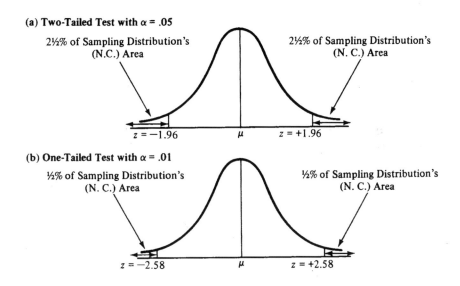

(a) Two-Tailed Test with α = .05

2½% of Sampling Distribution's (N.C.) Area

2½% of Sampling Distribution's (N. C.) Area

$z = -1.96$ μ $z = +1.96$

(b) One-Tailed Test with α = .01

½% of Sampling Distribution's (N. C.) Area

½% of Sampling Distribution's (N. C.) Area

$z = -2.58$ μ $z = +2.58$

Let's compare Figure 8.3 with its two-tailed counterpart, Figure 8.4. A moment's consideration enables you to see that a one-tailed test requires a smaller critical value, for example, 1.645 versus 1.96, than does a two-tailed test to reject the null hypothesis at the selected alpha level. Furthermore, a one-tailed test is more powerful than a two-tailed test since there is a smaller area within which the probability of a type II error may occur and power is defined as 1 − probability of a type II error.

Two-Tailed Test

A two-tailed test is ordinarily used in instances where research is exploratory in nature. It is also practiced when there exists no theory to guide the specific expression of the alternative hypothesis or when the previous research has been inconsistent. The alternative hypothesis in these cases is simply that the population parameter is different from the hypothesized one. With a two-tailed test we must divide the critical region of the sampling distribution into *two* equal (generally) parts. Consequently, the *location* of the region of rejection is affected by the nature of the test although the *size* of the rejection zone is not. An illustration of population means is in order.

A **two-tailed test**, sometimes called a *nondirectional test*, asserts that two means are merely different, that is, $\mu_1 \neq \mu_2$. Note that no statement about the direction of difference is made, in contrast to a one-tailed test; hence, a nondirectional hypothesis. In a two-tailed test, the researcher is concerned with both ends of the statistic's sampling distribution. When $\alpha = .05$ and a two-tailed test is used, 2½ percent of the curve's area is located in the right tail and 2½ percent in the left tail. In the N.C. table a z value of 1.96 divides the curve so that .0250 of the area is beyond it. Since this is done for both tails, we say that with the .05 level of significance the region of rejection consists of all values equal to and greater than 1.96 standard errors away from the mean in *both* directions. A two-tailed test or hypothesis may be employed when the investigator has no compelling reason for expecting one group (experimental group) to perform better than another group (control group). If, for example, a person wished to compare a revolutionary reading method (call it μ_1) with a conventional method (call it μ_2) and had no reason for expecting one method to be more efficacious than another, a two-tailed test asserting that $\mu_1 \neq \mu_2$ would be warranted.

The critical value for a two-tailed test in which alpha = .01 is similarly found. We locate the value that excludes 1 percent of the normal curve's area. In the N.C. table this could be either 2.57 or 2.58, and since 2.58 is slightly more precise we use this latter figure. In a two-tailed test in which the .01 level of significance is used, the critical region consists of all values equal to or greater than 2.58 standard errors from the mean in *both* directions.

The *logic* behind the one- and two-tailed test applications is identical. However, the critical values and the location of the critical regions, not their sizes, will be a function of the nature of the test. Table 8.2 portrays the relationships between the nature of the test, levels of significance, and critical values.

TABLE 8.2

Summary and Comparison of One- and Two-Tailed Tests, Levels of Significance, and Critical z Values

Nature of Test	Level of Significance (α)			
	.05	.01	.001	
One-tailed test	$z = 1.645$	$z = 2.33$	$z = 3.08$	Critical
Two-tailed test	$z = 1.96$	$z = 2.58$	$z = 3.30$	z Values

To differentiate between one- and two-tailed tests that are statistically significant, the terms *point* and *level* are sometimes used when referring to one- and two-tailed tests, respectively. A one-tailed test is said to be significant (if it is) at the 5 percent *point*, or 1 percent *point*, whatever the case may be. Similarly, a two-tailed test is said to be significant at such-and-such a *level*, whatever the case may be.

The Sampling Distribution

When a researcher has chosen a certain statistical test to use with the data, and there are many tests as we will shortly see, the next step is to determine the appropriate **sampling distribution for the test statistic.** Many of the tables in the rear of any statistics book, including this one, are sampling distributions for various statistical tests, for example, *t*, *F*, *z*, and *chi-square*. The concept of sampling distribution is one of the most important notions in sampling statistics. In the chapter on statistical estimation (Chapter 7) an empirical sampling distribution was generated. Refer to that chapter for a review. Blalock (1979: 153) defines it as follows: "*Whenever we associate probabilities with each possible outcome of an experiment, or with sets of outcomes, we refer to the resulting probability distribution as a sampling distribution. . . . A* sampling distribution refers to the relative number of times we would expect to get certain outcomes in a very large number of experiments.*"

Another way of defining it, which makes more sense to this writer, is to say that it is *a probability distribution of some statistic which would occur if one were to select all possible samples of a fixed size from a given population.*

Fortunately, the researcher does not have to generate a sampling distribution for each test statistic. Furthermore, the necessary information to do this is often not available. This has already been done by our mathematician and statistician forbearers, and some of these are located in Appendix A of this book. We could enumerate our own sampling distributions but it would be impractical (since they've already been enumerated) and tedious. This being the case, we have recourse to the authority of proven *mathematical theorems*. These theorems usually involve assumptions about the distribution of the population and/or the size of the sample and were mentioned in Chapter 7. They are sufficiently important in this context to reiterate in a slightly different way.

Two of the most salient theorems in statistics are: (1) the **central limit theorem** and (2) the **law of large numbers.** The central limit theorem tells us that if repeated random samples of size *n* are drawn from a *normal* population, with mean μ and variance σ^2, the sampling distribution of sample means will be normal with mean μ and variance σ^2/n. The law of large numbers indicates that if repeated random samples of size *n* are drawn from *any* population (whatever form) having a mean μ and variance σ^2, then as *n* becomes larger the sampling distribution of sample means approaches normality with mean μ and variance σ^2/n.

In summary, let us pose and briefly answer the query: *Why is the concept of sampling distribution important?* Whenever we estimate a population parameter from a sample or test hypotheses we want a knowledge of what we would expect if chance were the only factor operating. These expected chance results are contained and made explicit in a test statistic's sampling distribution.

Every useful statistical test has a sampling distribution. Since a sampling distribution makes explicit the probability of different outcomes of the statistic, without it one would never be able to make accurate inferences from the sample to the larger population. Up to this point we have relied heavily upon the normal curve as a sampling distribution since its properties and nature were carefully described in Chapter 6. By focusing exclusive attention on the N.C. it was hoped that such discussion would facilitate an intuitive comprehension of the sampling distribution concept. When large samples are selected the normal curve is appropriate for such statistics as means and proportions. What is so remarkable is that the nature of sampling distributions can sometimes be *deduced* without ever taking even a single sample. Such deductions stem from what the statistician knows about random sampling. By combining what is known about probability theory in relation to random sampling techniques, the sampling distribution and its statistical properties can be identified. In the next few chapters we will see that there are many other sampling distributions. Although there are fewer sampling distributions than there are statistical techniques (since a specific sampling distribution can sometimes be used with more than one statistic), it is imperative for the researcher to match the statistical technique with its appropriate sampling distribution in order to make a legitimate generalization from sample to population.

The Region of Rejection

By definition, the **region of rejection** (sometimes called the **zone of rejection** or **critical region**) is that area of a statistic's sampling distribution that warrants rejection of the null hypothesis at a predetermined level of significance. The level of significance specifies the area of the sampling distribution within which the null hypothesis will be rejected if the statistic falls. In order to choose a critical region, the researcher must ask at least two questions:

1. *What risk am I willing to take of making a type I and/or type II error?* The answer to this query will influence the significance level chosen as well as the power of the test.

2. *Will I use a one- or two-tailed test?* This question amounts to deciding whether the critical region will include one tail or both tails of the appropriate sampling distribution. Previously we've seen that one-tailed tests (directional) and two-tailed tests (nondirectional) differ in location, but not in size, of the region of rejection. In a one-tailed test the region of rejection is entirely at one end or tail of the sampling distribution, whereas in a two-tailed test the regions of rejection are at both ends or tails of the sampling distribution.

The Decision

The goal of hypothesis testing is to decide on the suitability of hypotheses derived from our theories of behavior. The preceding steps are instrumental in making an ultimate decision for a specific study.

If the test statistic yields a value which is in the region of rejection of the sampling distribution, the null hypothesis is rejected and the alternative one temporarily retained. The rationale behind the decision-making process is simply this: If a value occurs that is highly improbable under the assumption of the truth of the null hypothesis, its occurrence may be accounted for in two ways: (1) H_0 is false, or (2) a rare and remote event has occurred. Statisticians choose the former logic even though there will be occasions when the second one is correct. In fact, the level of significance selected is the probability of the second outcome being true.

When H_0 is rejected, the results are said to be statistically significant at the selected alpha level. If the results were statistically significant at the .05 level we interpret this as an event whose occurrence could have been produced by chance only 5 times in 100. Findings significant at the .01 level are interpreted likewise: this event or outcome could have been due to chance 1 time in 100. Similarly, an outcome significant at the .001 level is one in which only 1 time in 1,000 could chance have produced it. In research reporting it is customary to indicate statistical significance like this: $p < .05$ (or .01 or .001). This is interpreted to mean that the probability of chance producing the outcome is less than ($<$) 5/100 (or 1/100 or 1/1,000).

In this chapter the fundamental dimensions of hypothesis testing have been covered in a step-by-step fashion. Ultimately the researcher makes a statement to the effect that his or her findings are statistically significant, that is, unlikely to be due to chance factors, or not. It is of utmost importance to be cognizant that **statistical** and **theoretical** and **practical significance** are independent dimensions.[6] Much reputable research is theoretically or practically significant but not statistically significant. On the other hand, research outcomes may be statistically significant but not theoretically or practically meaningful.

PARAMETRIC AND NONPARAMETRIC STATISTICAL TECHNIQUES

Many of the traditional statistical techniques used in social research were derived on the assumption that the population(s) from which samples were selected were normally, or approximately normally, distributed. In fact, our discussion in Chapter

---

[6] For a classic critique of tests of significance see H. C. Selvin's article in the *American Sociological Review*, vol. 23, no. 4 (August 1958).

6 of the normal curve, particularly its theoretical importance, was to be understood in terms of its use as a mathematical model whose form is approximated by a variety of statistics. Stemming from this normality assumption, those tests that use the normal curve as a mathematical model are referred to as *parametric* or *distribution-bound* techniques.

In the past quarter of a century there has been an accelerated recognition that often this assumption of normality is not adequate; that is, many populations that social researchers study are *not* normally distributed. Consequently, the derivation of statistical techniques with less stringent assumptions about the nature of the universes from which samples are selected has come into its own. Those statistical techniques that do not require the normality assumption and make generally less stringent test assumptions are referred to as *nonparametric* or *distribution-free* techniques. Actually, these two concepts, nonparametric and distribution-free, are misnomers since it is not true that such tests have no parameters nor are their universes distribution-free. Both terms refer to a whole host of tests, generally nominal and ordinal level measurement techniques, that *do not require the normality assumption and/or make less stringent assumptions about the universe.* Moreover, even nonparametric tests make some assumptions, such as: the samples are randomly selected, the observations are independent in nature, and, in some cases, the variable is a continuous one.

Several statisticians (Bradley, 1968; Siegel, 1956; and Moses, 1952) have pointed to some major advantages of nonparametric statistics. Some of these assets include simplicity of derivation, ease, speed, and scope of application, utility with small samples, and, of course, not having to make stringent mathematical assumptions about either one's data or the population from which the observations have been drawn. There are certain disadvantages such as the fact that a nonparametric statistic used on data conforming to interval/ratio measurement wastes information, and a technical consideration involving problems dealing with the higher-order interactions. For those wishing to pursue these ideas the sources listed above should be consulted.

In the next three chapters (9, 10, and 11) tests of significance for nominal, ordinal, and interval/ratio level data will be discussed and explained. The nominal (Chapter 9) and ordinal (Chapter 10) tests of significance are nonparametric techniques, and the interval/ratio (Chapter 11) tests of significance are parametric procedures. The distinction between parametric and nonparametric techniques is not exclusively reserved to tests of significance (*inferential statistics*). There are also nonparametric *descriptive statistics*, particularly nominal and ordinal measures of association. Some nonparametric descriptive techniques will be addressed in Chapters 12 and 13. One of the basic general features that will facilitate your understanding of the nonparametric/parametric distinction lies in a test statistic's sampling distribution. Consequently, you should be especially attuned to the sampling distributions of the different statistics.

SUMMARY

In this chapter we have elaborated upon the general logic of hypothesis testing. Usually students discover that a single reading of this material is not sufficient to master its contents. Therefore, re-reading may be helpful.

To recapitulate the rationale of hypothesis testing consider the following. Having decided to put to empirical test a certain idea, sometimes called a research or working hypothesis, we translate it into a statistical hypothesis called the alternative hypothesis. To test it we assume the truth of the null hypothesis and choose an appropriate statistical technique using the level of measurement, number of samples, and whether the samples are related or independent criteria.

For the test selected we determine the appropriate sampling distribution, collect a random sample, and compute the relevant statistic and decide if it's reasonable that the statistic came from the chosen sampling distribution. The decision of whether the statistic could frequently come from the sampling distribution is made assuming the correctness of the null hypothesis. The predetermined level of significance defines the area of the curve in which the truth of the null becomes increasingly suspect. If the computed statistic falls in the critical region the null hypothesis is rejected and the alternative accepted; if it does not fall within the zone of rejection we fail to reject the null.

Finally, the generic structure for hypothesis testing developed in this chapter will be systematically worked through for all tests of significance presented in Chapters 9 (nominal level techniques), 10 (ordinal level tests), and 11 (interval/ratio measures).

IMPORTANT CONCEPTS DISCUSSED IN THIS CHAPTER

Inferential statistics

Parameter estimation

Hypothesis testing

Sample

Probability sampling

Nonprobability sampling

Simple random sampling

Population

Representativeness

Adequacy (of sample)

Sampling fraction

Parameters

Statistics

Classical statistical inference

Tests of significance

Research hypothesis

Causality

Null hypothesis (H_0)

Alternative hypothesis (H_1)

One-, two-, and k-sample tests

Related samples (matched or correlated samples)

Independent samples

Level of significance

Normal curve

z statistic

Sample size

Decision errors

Type I (alpha) error

Critical region (region of rejection, zone of rejection

Critical value

Type II (beta) error

Power

One-tailed test

Two-tailed test

Sampling distribution for the test statistic

Central limit theorem

Law of large numbers

Statistical and theoretical and practical significance

Bayesian statistical inference

p-value

REVIEW QUESTIONS

1. How does hypothesis testing, in general, dovetail with the major objective of inferential statistics? What are tests of significance?

2. Suppose you were interested in empirically studying the relationship between race and intelligence. How would you proceed in light of the steps in hypothesis testing outlined in this chapter.

3. Explain the similarities and differences between parameter estimation and hypothesis testing.

4. A good sample must be representative and adequate. Explain the meaning of both these concepts and illustrate how they are important to the sampling procedure.

5. Why is the concept of sampling distribution so important in hypothesis testing?

6. Why is the size of a sample important?

7. If proof of the null and alternative hypothesis is indirect, why do we commence research with the null?

8. What are the criteria used for choosing a statistical test in hypothesis testing?

9. What are one-, two-, and k-sample tests? Why are such distinctions important?

10. Explain briefly the concept of power and how it is important in hypothesis testing.

11. Explain the relationship between one- and two-tailed tests considering: (1) direction of hypothesis, (2) alpha level, and (3) z value.

12. What are the considerations involved in deciding on whether to use a one-tailed or two-tailed test in hypothesis testing?

13. Examine the final decision-making process of an empirical study and explain the rationale behind it.

14. What does it mean to say that a finding is statistically significant at the .05 (.01 or .001) level?

15. How are the central limit theorem and the law of large numbers meaningful in statistical analysis?

16. What is meant by the p-value?

Table 8.3

Approximate 95% Confidence Intervals for an Observed Sample Frequency of .50 in Samples of Various Sizes

Sample Size	Confidence Interval	Margin of Error
10	.20 to .80	+/−.30
25	.28 to .72	+/−.22
50	.36 to .64	+/−.14
100	.40 to .60	+/−.10
250	.44 to .56	+/−.06
500	.46 to .54	+/−.04
1000	.47 to .53	+/−.03
1500	.48 to .52	+/−.02

9

NOMINAL LEVEL
TESTS OF SIGNIFICANCE

FIGURE 9.1

Nominal Level Tests of Significance

One-Sample Test	Two-Sample Tests		k-Sample Tests	
	Independent Samples	*Related Samples*	*Independent Samples*	*Related Samples*
Chi-square goodness-of-fit test	Chi-square test of independence Fisher's exact test z test for differences between proportions	McNemar test	Chi-square test for k independent samples	Cochran Q test

In the previous chapter the fundamental dimensions of hypothesis testing were presented. The sequence of steps and general logic apply to virtually all tests of significance. In this chapter we will focus exclusively upon *nominal* level significance tests. Remember that tests of significance are simply statistical techniques whereby we can establish the probability of obtaining certain results. In other words, to determine whether an hypothesis is statistically significant, chance is used as a standard against which to compare our observations. When our observed data depart markedly from chance expectations, we conclude that our observations differ from chance at a certain probability level. Hypothesis testing helps us to evaluate differences between what we expect under the truth of the null hypothesis and what is actually revealed in our data. In this chapter we will categorize the tests on the basis of: (1) the number of samples, that is, one, two, or k, and (2) whether the samples are independent or related. The structure for this chapter appears in Figure 9.1.

CHI-SQUARE TEST OF SIGNIFICANCE

Probably the most versatile nominal level test of significance is chi-square. The **chi-square** (symbolized χ^2) **test** is the most popular measure of significance at this level of analysis. There are two broad uses of chi-square: (1) as a test of **goodness-of-fit**, and (2) as a **test of statistical independence**.

Let us consider the *goodness-of-fit* approach first. This approach gets its name from the fact that it provides a procedure for testing the "fit" of a theoretical model to some empirical outcome. As such, the goodness-of-fit technique may be considered a rudimentary example of the general interests of mathematical sociologists. Mathematical sociology, a growing and sophisticated specialty within the sociological enterprise, uses mathematics and mathematical models for understanding social phenomena. When this subtype of chi-square is employed, the researcher is trying to find out if an observed distribution of empirical data is similar to that of some predetermined hypothesized distribution. Another way of expressing this is that the chi-square goodness-of-fit test attempts to determine whether a certain observed distribution differs from a predetermined theoretical distribution. For example, the probability that a *fair* coin will land heads is 1/2 ($p = .50$). Now, if we tossed a single coin 1,000 times, we could compare the obtained or observed heads with the number of heads we would expect if chance were the only factor affecting the outcome of the coin tossing experiment. Using the formula (7.8) for the mean of a binomial distribution (np), the expected number of heads would be 500 and the expected number of tails would be 500. Although it is unlikely that we would obtain these *exact* results, the goodness-of-fit test would allow us to determine if the results we obtained could or could not be likely to have occurred assuming the coin was *honest*. In other words, we compare how *good* our observed distribution of coin flips fits the expected distribution of coin tosses. Another illustration involves our expectations for the outcome of rolling a die (singular of dice) in a large number of trials. The probability of tossing a 1, 2, 3, 4, 5, or 6 should be theoretically identical; otherwise, we would begin to be suspicious of our *unbiased* die. As these examples have demonstrated, the goodness-of-fit approach enables us to systematically and statistically compare observed (or obtained) results with theoretical (or expected) results. A real application of this test is presented in the next section.

The second generic use of chi-square is as a *test of statistical independence*. Here a brief review of **contingency tables** is in order. Some statisticians refer to the most rudimentary contingency tables as **bivariate frequency tables**. *Bivariate* indicates that two variables have been employed ("bi" = two; "variate" = variable). In statistics, a contingency table is a tabular representation of cases classified in terms of two or more attributes (or variables). Sometimes the concept **matrix is** used synonymously with contingency table, although it is generally thought of as a more inclusive term. A contingency table is an arrangement of data whereby two (or more) variables have been cross-classified as shown in Table 9.1. This table is called a **2 × 2 table.** It is a 2 × 2 table since each variable has been dichotomized, that is, has two subdivisions. Although contingency tables may have any dimensions, for example, 2 × 3, 3 × 5, 10 × 15, and so forth, the basic logic behind their construction remains the same. Notice that the individual **cell frequencies,** for example, A, B, C, D, are labeled from left to right beginning with the intersection of row 1 and column 1. Note, too, that there are both *row marginal frequencies* for example A + B and C + D, and *column marginal frequencies,* for example, A + C and B + D, as well as a **grand total** *(frequency),* for example, A + B + C + D. Sometimes the marginal frequencies are simply called **marginals** or **marginal totals.** As we will see shortly, the marginal and grand totals are used to obtain the expected (or theoretical) frequencies in the chi-square test of independence.

When data are arranged in the contingency table format, the investigator is testing the null hypothesis that there is no relationship or association between the variables under examination. That is, a test is made to determine whether or not the variables can be considered independent or unrelated vs. dependent or related in the larger population from which the samples have been drawn. To repeat, *the typical hypothesis the social scientist tests is the hypothesis that two variables are independent of each other (or unrelated) in some larger universe.*

TABLE 9.1

Arrangement of a 2 × 2 Contingency Table

| Variable Y | Variable X | | Marginal Totals |
	Column 1	Column 2	
Row 1	A	B	A + B
Row 2	C	D	C + D
Marginal totals	A + C	B + D	A + B + C + D Grand total = N

The chi-square test is an inferential statistic and *not* a measure of association, even though it is used in the calculation of some nominal measures of association. To repeat, the chi-square test enables us to determine the acceptability of an hypothesis and, as such, is a test of significance. It is *not* and *cannot* be used alone for assessing the degree of relationship between attributes or variables. An actual example follows shortly. The *basic difference* between the chi-square goodness-of-fit test and the test of independence resides in the *method* used to obtain the theoretical or expected frequencies. In the goodness-of-fit type the expected frequencies are generated on an a priori or theoretical basis; in tests of independence the marginal and grand total frequencies are used for determining a pattern of cell frequencies that would yield a model of no association. The method for generating expected frequencies in the test of independence is an a posteriori one.

SINGLE-SAMPLE TEST

Chi-Square Goodness-of-Fit Test

The proper use of this test, as well as the test of independence, assumes that your sample has been randomly and independently selected. Since we have previously discussed the nature of a random sample we need only mention the character of an independently selected one. *Independence* in this context means that we may not make several observations of the same person and then treat these observations as if they were made on different persons. If this assumption is violated the chi-square goodness-of-fit test is not appropriate. An example from this writer's research will demonstrate the logic and calculations involved.

The cry for course relevance is frequently heard on college campuses today. We hear much about the precarious role of college professors. They are, to use the hackneyed phrase, "damned if they do and damned if they don't!" Given this social climate, this writer attempted to determine student preferences for what makes a good college teacher by employing an instrument consisting of a series of forced-choice questions to which the students responded. One of these items was this: Are professors better teachers if they: (1) require students to follow the syllabus strictly or (2) do not require students to follow the syllabus strictly but allow self-direction on the part of the students? A randomly selected sample of 340 students was "forced" to check one of these two responses. When the data were tabulated it looked like this:

Professors are better teachers if they:

	N	%[1]
1. Require students to follow syllabus directly	72	21
2. Allow self-direction	268	79
	N = 340	100

This is the type of problem to which the chi-square goodness-of-fit test lends itself. Since we already have the **observed frequencies** (72 and 268) we must

[1]This percentage column is included to facilitate your understanding of the data distribution. It is *not* necessary nor used in the computation of the chi-square statistic. Chi-square analysis requires *frequencies*, and if one's data are in percentages or some other form, they must be converted into frequency counts to employ this data processing tool.

decide, logically, how to generate the **expected frequencies.** If there were absolutely no difference in student preference for one mode of instruction over the other, then we'd expect a "50-50" split of our total frequency. In other words, were there no real differences in preference in a sample of 340 students, we'd expect about 170 to select the first alternative and 170 to select the second alternative. In this case, the expected frequencies would be obtained by dividing the sample size by two or $340/2 = 170$. In general, where the null hypothesis states that the number of cases in each category is the same, then the expected frequencies will equal N/k where N = total number of observations and k = the number of categories into which the observations are distributed. One should be cognizant that there should be a logical and/or theoretical reason for determining the expected frequencies. If one has a different but theoretically acceptable rationale, then the expected frequencies could be *other* than those stated here.

Obviously, there is not an even split in student preferences since 72 (21 percent) selected the former alternative while 268 (79 percent) selected the latter one. *Variations are quite common in any sample data, but the statistical query is whether or not these responses could be due to chance factors alone.* To answer this question requires the calculation of the chi-square goodness-of-fit statistic and a knowledge of its sampling distribution.

The formula for the chi-square goodness-of-fit test is:

$$\chi^2 = \sum \frac{(O_f - E_f)^2}{E_f}$$
(9.1)

where: χ^2 = chi-square test statistic
O_f = observed frequency for a particular cell
E_f = expected frequency for the same cell
Σ = summation operator

We will systematically work through the steps outlined in the previous chapter.

Stating the Null and Alternative Hypotheses. Substantively speaking, the null hypothesis (H_0) is that students do not prefer one mode of instruction over another. Or, the number of preferences for one mode is equal to the number of preferences for the other. Or, simply, there is no difference between observed and expected frequencies.

The alternative hypothesis (H_1) is that there is a difference in students' preferences for one mode of instruction over another. Or, they do prefer one instructional mode over the other.

The Choice of a Statistical Test. Since the data consist of frequency counts and the notion of related samples isn't applicable, the chi-square goodness-of-fit test statistic is appropriate.

The Level of Significance and Sample Size. Let us test these data at the .01 level. Remember that alpha = .01 indicates the probability of rejecting H_0 when it should have been accepted. In statistical jargon, .01 is the probability of making a type I error. The sample size, as has already been noted, is 340.

One- versus Two-Tailed Tests.[2] Since the alternative hypothesis is stated in non-directional terms a two-tailed test is called for. For a one-tailed application, simply *halve* the probability value shown in the chi-square sampling distribution table; that is .10 becomes .10/2 or .05, and .05 becomes .05/2 or .025, and .01 becomes .01/2 or .005, and .001 becomes .001/2 or .0005.

The Chi-Square Sampling Distribution. Every useful test statistic has a corresponding sampling distribution that must be consulted in order to determine the probability of obtaining certain outcomes. The chi-square sampling distribution, actually a family of distributions, is a function of the number of **degrees of freedom** (designated *df*). In other words, there is a different sampling distribution for every value of *df*.

What does the degrees of freedom (*df*) concept mean? Degrees of freedom are defined as *the number of quantities that are free to vary, given certain restrictions on the data.* Two examples will make this clear. First of all, assume we have the following equation: $A + B = C$. Now, if quantity C has been identified (or determined), let's say it equals 500, only *one* of the other quantities, A or B, is free to vary. If B equals 225, we know that A must equal 275 since $A(275) + B(225) = C(500)$. Consequently, there is *one degree of freedom.*

This logic applies to determining the degrees of freedom in a chi-square *goodness-of-fit test.* The degrees of freedom value is computed as $k - 1$ where $k =$ the number of categories into which observations have been distributed. A second example, more germane to contingency table analysis, is this. In a contingency table there are a certain number of rows and columns. For illustrative purposes we will confine ourselves to a 2 × 2 table. In computing the **expected frequencies** (designated E_f) we assume that the marginal frequencies are already known. Given the marginal frequencies, there are only a certain number of cell frequencies that are free to vary. The example in Table 9.2 will make this clear. If we know the marginal frequencies, and if we know one cell frequency, the remaining three cell frequencies are known (or can be easily determined). If Table (a) were the case, we know that cell B must equal 70 since cell $A = 50$ and the row marginal frequency = 120. Consequently, $A(50) + ? = 120$ or $A(50) + B(70) = 120$. Similarly, to deter-

---

[2]A technical point, about which statisticians are not in complete agreement, concerns one- and two-tailed chi-square hypotheses. Some (Anderson and Zelditch, 1975: 289) argue that chi-square should be used only with nondirectional hypotheses. Their reasoning is that in the process of squaring the $O_f - E_f$ values the two ends of the sampling distribution become combined and virtually impossible to untangle. On the other hand, some statisticians (Blalock, 1979: 288 and Champion, 1970: 133) acknowledge that chi-square is insensitive to direction since the act of squaring always produces positive values, but that direction can be accounted for by halving the level of significance obtained.

mine the value for cell C, 50 + ? = 60 or 50 + 10 = 60. Finally, to determine cell D, since we know B = 70 and the column marginal frequency = 140, D must equal 70 since 70 + ? = 140 or 70 + 70 = 140. The completed table looks like (b) in Table 9.2.

TABLE 9.2

Illustration of Logic for Computing the Degrees of Freedom in a 2 × 2 Contingency Table

(a)			(b)		
50	B?	120	50	70	120
C?	D?	80	10	70	80
60	140	200	60	140	200

In a 2 × 2 contingency table df will always equal one since by knowing the marginal frequencies, if one cell frequency is known, the others can be determined. The number of degrees of freedom in any *contingency table* can always be determined by $(r - 1)(c - 1)$ where r = the number of rows and c = the number of columns.

The *shape* of the chi-square sampling distribution is a function of the degrees of freedom. Figure 9.2 illustrates the different forms the curve takes as df changes. Notice that for one degree of freedom the distribution is a reverse-J in shape with most chi-square values near zero. Only 5 percent of those values are equal to and larger than 3.8416. With 1 df the distribution is identical to that of z^2. For example, the critical value for z at the .05 level is equal to 1.96 and for χ^2 it is 3.8416 (or 1.96^2). However, there is a difference in the sense that $1.96z$ divides the curve so that 2.5 percent of the area is in *each* tail whereas χ^2 = 3.8416 places the entire area in *one* (the right) tail.[3] When df = 5 the chi-square sampling distribution looks like a positively skewed curve and when df = 10 it begins to resemble the normal curve, although it is not yet symmetrical. In general, as df increases the sampling distribution becomes less and less skewed. When the df value exceeds 30 the normal curve becomes a reasonably accurate approximation of the chi-square sampling distribution.

As we know, each test statistic has a sampling distribution, usually displayed in tabular form. The χ^2 test statistic has the chi-square sampling distribution which appears in Table C of Appendix A. Notice in this table that df's are listed down the

---

[3] If the level of significance cannot be obtained from the chi-square table, or if the table is unavailable, an approximation can be made by taking the square root of chi-square ($\sqrt{\chi^2}$) and entering the normal curve table. This technique can only be used in 2 × 2 table setups.

extreme left column and the various probability levels are lined up horizontally at the top of the table and proceed from .99 to .001.

FIGURE 9.2

The Shape of the Chi-Square Sampling Distribution When *df* = 1, 5, and 10

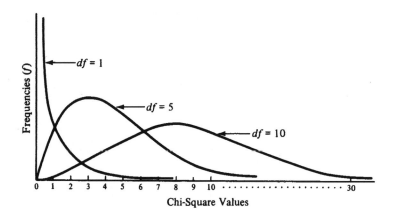

Chi-Square Values

The Region of Rejection. The intersection of a specific *df* and probability level (level of significance) tells us the critical value sufficient to reject the null hypothesis. Remember, if the computed chi-square value is *equal to or larger than the critical value in the table, H_0 is rejected*. From a knowledge of the chi-square sampling distribution notice that a χ^2 value of 6.635 (critical value) or larger is needed to reject H_0 at the .01 level of significance, *df* = 1.

Let us now set up our data for computing the chi-square value. The following steps are recommended:

1. Indicate the observed frequencies for each category, in this case *follow syllabus* and *self-direction*. Hence,

	O_f*	E_f†	$O_f - E_f$	$(O_f-E_f)^2$	$(O_f-E_f)^2/E_f$
Follow syllabus	72	170	−98	9,604	9,604/170=56.49
Self-direction	268	170	98	9,604	9,604/170=56.49
					$\Sigma=\chi^2=\overline{112.98}$

* Observed frequencies.
† Expected frequencies.

2. Indicate the expected frequencies for each category in a column adjacent to the O_f's. Our rationale was that if there were no difference in students' pre-

ferences, then there should be an equal split among the students. Hence, N/k (340/2 = 170) was used for generating the expected frequencies.

3. Subtract the E_f's from O_f's.
4. Square the differences, that is, $(O_f - E_f)^2$.
5. Divide the $(O_f - E_f)^2$ values by their corresponding E_f's.
6. Sum the values in the last column. This is the calculated chi-square value.

What does $\chi^2 = 112.98$ mean? To answer this question it is necessary to consult the chi-square sampling distribution, Table C in Appendix A, at the predetermined .01 alpha level according to the degrees of freedom. For the present problem the degrees of freedom value is determined by formula (9.2):

$$df_{GOF} = k - 1 \qquad\qquad (9.2)$$

where: df_{GOF} = degrees of freedom for χ^2 goodness-of-fit test
$\quad\quad\ \ k$ = number of categories

In our example, there are two categories, *follow the syllabus* and *self-direction*. Consequently, the appropriate degrees of freedom equals $k - 1$ or $2 - 1 = 1$. Therefore, we have one degree of freedom. Find the critical chi-square value where 1 df and the .01 level of significance intersect. That value is 6.635. Since the computed chi-square value is larger than the *table value,*[4] that is, $112.98 > 6.635$, we conclude that there is a statistically significant difference in our findings. In other words, there appears to be a real preference for one mode of instruction, that of self-direction, over another. With a chi-square value of this magnitude, only one time in 100 could our results have been due to chance or could we erroneously reject H_0. It is conventional to express this verbal description in statistical notation as $p < .01$.

TWO-SAMPLE TESTS: INDEPENDENT SAMPLES

Chi-Square Test of Independence

Some statisticians refer to this test as a *test of independence for categorical variables* or as a *test of the hypothesis of zero association*. Its use is recommended when two nominal level variables have been cross-classified.

To illustrate an application of this test, assume you are interested in voting behavior. More particularly, you are concerned with the relationship between political party registration and voting at the polls in the last gubernatorial election. To test this hypothesis you have selected two random samples of 100 voters from the voting list of a major municipality. Each of the 200 voters is asked two questions: (1) With which party are you officially registered? and (2) For whom (the

---

[4]The table value is the critical value ordinarily found in the test statistic's sampling distribution. Many tables are arranged in tabular form in the rear of this book.

Republican or Democratic candidate) did you vote in the last election? Assume the responses produce the following contingency table:

	Registered Republican	Registered Democrat	
Voted Republican	75 (A)	40 (B)	115
Voted Democrat	25 (C)	60 (D)	85
	100	100	200

To test our hypothesis let us work through the steps outlined in Chapter 8.

Stating the Null and Alternative Hypotheses. Substantively speaking, the null hypothesis (H_0) is that there is *no* association between voting behavior and political party registration.[5]

The alternative hypothesis is that there *is* an association between voting behavior and political party registration.

The Choice of a Statistical Test. Since the data consist of two independent cross-classified samples, the chi-square test of independence is appropriate.

The Level of Significance and Sample Size. For variety's sake, let's test these data with alpha = .05. The .05 level of significance indicates the probability of incorrectly rejecting H_0. That is, .05 is the probability of making a type I error. The sample size in this case is 200.

One- versus Two-Tailed Tests. Our alternative hypothesis simply stated that there is a relationship between voting behavior and political party registration. Since no direction was specified, a two-tailed chi-square test of independence is called for.

The Sampling Distribution. Table C in Appendix A provides the appropriate sampling distribution for the chi-square test of independence.

The Region of Rejection. With alpha equal to .05 and $(r-1)(c-1) = 1$ *df*, the

---

[5]There are a *variety* of ways that the null hypothesis (and alternative) can be stated. Since the chi-square test is not a measure of association it might be better not to use the hypothesis of no association since it is often confusing to students. Therefore, H_0 for this example could be: Voting behavior and registration with a political party are independent dimensions; or, there is no difference between observed and expected frequencies.

critical value in Table C indicates that we need a χ^2 value of 3.841 or larger to reject H_0.

Let us set up our data for computing the chi-square value.

1. In the extreme left column indicate the respective cells in the contingency table. Locate the observed frequencies for each cell in an adjacent column.

Cell	O_f	E_f	$O_f - E_f$	$(O_f - E_f)^2$	$(O_f - E_f)^2/E_f$
A	75	57.5	17.5	306.25	306.25/57.5 = 5.33
B	40	57.5	-17.5	306.25	306.25/57.5 = 5.33
C	25	42.5	-17.5	306.25	306.25/42.5 = 7.21
D	60	42.5	17.5	306.25	306.25/42.5 = 7.21
					$\Sigma = \chi^2 = 25.08$

2. Indicate the expected frequency for each cell in a column adjacent to the O_f's. The expected cell frequencies for the chi-square test of independence are determined differently than was the case with the goodness-of-fit test. Instead of obtaining them on an a priori basis, we obtain them by using the marginal and grand total frequencies. Refer to Table 9.1 for the letter designations involved in the following computations. For cell A the expected frequency is obtained by multiplying the row and column marginal frequencies that are common to that cell and then dividing by the grand total. Operationally, for cell A: $(A + B)(A + C)/N$ or $(115)(100)/200 = 57.5$. For cell B: $(A + B)(B + D)/N$ or $(115)(100)/200 = 57.5$. For cell C: $(C + D)(A + C)/N$ or $(85)(100)/200 = 42.5$; and for cell D: $(C + D)(B + D)/N$ or $(85)(100)/200 = 42.5$. Through this process the pattern of *expected* frequencies for a model of no association has been generated. Write these values in the expected frequency column (E_f).

To establish a **model of no association** we begin with the observed data distribution and then determine the pattern of cell frequencies in the body of the table that would be expected if there were, in fact, no relationship between the variables. The *logic* behind this operation is this: if there were no association between registration and voting behavior we would expect the same proportion of those who registered Democrat and Republican to be in the voted Republican and voted Democrat categories.

Let's be a bit more explicit. What is the proportion of the total sample that falls into the registered Republican, registered Democrat, voted Republican, and voted Democrat categories? By employing the formula for proportions (see Appendix B if you have forgotten how to perform this operation) we have 100/200 = .50; 100/200 = .50; 115/200 = .575; and 85/200 = .425, respectively. Notice that the sum of the column and row proportions equals unity. Since the *proportion* of registered Republicans is 100/200 or .50, we would expect this same figure in each of the two voting behavior categories. To obtain the expected *number* of persons in cell A we would multiply .50 by the total number of persons who voted Republican. Hence, .50(115) = 57.5. Similarly, the expectation for cell B would be .50(115) = 57.5, again. For cells C and D an analogous operation would be performed. For example, for cell C: .50(85) = 42.5 and for cell D: .50(85) = 42.5. We can also conceptualize what is entailed in establishing a model of no association a different way. Since 100 of the total sample registered Republican, the expectation would be that 100/200 × 115 would be found in cell A. For those registering Democrat, since 100 of the total sample registered that way, the expectation would be that 100/200 × 115 would be found in cell B. The same rationale would be applied for determining the expected frequencies in cells C and D. For those registering Republican it would be 100/200 × 85, and for those registering Democrat it would be 100/200 × 85. This logic boils down to the following operation for generating the expected frequencies in a contingency table:

Multiply the marginal frequencies common to a given cell and divide by the grand total.

Employing this rule for our data the *expected* cell frequencies would be:

Cell	Expected Cell Frequencies (E_f)
A	$(115)(100) \div 200 = 57.5$
B	$(115)(100) \div 200 = 57.5$
C	$(85)(100) \div 200 = 42.5$
D	$(85)(100) \div 200 = 42.5$

Notice that the *expected* frequencies when summed (57.5 + 57.5 + 42.5 + 42.5 = 200) are identical to the grand total and the *observed* cell frequencies when added together (75 + 40 + 25 + 60 = 200).

In notation form:

$$E_f = \frac{\text{(row marginal total)(column marginal total)}}{\text{grand total}}$$

where: E_f = expected frequency of any cell

3. Subtract the E_f's from the O_f's.
4. Square the differences, that is, $(O_f - E_f)^2$.
5. Divide the $(O_f - E_f)^2$ values by their corresponding E_f's.
6. Sum the values in the last column.

What does χ^2 = 25.08 mean? To answer this question we must consult the chi-square sampling distribution at the selected alpha level according to the degrees of freedom. Since alpha was set at the .05 level, the only task remaining is to determine the appropriate degrees of freedom. In any (chi-square) contingency problem the *df* is determined by formula (9.3):

$$df_{CT} = (r - 1)(c - 1) \tag{9.3}$$

where: df_{CT} = degrees of freedom for contingency *tables*
  r = number of rows
  c = number of columns

For the present problem there are two rows and two columns. Substituting these values in formula (9.3) yields the degrees of freedom: $(2-1)(2-1) = 1$. Now we locate the critical value of chi-square where 1 df and the .05 level of significance intersect. The critical value is 3.841. Since our computed chi-square value is larger than the table value, that is, $25.08 > 3.841$, we conclude that there is a statistically significant relationship between voting behavior and voting registration. That is, voting behavior and registration are *not* independent dimensions. To determine the *substantive* meaning of this requires the researcher to scrutinize the table itself. Since alpha was set at the .05 level, we would expect these results to have occurred 5 times (or less) in 100 if chance were the only factor operating. Consequently, only 5 times in 100 would we entertain the probability of rejecting H_0 when it should have been accepted. Consequently, $p < .05$.

With any *fourfold* (or 2 X 2) *table*, an easy chi-square computing formula is noted in formula (9.4):

$$\chi^2 = \frac{N(AD-BC)^2}{(A+B)\,(C+D)\,(A+C)\,(B+D)} \qquad (9.4)$$

Notice that this formula uses the cell and marginal totals, but it is restricted to 2 X 2 tables. Let us employ formula (9.4) for the above data:

$$\chi^2 = \frac{200\,[(75)\,(60)-(40)\,(25)]^2}{(75+40)\,(25+60)\,(75+25)\,(40+60)}$$

$$= \frac{200\,(4,500-1,000)^2}{(115)\,(85)\,(100)\,(100)}$$

$$= \frac{200\,(3,500)^2}{97,750,000}$$

$$= \frac{200(12,250,000)}{97,750,000}$$

$$= \frac{2,450,000,000}{97,750,000}$$

$$= 25.06$$

The slight difference between the value provided by formula (9.1) and that by formula (9.4) for the same data is due to rounding errors.

Yates' Correction for Continuity. The chi-square sampling distribution is a continuous one whereas the empirical distribution of categorical variables, or attributes, is discrete. Consequently, it is recommended that an adjustment be made in the computational format for chi-square. **Yates' correction for continuity** is ordinarily only applied to 2 × 2 tables and should be employed when *expected* frequencies are less than five. If this is not done, the computed χ^2 is actually an inflated value.

To correct for continuity, .5 is subtracted from the absolute difference $|O_f - E_f|$. When $df = 1$ the computing formula becomes:

$$\chi_c^2 = \Sigma \frac{(|O_f - E_f| - .5)^2}{E_f} \tag{9.5}$$

Hence, for the above data:

Cell	O_f	E_f	$(|O_f - E_f| - .5)^2/E_f$
A	75	57.5	$|75 - 57.5| - .5 = \;\;17^2 = 289/57.5 = 5.026$
B	40	57.5	$|40 - 57.5| - .5 = -17^2 = 289/57.5 = 5.026$
C	25	42.5	$|25 - 42.5| - .5 = -17^2 = 289/42.5 = 6.800$
D	60	42.5	$|60 - 42.5| - .5 = \;\;17^2 = 289/42.5 = 6.800$

$$\Sigma = \chi_c^2 = 23.652$$

Notice the slight difference between the original uncorrected χ^2 of 25.08 (or 25.06) and the corrected χ_c^2 of 23.652.

Similarly, formula (9.4) when corrected for continuity becomes formula (9.6):

$$\chi_c^2 = \frac{N(|AD - BC| - N/2)^2}{(A+B)(C+D)(A+C)(B+D)} \tag{9.6}$$

Substituting our values into formula (9.6):

$$\chi_c^2 = \frac{200\,[(|4,500 - 1,000|) - 200/2]^2}{(115)(85)(100)(100)}$$

$$= \frac{200\,[(|4,500 - 1,000|) - 100]^2}{97,750,000}$$

$$= \frac{200\,(3,400)^2}{97,750,000}$$

$$= \frac{200(11,560,000)}{97,750,000}$$

$$= \frac{2,312,000,000}{97,750,000}$$

$$= 23.652$$

With Yates' correction the overinflated χ^2 value is brought more in line with the known values of the chi-square sampling distribution. Whereas some statisticians maintain it should be used when expected frequencies are less than five, a more conservative position is to employ it in any 2 × 2 table.[6]

Fisher's Exact Test

The **Fisher exact test** is a most useful test of significance when we have two independent samples which can be arranged in a 2 × 2 table *where the sample size is small.* This test gets its name from the fact that it yields an *exact*, not approximate, probability associated with a given data-set. The chi-square test should not be used when the expected frequencies are less than 5 (in a 2 × 2 table). Fisher's exact test does not have this limitation.

Suppose we were interested in the incidence of drug use among children from white-collar and blue-collar families. Assume we have the tabular arrangement given in Table 9.3. Let us set up this problem in formal statistical terms.

TABLE 9.3

Illustration of Fisher's Exact Test: Hypothetical Drug Use among Children from White-Collar and Blue-Collar Families

Drug Usage	Family Type		
	White Collar	Blue Collar	
Drug user	0	3	3
Drug nonuser	6	4	10
	6	7	13

Stating the Null and Alternative Hypotheses. Substantively speaking, the null hypothesis states that the proportion (or frequency) of drug use is the same in white-collar and blue-collar family types. We could state H_0 differently: our observations do not differ from what would be expected by chance. The alternative hypothesis would be that there is a difference in drug usage between children from white-collar and blue-collar families.

The Choice of a Statistical Test. The Fisher exact test is appropriate since we have two independent samples categorized in a 2 × 2 table. In addition, the frequencies are too small to legitimately employ the chi-square test.

---

[6] See Conover (1974) and Mantel (1974) for a discussion of this controversy.

The Level of Significance and Sample Size. For variety's sake let alpha equal .10. Our sample size is 13.

One- versus Two-Tailed Tests. Since the alternative hypothesis is stated in non-directional fashion, a two-tailed test is called for.

The Sampling Distribution. The exact probability of the occurrence under H_0 of an observed set of values in a 2×2 table may be found by employing formula (9.7) for a one-tailed test and (9.8) for a two-tailed test.

$$p = \frac{(A+B)!\,(C+D)!\,(A+C)!\,(B+D)!}{N!\,A!\,B!\,C!\,D!} \quad one-tailed\ test \qquad (9.7)$$

$$p = 2\frac{(A+B)!\,(C+D)!\,(A+C)!\,(B+D)!}{N!\,A!\,B!\,C!\,D!} \quad two-tailed\ test \qquad (9.8)$$

where:
$$p = \text{probability of a given data set}$$
$$A,\ B,\ C,\ D = \text{cell frequencies as indicated in Table 9.1}$$
$$N = \text{total number of observations in the table}$$

In statistics the exclamation mark (!) is called a *factorial sign*. In the generic sense it may be thought of as a mathematical verb that directs us to multiply the indicated value by all integers less than it but greater than zero. For example, 6! = (6)(5)(4)(3)(2)(1) = 720. In the same fashion, 3! = (3)(2)(1) = 6. It is important to remember that 0! = 1, and any value other than zero raised to the zero power = 1, for example, $X^0 = 1$.

The probability distributions generated by formulas (9.7) and (9.8) are known as **hypergeometric distributions.** When the marginal totals are fixed, the probability of any cell arrangement can be generated by using these formulae. If the researcher is satisfied to use levels of significance rather than exact probability values, tables (of the sampling distribution) are available. Since this sampling distribution, in table form, is more complicated than most, the interested reader is asked to refer to Siegel (1956). Furthermore, the advantages of Fisher's test accrue when exact probability values are to be obtained.

The Region of Rejection. Any p value *equal to or less than* .10 is sufficient to reject H_0. To compute the value of the Fisher exact test statistic formula (9.8) is employed for a two-tailed test. Hence:

$$p = 2\frac{3!\,10!\,6!\,7!}{13!\,0!\,3!\,6!\,4!}$$

$$= 2\frac{(6)(3,628,800)(720)(5,040)}{(6,227,020,800)(1)(6)(720)(24)}$$

$$= 2(.12238)$$

$$= .24476$$

Consequently, the exact probability of obtaining a data arrangement like that in Table 9.3 under the null hypothesis is .24.

In many instances, Fisher's exact test is not so easily computed. This one was facilitated by the 0 cell frequency in cell A. If there is no cell frequency that is initially zero, the computational procedure becomes more involved.

Ordinarily, in a test with the hypergeometric distribution, we are concerned with the probability of getting our particular data-set *and* all the more extreme distributions which could occur, assuming the marginal totals in a given table are fixed. To illustrate we rearrange the data in Table 9.3, and this alteration appears in Table 9.4 (a). To employ Fisher's exact test we must modify the cell frequencies until the most extreme table arrangement is produced. In the present case, Table 9.4 (b) contains this modification.

TABLE 9.4

Rearranging Data in Table 9.3 to Illustrate the Computation of Fisher's Exact Test

	(a) *Rearranged Table*		
	White Collar	*Blue Collar*	
Drug user	1 (*A*)	2 (*B*)	3
Drug nonuser	6 (*C*)	4 (*D*)	10
	7	6	13
	(b) *Most Extreme Table*		
	White Collar	*Blue Collar*	
Drug user	0 (*A*)	3 (*B*)	3
Drug nonuser	7 (*C*)	3 (*D*)	10
	7	6	13

Note what has been done in Table 9.4 to produce the most extreme data arrangement. The frequency of cell A has been reduced by one, and then all other cell frequencies are made to fit the original marginal totals. *This procedure terminates when one of the cell frequencies reaches zero.* Any original table containing a 0 frequency is already in its most extreme form.

To compute the probability of getting our original distribution and all more extreme ones, we compute p for each table and sum the respective probabilities obtained. Doing this:

$$P_{\text{rearranged Table 9.4a}} = 2\frac{3!\,10!\,7!\,6!}{13!\,1!\,2!\,6!\,4!}$$

$$= (2).36713$$

$$= .73426$$

$$P_{\text{most extreme Table 9.4b}} = 2\frac{3!\,10!\,7!\,6!}{13!\,0!\,3!\,7!\,3!}$$

$$= (2).06993$$

$$= .13986$$

$$p_c = .87412(.73426 + .13986)$$

The symbol p_c is the cumulative probability. In this illustration, $p_c = .87412$. What does $p_c = .87412$ mean? Since our computed value is greater than the selected alpha value, that is, $.87412 > .10$, we fail to reject H_0. We may conclude, substantively, that there is not a statistically significant difference in drug usage among children from white-collar and blue-collar families. For these data $p > .10$. Sometimes the letters $N.S.$ are used, and this means the findings are not (N) statistically significant (S).

Observations on Fisher's Exact Test. To use this test the data should be arranged in a 2 × 2 table. For a broader application, Pierce (1969) has extended the Fisher exact test for 2 × 3 tables. Intuitively you may see that in larger tables the calculation of the factorial values would become a time-consuming and laborious task.

The major advantage of this test is that it is applicable to 2 × 2 tables with small cell frequencies (< 5) and it is more precise than chi-square in that it gives the *exact* probabilities associated with the data-set.

Finally, when a one-tailed test application is called for, we would simply divide p_c by two or use formula (9.7). Were this the case, we still could not reject H_0 since $.10 < .43706$ ($.87412/2 = .43706$). Again, $p > .10$ and not statistically significant ($N.S.$).

z Test for Differences between Proportions

This test is a two-sample alternative to the chi-square test of independence, but is used with *proportions* rather than frequencies. The z test for differences between proportions may be used to evaluate whether or not there are significant differences between two proportions as in the following example.[7]

This writer once was concerned with attitudes toward differential forms of alternate civilian work for conscientious objectors (COs). One hypothesis from a

[7]See Appendix B for a discussion of the computations for proportions.

large battery was this: Male students, because they are more susceptible than female students to orders for military duty, will be more favorable than female students toward allowing conscientious objectors to perform a wide variety of alternative service work activities. After establishing twenty-seven approved alternate service work jobs for COs, the instrument was administered to two samples, one of males ($n_1 = 59$) and the other of females ($n_2 = 95$). For present purposes, the researcher was concerned with the mean percent (or proportion) of favorable responses to the twenty-seven items. The results of the survey appear in Table 9.5. It should be noted that p and q are proportions and the $p_1 + q_1 = 1.000$ and $p_2 + q_2 = 1.000$. In any event, the focus here is upon whether there is a significant difference between males and females in their attitudes toward alternative military service work. Let us systematically outline the formal steps involved.

TABLE 9.5

Illustration of z Test for Differences between Proportions: Proportion of Favorable Responses to Alternate Service Items by Sex

	Sex	
	Male ($n_1 = 59$)	Female ($n_2 = 95$)
Proportion favorable	.685 (p_1)	.577 (p_2)
Proportion unfavorable	.315 (q_1)	.423 (q_2)
	1.000	1.000

Stating the Null and Alternative Hypotheses. Substantively speaking, the null hypothesis (H_0) is that there is no difference in the proportion of males (p_1) and females (p_2) favorable to alternative modes of service for COs. Symbolically, $p_1 = p_2$ or $p_1 - p_2 = 0$.

The alternative hypothesis (H_1), in line with our contention, is that the proportion of males (p_1) favorable to alternative modes of service for COs is greater than the proportion of females (p_2) favorable. Symbolically, $p_1 > p_2$.

The Choice of a Statistical Test. Since we have the proportion of favorable (and unfavorable) responses for two samples, the z test for differences between proportions is appropriate. It should be apparent that this test of significance is also applicable to percentages by simply converting the respective percentages to proportions.

The Level of Significance and Sample Size. For variety's sake, let us set alpha at the .10 level. The sample sizes for males (n_1) and females (n_2) are 59 and 95, respectively.

Leonard–Basic Social Stats.—14

One- versus Two-Tailed Tests. Since the alternative hypothesis was symbolized H_1 = $p_1 > p_2$, a one-tailed test is called for.

The Sampling Distribution.   The N.C. table (Table B in Appendix A) is the appropriate sampling distribution for this test. The form of the sampling distribution of p only approaches the normal curve under certain conditions. Whenever p departs widely from .50, say .10 or .95, the sampling distribution does not look very much like the normal one. In general, the approximation of the normal curve occurs the closer p is to .50 and the larger the sample.

The Region of Rejection.   The N.C. table indicates that we must have a z value of 1.28 or larger in order to reject H_0.

To calculate z in the present example, formula (9.9) is employed:

$$z = \frac{p_1 - p_2}{s_{p_1 - p_2}} \qquad (9.9)$$

where: z = z test for differences between proportions
p_1 = the proportion of male students expressing favorable responses
p_2 = the proportion of female students expressing favorable responses
$s_{p_1 - p_2}$ = the standard error of the difference between two proportions

The standard error term is calculated:

$$s_{p_1 - p_2} = \sqrt{\frac{p_1 q_1}{n_1} + \frac{p_2 q_2}{n_2}}$$

If we substitute the tabled data (Table 9.5) into formula (9.9):

$$z = \frac{.685 - .577}{\sqrt{\dfrac{(.685)\,(.315)}{59} + \dfrac{(.577)\,(.423)}{95}}}$$

$$= \frac{.108}{\sqrt{\dfrac{.2158}{59} + \dfrac{.2441}{95}}}$$

$$= \frac{.108}{\sqrt{.0036 + .0026}}$$

$$= \frac{.108}{\sqrt{.0062}}$$

$$= \frac{.108}{.079}$$

$$= 1.37$$

What does a z of 1.37 mean? To answer this we must consult the normal curve table at the .10 level of significance. We find the critical value equal to 1.28 (approximately). As is our custom, whenever our computed value is larger than the table value, H_0 is rejected. Since $1.37 > 1.28$ we reject the null hypothesis knowing that we may have done so erroneously 10 times out of 100. Substantively speaking, there is a statistically significant difference between male and female favorable attitudes toward alternate modes of service for COs at the .10 level of significance. It also means that the probability of a type I error is 10 percent. Thusly, $p < .10$.

The above z equation is most appropriate when $n > 30$. When n is small, that is, less than 30, a modification in the formula is made. This alteration, reflected in the denominator of formula (9.10), is a *pooled* estimate of the standard error of the difference between two proportions. In this instance, the t test, with the following formula (9.10), is appropriate:

$$t = \frac{P_1 - P_2}{s_{p_1 - p_2}} \qquad (9.10)$$

where: $t = $ difference of proportion test for small samples ($n < 30$)
$p_1 = $ the same as in z formula (9.9)
$p_2 = $ the same as in z formula (9.9)
$s_{p_1 - p_2} = \sqrt{pq(1/n_1 + 1/n_2)}$

p (in the standard error formula above) is determined as follows:

$$p = \frac{p_1 n_1 + p_2 n_2}{n_1 + n_2}$$

where: $p = $ proportion of cases of interest

To illustrate, suppose that $n_1 = 11$ and $n_2 = 15$ and $p_1 = .45$ ($q_1 = .55$) and $p_2 = .55$ ($q_2 = .45$). Substituting these values:

$$p = \frac{(.45)(11) + (.55)(15)}{11 + 15}$$
$$= .51$$
$$q = 1.00 - .51 = .49$$

Determining $s_{p_1 - p_2}$:

$$s_{p_1 - p_2} = \sqrt{(.51)(.49)(1/11 + 1/15)}$$
$$= \sqrt{(.2499)(.09 + .07)}$$
$$= \sqrt{(.2499)(.16)}$$
$$= \sqrt{.039984}$$
$$= .19996$$

Substituting these values into formula (9.10):

$$t = \frac{.45 - .55}{.19996}$$
$$= \frac{-.10}{.19996}$$
$$= -.50$$

What does a $t = -.50$ mean? Before answering this question let us turn to the sampling distribution of the t statistic.

The t Sampling Distribution.   The t sampling distribution appears in Table E of Appendix A. A discussion of its key characteristics is in order. With samples equal to or less than 30, the normal curve is not adequate for representing one's data. Consequently, we must turn to another sampling distribution, actually a family of distributions that are a function of the **degrees of freedom** (*df*). These distributions were described by William S. Gosset (1876 1937), who published under the name of "Student," and are sometimes called *Student's t distribution* (or simply the *t distribution*).

You will recall from our previous discussion that degrees of freedom refer to the number of values free to vary given certain restrictions on our data. For the present illustration, *df* is equal to $n_1 + n_2 - 2$ or $11 + 15 - 2 = 24$.

The diagram in Figure 9.3 provides a visual display of the form of the t sampling distribution with different *df*'s. Notice that the t distribution, like the normal one, is *symmetrical* but more *platykurtic* (flatter) than the normal curve, particularly when *df* is small. Because t is more spread out it means that the area beyond a specific t value is greater than the area beyond a corresponding z value. However, as *df* becomes larger, that is, approaches 100, the areas encompassed by different t values are virtually identical to those for corresponding z values. In other words, when *df* approaches 100 the shapes of the N.C. and t distributions are just about the same.

To assess the statistical meaning of our t value we consult the t sampling distribution and locate the critical value at the intersection of our *df* and preselected alpha (level of significance) according to the nature of our alternative hypothesis. Assume we had selected an alpha value of .05 for a two-tailed test. Since $df = 24$ ($n_1 + n_2 - 2$ or $11 + 15 - 2 = 24$) we discover that a critical value of 2.064 or larger is needed to reject the null hypothesis. Since our t value of $-.50$ is less than the critical value we fail to reject the null. Therefore, $p > .05$ and "N.S."

Observations on the z and t Tests for Differences between Proportions.   The appropriate application of the z test requires n's equal to or larger than 30. When n's are small, less than 30, the t test should be employed. In fact, when one is in doubt about which to employ, the t test would be more appropriate since it provides more conservative values.

FIGURE 9.3

The Shape of the *t* Sampling Distribution with Different *df*'s

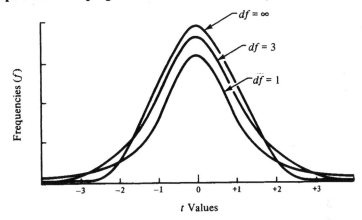

TWO-SAMPLE TEST: RELATED SAMPLES

McNemar Test

In the pre-post test research designs, the researcher is often interested in the effect of some intervening variable or experimental stimulus upon his or her sample. Such a design requires the phenomenon of interest to be measured *both* before (the "pre" phase) and after (the "post" phase) the introduction of some stimulus. By comparing the two measurements, one may then garner some insights into the effect of the experimentally induced stimulus. If a significant change *has* been observed, it *may* be due to the intervening variable. An example will make this clear.

Professors are perennially interested in the effect their courses have upon a person's ability to think about the particular discipline being discussed. Suppose a sociology prof wishes to determine the influence of a course on students' ability to think about the relativity of cultural norms. More specifically, interest is in whether the gestalt nature of the class (that is, lectures, textbooks, and discussion) has an effect on changing their intital perspective of societal norms. Let us assume that a valid instrument has been devised that permits us to categorize students into two brackets: (1) ethnocentric and (2) nonethnocentric. The students are categorized during the first week of classes into ethnocentric and nonethnocentric on the basis of their responses and then again the final week of school. This is the type of question the **McNemar Test** is geared to answer. Before presenting the equation, let us set up this problem in formal statistical terms.

Stating the Null and Alternative Hypotheses. In substantive terms, the null hypothesis is that there is no change in students' ability to think about the relativity of cultural norms as a result of an introductory sociology course. The alternative hypothesis is, substantively speaking, that there is (or will be) a change in their ability to do this.

The Choice of a Statistical Test. Since we have a two-sample situation dealing with before and after measurements, the *McNemar test for significance of changes* is appropriate. Any time the *same* subjects are tested at two different points in time, the samples are said to be *matched* or *related*. Furthermore, our tabulation of data into mutually exclusive categories such as this summons us to employ a nominal level test of significance.

The Level of Signficance and Sample Size. Let us set alpha at the .05 level and use a sample of 350 students from a mass lecture section of introductory sociology.

One- versus Two-Tailed Tests. Since the alternative hypothesis is nondirectional in nature, we will use a two-tailed test. Had we specified the direction of change, a one-tailed test would have been called for.

The Sampling Distribution. The McNemar test uses the chi-square sampling distribution. Consequently, we must consult this table for determining the test statistic's significance.

The Region of Rejection. To determine the critical value (as well as the entire critical region) we enter the chi-square table (Table C in Appendix A) at the selected alpha level according to the degrees of freedom. In a 2×2 table the *df* will always equal 1: $(r - 1)(c - 1)$ or $(2 - 1)(2 - 1) = 1$. Since the McNemar test is restricted to a 2×2 contingency table, it will always have 1 *df*.

Examining the table indicates that a χ^2 value of 3.841 or larger is necessary to reject H_0 at the .05 level.

To employ the McNemar test we construct a contingency table with both the pre- and post-test measures categorized. Table 9.6 has been constructed for our use.

It should become apparent that McNemar's test focuses only on those students whose thinking ability has changed from one time period to the next. Consequently, these changes are reflected in cells A and D. In cell A appears the number of students whose thinking changed from nonethnocentric to ethnocentric while cell D contains the number of students whose thinking changed from ethnocentric to nonethnocentric. Since the total number of students who change are located in cells A and D, the expectation of the pattern of cell frequencies under the null hypothesis is that $\frac{1}{2}(A + D)$ of the students will change in one direction and $\frac{1}{2}(A + D)$ of the students will change in the other direction. In short, $\frac{1}{2}(A + D)$ is the expected frequency of both cells (A and D) under the truth of the null.

TABLE 9.6

Illustration of McNemar Test: Hypothetical Changes in Students' Ability to Think about the Relativity of Cultural Norms

Classification before Course	Classification at the End of the Course		
	Ethnocentric	Nonethnocentric	
Nonethnocentric	25 (A)	50 (B)	75
Ethnocentric	125 (C)	150 (D)	275
	150	200	350

To compute the McNemar test statistic formula (9.11) is used:

$$\chi^2_M = \frac{(|A - D| - 1)^2}{A + D} \qquad (9.11)$$

where: χ^2_M = McNemar test for significance of changes

A and D = refer to cell frequencies (as labeled in Table 9.1)

| | = indicates concern with absolute values

Formula (9.11) has a correction for continuity built into it. Substituting our data into the formula:

$$\chi^2_M = \frac{(|25 - 150| - 1)^2}{25 + 150}$$

$$= \frac{(|125 - 1|)^2}{175}$$

$$= \frac{15,376}{175}$$

$$= 87.86$$

What does χ^2_M of 87.86 mean? We enter the chi-square table at the .05 level of significance with 1 *df*. Since our computed value exceeds the table value, that is, $87.86 > 3.841$, we conclude that there has been a statistically significant ($p < .05$) change in students' ability to think about societal affairs at the end of the course in introductory sociology. One caution is in order: since no other variables were considered, we *cannot* conclude that the course per se caused the perspective change. To make a statement of this nature would require a more elaborate research design with other variables controlled.

Suppose we had hypothesized that a change from ethnocentric to nonethnocentric is more likely to occur. Hence, we have a one-tailed, that is, directional, hypothesis. Since the chi-square sampling distribution lists only two-tailed values, we must halve the two-tailed probability value. Therefore, $\frac{1}{2}(.05) = .025$. Consequently, the probability associated with the data in Table 9.6 is equal to or less than .025. Moreover, had we selected an alpha value of .01 the critical value would be 6.635 for 1 df for a two-tailed application. Had the hypothesis been directional we would divide .01 by 2 $(.01/2 = .005)$ and assert that these data are significant at the .005 level since $87.86 > 6.635$ and express this as $p < .005$.

Observations on the McNemar Test. To employ this test the samples must be related in some way. Ideally, this test works best when individuals act as their own controls in a before-after research design such as in the illustration above.

The McNemar test should not be used with relatively small frequencies, that is, where $(A + D)/2$ is less than 5. It should be obvious that its use is restricted to a fourfold table.

k-SAMPLE TESTS: INDEPENDENT SAMPLES

Chi-Square Test for k Independent Samples

A previous section dealt with the chi-square test of independence for two independent samples. k refers to contingency tables larger than 2×2. For example, 3×3, 2×3, 6×7, 10×15, and so forth, are possible table arrangements for which the chi-square test may be appropriate. Table 9.7 depicts a hypothetical situation whereby persons of different religious denominations and their attitudes toward abortion have been cross-tabulated. Instead of designating cell *frequencies*, a *letter* designation for each of the 20 cells is noted.

TABLE 9.7

Illustration of Chi-Square for *k* Independent Samples: Attitudes toward Abortion by Religious Groups

Attitude Toward Abortion	Religion				Row Marginal Totals
	Protestant	Catholic	Jew	Other	
Strongly oppose	A	B	C	D	A+B+C+D
Oppose	E	F	G	H	E+F+G+H
Undecided	I	J	K	L	I+J+K+L
Support	M	W	O	P	M+W+P+P
Strongly support	Q	R	S	T	Q+R+S+T
Column marginal totals:	A+E+I +M+Q	B+F+J +W+R	C+G+K +O+S	D+H+L +P+T	N (grand total)

Technically speaking, Table 9.7 is a 5 (attitude toward abortion using five categories of response) by 4 (four religious groupings) table. The didactic point is that virtually any arrangement of rows and columns can be created for a data-set. The computational logic behind $r \times c$ contingency tables remains the same. In this illustration, the researcher would be testing the null hypothesis that there is no difference in attitudes toward abortion among the various religious groups. The steps outlined previously will *not* be worked through. However, several features of the chi-square test should be made explicit at this point.

First of all, regardless of the table's dimensions, the *expected* frequencies are obtained by multiplying the marginal frequencies (row and column) common to a particular cell and dividing by the grand total. The expected frequency in cell *A* would be: $[(A + B + C + D)(A + E + I + M + Q)]$/the grand total.

Secondly, regardless of the number of cells, the degrees of freedom are determined by $(r - 1)(c - 1)$. In the present example there are 5 rows and 4 columns, hence, $df = (5 - 1)(4 - 1)$ equals 12. Notice that the *df* formula (9.3) included in the section on the chi-square test of independence is applicable to *all* contingency tables.

Thirdly, the chi-square computational formula (9.1):

$$\chi^2 = \sum \frac{(O_f - E_f)^2}{E_f}$$

is worked through in the same manner as we illustrated with the test of independence for two samples.[8] The obtained chi-square value is compared with the critical value in the chi-square sampling distribution table according to *df* and alpha. If the computed value is equal to or larger than the table value then H_0 is rejected; if smaller, we fail to reject H_0.

Observations on the Chi-Square Test Statistic. Blalock (1979: 290–291) has noted that the frequency chi-square test statistic requires a relatively large *n* because the sampling distribution of the test statistic approximates the sampling distribution found in chi-square tables only when *n* is large. In contingency tables a large *n* depends upon the number of cells and marginal frequencies. Whenever the *expected* frequencies (E_f) are in the neighborhood of 5 or less, it is advisable to make a modification in the tabled data. Since the chi-square distribution is assumed to be continuous and since observed frequencies are restricted, that is, must always be integers, some correction should be made. One convention, which we previously employed, known as **Yates' correction for continuity,** assumes that the observed frequencies (O_f) actually take on all possible values, and we make use of those values within a distance of one-half unit on both sides of the integer reported.

---

[8]An alternative formula for computing chi-square is: $\chi^2 = \sum [(O_f)^2/E_f] - N$. If we used this formula for the "professors are better teachers" data, we have: $\chi^2 = [(72)^2/170 + (268)^2/170] - 340 = 112.98$.

Ordinarily, .5 (one-half unity) is subtracted from the $(O_f - E_f)$ differences as illustrated in formula (9.5). This is a *conservative* approach which generally reduces the magnitude of the chi-square value. Runyon and Haber (1976: 334) state that "When $df > 1$, the expected frequency should be equal to or greater than 5 in at least 80% of the cells." It should be noted that some of the more recently developed computer programs (e.g., SPSS, SAS) have this correction for continuity built into the analysis. Finally, when larger tables can be *collapsed*, the small expected frequency problem can often be circumvented.

The computed chi-square value will always be *positive*, varying from 0 to infinity, theoretically. This becomes obvious in examining the chi-square formula in which the $(O_f - E_f)$ numerical values are squared.

Chi-square is most often considered to be a *nondirectional* or *two-tailed test*. Just the same, its use is *not* confined to nondirectional applications. Although most chi-square tables are set up for two-tailed tests, for one-tailed applications the researcher simply halves the probability values listed, for example, .10 (two-tailed test) becomes .10/2 or .05 for one-tailed hypotheses. This also implies that the substantive interpretation of the data can only be ferreted out by scrutinizing the cellular composition of the table.

The use of the chi-square test assumes random sampling and that the frequency counts be independent of one another. In short, the same person cannot be questioned or surveyed more than once; otherwise, this produces what is termed the inflated n dilemma and will play havoc with both the computation and interpretation of the chi-square value.

A very important matter surrounds χ^2 sensitivity to grouping. In other words, if categories are collapsed or subdivided differently, different chi-square values will result.

Chi-square is also related to the sample size. Consider the following table (a):

(a)

7	3	10
5	10	15
12	13	25

$\chi_c^2 = 1.93$

The corrected chi-square value is 1.93 and not significant at the .05 level. Now, if we simply double the frequencies in each cell of (a), for example,

(b)

14	6	20
10	20	30
24	26	50

$\chi_c^2 = 5.08$

the corrected chi-square value is now significant at the .05 level. In table (b) the chi-square is 5.08. Finally, if we double the cell frequencies in table (b), that is,

(c)

28	12	40
20	40	60
48	52	100

$\chi_c^2 = 11.50$

the corrected chi-square is now significant at the .01 level. In this case $\chi^2 = 11.50$ and $p < .01$.

This illustration of how χ^2 is affected by n should be understood in this manner. If *real* differences between the observed and expected frequencies exist, the difference will increase as sample size increases. However, if no actual differences exist between observed and expected frequencies, χ^2 will not alter with an increase in the sample size.

Finally, chi-square is a **test of statistical significance**, not a measure of association. This is often confusing since the chi-square value is used in the computation of a variety of delta-based measures of relationship. More will be said about this in the chapter devoted to nominal measures of association.

k-SAMPLE TEST: RELATED SAMPLES

Cochran *Q* Test

This test may be thought of as an extension of the McNemar test. Whereas the McNemar test is geared to deal with two related samples, the **Cochran *Q* test** has a wide variety of research applications and may be used for determining whether three or more matched frequencies differ significantly. For this test the samples must be related, that is, the k samples must include subjects who act as their own controls or the k samples must have been matched according to certain criteria.

To demonstrate Cochran Q's affinities with the McNemar test let us alter the example previously discussed concerning changes in students' ability to think of the relativity of societal norms as a result of an introductory sociology course. For illustrative purposes we will focus on six individuals' scores on an ethnocentrism scale at three different measurement periods during the course (the first week, the middle of the semester, the last week of school). In this example, each student is acting as his or her own control and would be studied at different times during the semester. In Table 9.8 the matched individuals' responses are categorized as zero (0) when ethnocentrism has been determined and one (1) when nonethnocentrism has been established.

TABLE 9.8

Illustration of Cochran's Q Test: Hypothetical Students' Ethnocentrism Scores at Three Different Points during the Semester

Individuals	Measurements			F	F^2
	First	Second	Third		
A	0	1	1	2	4
B	0	0	1	1	1
C	1	1	1	3	9
D	0	1	0	1	1
E	0	0	1	1	1
F	1	1	0	2	4
	$S_1 = 2$	$S_2 = 4$	$S_3 = 4$	$\Sigma = 10$	$\Sigma = 20$

Let us set up this problem in formal statistical terms.

Stating the Null and Alternative Hypotheses. Substantively speaking, the null hypothesis is that there is no difference (or change) among the students from one measurement period to the next. The alternative hypothesis is that there is a change in students' attitudes from one period to the next.

The Choice of a Statistical Test. The Cochran Q test is chosen because the data consist of measurements for the same individuals acting as their own controls and are dichotomized into ethnocentric (0) and nonethnocentric (1).

The Level of Significance and Sample Size. Let us set alpha at the .001 level and study six individuals. Table 9.8 contains the necessary information for computing the Cochran Q statistic.

One- versus Two-Tailed Tests. Since the alternative hypothesis is stated in non-directional fashion, a two-tailed test is called for.

The Sampling Distribution. The chi-square sampling distribution is appropriate for use with the Cochran Q test.

The Region of Rejection. The region of rejection is determined by consulting the chi-square table (Table C in Appendix A) with $k - 1$ degrees of freedom at the .001 level of significance. The critical value for 2 *df* at the .001 level is 13.815. All values equal to or larger than 13.815 are sufficient to reject H_0.

The following steps are recommended for computing Cochran's Q statistic:

1. Indicate the individuals' ethnocentrism scores during the different phases

using a zero (0) for ethnocentric responses and a one (1) for nonethnocentric attitudes. Note that this has been done in Table 9.8.

2. In a column labeled F sum, *horizontally*, the number of nonethnocentric (1) responses for each individual. See Table 9.8.

3. In an adjacent column (to F) set up an F^2 column where the sum of each subject's nonethnocentric responses is squared. This has been done in Table 9.8.

4. Sum, *vertically*, all (five) columns. To test our hypothesis the following formula is employed:

$$Q = \frac{(k-1)\ [k\Sigma S_i^2 - (\Sigma S_i)^2]}{k(\Sigma F) - \Sigma F^2} \qquad (9.12)$$

where: Q = Cochran's Q statistic
  k = number of different measurement periods
  Σ = summation operator
  S_i = total number of nonethnocentric responses for each measurement period
  F = total number of nonethnocentric responses for each individual across the three measurement periods

Substituting our values into formula (9.12):

$$Q = \frac{(3-1)\ [3(2^2 + 4^2 + 4^2) - 10^2]}{3(10) - 20}$$

$$= \frac{2\ [3(36) - 100]}{30 - 20}$$

$$= \frac{2(108 - 100)}{10}$$

$$= \frac{2(8)}{10}$$

$$= \frac{16}{10}$$

$$= 1.6$$

What does Q equal to 1.6 mean? To answer this question requires us to consult the chi-square table (the appropriate sampling distribution for Cochran's Q) with $k-1$ degrees of freedom at the predetermined .001 level of significance. We find the critical value to be 13.815. Since our computed value is less than the table value, that is, 1.6 < 13.815, we cannot reject H_0 at the .001 level. Substantively speaking, a statistically significant difference (at the .001 level) has not been found in students' attitudes during three different measurement periods as a result of an introductory sociology course. Therefore, $p > .001$ and not statistically significant.

Observations on Cochran's Q Test. This test is most appropriate for naturally dichotomous variables such as black-white, agree-disagree, and so forth. Nevertheless, data which are continuous may be used as long as the researcher has some rationale for dichotomizing the observations.

SUMMARY

In this chapter we have demonstrated the application of various nominal level tests of significance. The statistical techniques were categorized and discussed on the basis of: (1) the number of samples, one, two, or k, and (2) whether the samples were independent or related. Figure 9.1 summarizes the discussion contained in this chapter.

IMPORTANT CONCEPTS DISCUSSED IN THIS CHAPTER

Chi-square test

Test of statistical independence

Goodness-of-fit

Contingency tables

Bivariate frequency tables

Matrix

2×2 table

Cell frequencies

Grand total

Marginals or marginal totals

Row marginal total

Column marginal total

Observed frequencies (O_f)

Expected frequencies (E_f)

Degrees of freedom (df)

Model of no association

Yates' correction for continuity

Fisher's exact test

Factorial

Hypergeometric distribution

McNemar test

z Test for differences between proportions

Chi-square test for k independent samples

Cochran Q test

REVIEW QUESTIONS

1. Suppose we are interested in student opinions as to whether or not O.J. Simpson was guilty. In a random sample of 500 students our hypothetical results showed that 426 said "Yes" and 72 said "No." From these data compute the *chi-square goodness-of-fit test* statistic and make a decision as to whether or not the null hypothesis is rejected or retained at the .01 level of significance.

2. Assume we want to determine if there is a significant difference in marijuana smoking among children of divorced parents and among children of parents who are not divorced. Using the data below, employ the *Fisher exact test* to determine if there is a statistically significant difference at the .05 level (do this for both one- and two-tailed hypotheses).

	Divorced Parents	Not Divorced
Smoke marijuana	2	0
Do not smoke marijuana	4	5

3. Many college students find temporary summer work as a means of supplementing their income. Suppose, we wish to measure the self-esteem of working college students (in terms of high and low) at the beginning and end of their summer employment. For the data below, use the *McNemar test* and determine whether a significant change at the .05 level can be supported.

	End of Summer	
Beginning of Summer	Low Esteem	High Esteem
High esteem	55	70
Low esteem	175	200

4. Let us assess the attitudes that college students have toward working-class individuals. Focusing on five students, we measure their attitudes at the beginning, middle, and end of the summer to determine if there is a significant change from one time period to the next (remember that 0 means there is no change and 1 means that some change has occurred). Employ *Cochran's Q* test for these data and test the null hypothesis at the .10 level of significance.

Individual	Beginning	Middle	End
A	0	1	1
B	1	1	1
C	0	0	1
D	1	1	0
E	0	0	1

5. It has been said that females have a more favorable opinion toward abortion than males. Using the hypothetical data below, employ the *z test for differences between*

proportions to determine if there is a significant difference between male and female attitudes at the .01 level.

	Sex	
Attitudes toward Abortion	*Female (n_1 = 50)*	*Male (n_2 = 50)*
Favorable	.790	.415
Unfavorable	.210	.585

6. It is believed that attitudes toward the women's movement vary with age. Listed below are (hypothetical) different age groups' attitude towards the movement. From these data, calculate the *chi-square test for k independent samples* and decide whether there is a statistically significant difference at the .001 level.

	Age Categories			
Attitudes towards Women's Movement	11–25	26–40	41–55	56–70
Strongly accept	7(A)	5(B)	3(C)	1(D)
Accept	10(E)	7(F)	5(G)	4(H)
Indifferent	2(I)	5(J)	5(K)	8(L)
Reject	3(M)	4(N)	6(O)	5(P)
Strongly reject	3(Q)	4(R)	6(S)	7(T)

7. There are two broad uses of chi-square. What are they and how are they different?

8. Explain the degrees of freedom concept and show how *df*'s can be determined in a contingency table as well as in a goodness-of-fit situation.

9. If you had two related samples what criteria would be used in deciding whether the *z* or *t* test was more appropriate?

10. Explain the purpose of Yates' correction for continuity.

11. Choose one of the problem-solving problems above (questions 1 through 6) and outline the steps involved in the testing of the hypothesis. Use the step-by-step procedure presented in Chapter 8.

10

ORDINAL LEVEL TESTS OF SIGNIFICANCE

In this chapter the application of a variety of ordinal level significance tests will be explained. The discussion will be organized in terms of: (1) the **number of samples**, that is, one, two, or k, and (2) whether the samples are **independent or related** (it should be obvious that the distinction between independent and related samples is not applicable to one-sample tests). These tests are appropriate where data originally appear in or are reduced to rank form. Figure 10.1 contains the organizing framework for the contents of this chapter.

FIGURE 10.1

Ordinal Level Tests of Significance

One-Sample Tests	Two-Sample Tests		k-Sample Tests	
	Independent Samples	Related Samples	Independent Samples	Related Samples
Kolmogorov-Smirnov test One-sample runs test	Wald-Wolfowitz runs test Mann-Whitney U test	Sign test Wilcoxon matched pairs-signed ranks test	Kruskal-Wallis H test	Friedman two-way analysis of variance test

ONE-SAMPLE TESTS OF SIGNIFICANCE

Kolmogorov-Smirnov (K-S) One-Sample Test

The **Kolmogorov-Smirnov one-sample test** is a goodness-of-fit approach. Like the chi-square goodness-of-fit 'test, this technique is concerned with determining the correspondence between an observed distribution of scores and a specified theoretical distribution. The computed test statistic facilitates our deciding whether or not the observed scores could have come from a population with a specified theoretical distribution.

The Kolmogorov-Smirnov test involves specifying the *cumulative* frequency distribution which would occur under the null (theoretical distribution) and then comparing it with the *observed* cumulative frequency distribution. Then, the greatest divergence between theoretical and observed distributions is determined. Finally, the maximum divergence, symbolized as D, is compared with the Kolmogorov-Smirnov sampling distribution to assess its statistical significance.

Assume we are interested in disengagement scores among a random sample of elderly at a nursing home. The data tabulation produces four hypothetical ranked categories with the number of elderly in each shown in Table 10.1.

TABLE 10.1

Illustration of Kolmogorov-Smirnov Test: Hypothetical Disengagement Rankings for Twenty Elderly

	Disengagement Ranks			
	Low	Moderately Low	Moderately High	High
Number of elderly with various scores categorized into ranks ($N = 20$)	2	5	8	5

Let us set up this problem in formal statistical terms.

Stating the Null and Alternative Hypotheses. We are testing the null hypothesis that there is an equal distribution of disengagement ranks among the sample of elderly persons. The alternative hypothesis is that there is not an equal distribution of disengagement ranks in our sample.

The Choice of a Statistical Test. Since a single random sample has been drawn and the scores have been ranked into four categories, the Kolmogorov-Smirnov test is appropriate. Hereafter the Kolmogorov-Smirnov test will be designated by K-S.

The Level of Significance and Sample Size. Let alpha equal .05. The sample size has already been specified as 20.

One- versus Two-Tailed Tests. Since the alternative hypothesis is stated in non-directional fashion a two-tailed test is called for.

The Sampling Distribution. The various critical values of the D statistic are presented in Table F in Appendix A, along with the associated probabilities of occurrence under H_0.

The Region of Rejection. The rejection region consists of all the values of D which are equal to or larger than alpha = .05. In the sampling distribution table the critical value is .294, the number at the intersection of $n = 20$ and .05 level of significance.

    To test H_0 we must determine the theoretical distribution of the disengagement scores for these elderly. This is done by dividing the number of observations (in this case 20) by the number of categories (designated k) into which the observations are ranked. In other words, with $n = 20$ and $k = 4$, $20/4 = 5$. Five is the theoretically derived frequency for each category. Let us first list the observed frequencies (row 1) for each category and then place the expected frequencies in a row below the observed ones. This has been done in Table 10.2.

TABLE 10.2

Operations Involved in the K-S Test

		Disengagement Ranks		
	Low	*Moderately Low*	*Moderately High*	*High*
1. Observed frequencies	2/20	5/20	8/20	5/20
2. Theoretical frequencies	5/20	5/20	5/20	5/20
3. Cumulative observed frequencies	2/20	7/20	15/20	20/20
4. Cumulative theoretical frequencies	5/20	10/20	15/20	20/20
5. Absolute difference between cumulative observed and theoretical frequencies	3/20	3/20	0/20	0/20

    The next step is to determine the cumulative frequency distribution for *both* the observed and theoretical frequencies. This has been done in rows 3 and 4 of Table 10.2.

    The final step is to determine the largest absolute difference between the observed and theoretical cumulative frequencies, as we have done in Table 10.2 (row 5). Since the largest absolute difference is 3/20 (row 5) we shall label this difference D and consult the K-S sampling distribution at the preselected alpha level. D may be expressed as the maximum absolute observed-theoretical cumulative frequency difference. Turning to Table F we locate our sample size along the left-hand column at the .05 level and find the critical value to be .294. In order to reject H_0, the absolute difference between cumulative observed and theoretical frequencies must be equal to or larger than the table value. Since $3/20 = .15$ and since $.15 < .294$ we cannot reject H_0. Substantively speaking, there is an equal distribution of disengagement ranks among our sample of elderly. In short, there is not a statistically significant difference in disengagement ranks in our sample, that is, $p > .05$ and not statistically significant (N.S.).

Observations on the Kolomogorov-Smirnov Test. The K-S test, like virtually all others, assumes random sampling. The major advantage of this test is that, unlike chi-square in particular, it may be used with a small number of observations.

One-Sample Runs Test

The **one-sample runs test** is a useful technique for gauging whether a sample is random or not. It involves a computational procedure based on the *order* or *sequence* in which observations actually occur. A *run* is a series of identical elements which are followed or preceded by different elements or no elements at all.

For example, suppose a test containing twenty objective questions is administered to a class and an item analysis enables us to categorize each item as easy or difficult. Note that to employ this test the observations are assumed to be of a dichotomous nature. Assume that a systematic account of the twenty items results in the following sequence of easy and difficult items where E = easy and D = difficult. We will test whether or not the distribution of easy and difficult items occurs in a random sequence:

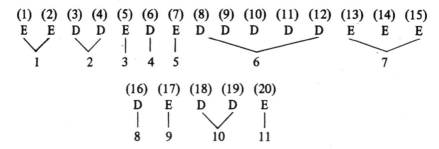

Item Number in Parentheses

In this exam there were 11 runs. The total number of **runs** (designated r) permits us to determine whether or not a sample (of questions in this case) is random.

Let us set up this example in formal statistical terms.

Stating the Null and Alternative Hypotheses.   The null hypothesis is that the number of easy and difficult items occur in a random order. The alternative hypothesis is that the sequence of questions is not random in nature.

The Choice of a Statistical Test.   Since our research question concerns whether or not the items of a single sequence are randomly distributed, the one-sample runs test is appropriate.

The Level of Significance and Sample Size.   We will set alpha at the .05 level. The sample size is 20.

One- versus Two-Tailed Tests.   Since no prediction of direction is made (see alternative hypothesis), a two-tailed test is called for.

The Sampling Distribution.   Table G in Appendix A gives the critical values of r for the runs test under the assumption of the truth of H_0. Notice that the runs table includes the number of runs that are *too few* as well as *too many* to be sufficient to reject H_0.

The Region of Rejection. From the sampling distribution we discover that if $r < 3$ or > 10 the H_0 can be rejected.
  To compute r let $n_1 =$ the number of easy items and n_2, the number of difficult items. Of course, $n_1 + n_2 =$ the total number of test items. To use the one-sample runs test, we must determine the *sequence* in which the n_1 and n_2 items occur and then count r, the number of runs. In our example there are 11 runs and $n_1 = 9$ while $n_2 = 11$. In the runs table we locate the intersection of n_1 and n_2 and find that any observed r of 6 or less or of 16 or more is in the rejection region for alpha $= .05$.
  Notice that if our observed number of runs is smaller than 6 or larger than 16 we can reject H_0 that the exam questions are randomly arranged. Since our $r = 11$ we may not reject H_0 and may conclude that the sequence of questions is random insofar as easy and difficult questions are concerned. In notation form, $p > .05$.

TWO-SAMPLE TESTS OF SIGNIFICANCE: INDEPENDENT SAMPLES

Wald-Wolfowitz Runs Test

The **Wald-Wolfowitz runs test** is appropriate when the researcher wishes to test the null hypothesis that two independent samples have been drawn from the same population. This test is a nonspecific one in the sense that it will pick up any differences, for example, central location, variation, and form (skewness and/or kurtosis), if there actually are differences. In a practical sense this means that H_0 and H_1 may be expressed in a variety of ways.

The Wald-Wolfowitz runs test assumes that the variable under investigation is continuous. Although ties can occur, these are usually due to imperfect measurement. The rationale for the runs test is that if the scores of the two independent samples are arranged into one continuous series (low to high or high to low), and if the null hypothesis is true, there should be no systematic concentration of either high or low scores in either of the samples. In other words, high and low scores should be evenly divided between the two samples.

Suppose we are interested in assessing the differences in attitudes of a civilian and a military sample toward the U.S.'s involvement in Southeast Asia. Furthermore, assume an instrument has been devised to measure both pro and con attitudes toward such involvement and a high score is indicative of favorable attitudes and a low score is indicative of unfavorable attitudes. The hypothetical data appear in Table 10.3. Let us set up this problem in formal statistical terms.

TABLE 10.3

Illustration of Wald-Wolfowitz Runs Test: Hypothetical Scores of Civilian and Military Attitudes toward U.S.'s Involvement in Southeast Asia

Civilian Scores ($n_1 = 8$)	Military Scores ($n_2 = 10$)
12	13
24	15
20	22
21	23
9	26
11	25
10	8
7	16
	28
	27

Stating the Null and Alternative Hypotheses. Although there are several ways of expressing these hypotheses, let the null hypothesis be that there is no difference between civilian and military attitudes toward the U.S.'s involvement in Southeast Asia. The alternative hypothesis is that there is (or will be) a difference between these two independent samples' attitudes on the issue.

The Choice of a Statistical Test. Since the data can be ranked and the hypothesis concerns differences of *any kind* between the two independent samples, the Wald-Wolfowitz runs test is selected.

The Level of Significance and Sample Size. Let us set alpha at the .05 level. The civilian sample size is equal to eight ($n_1 = 8$), and the military sample size is equal to ten ($n_2 = 10$).

One- versus Two-Tailed Tests. Since the alternative hypothesis is nondirectional, a two-tailed test is called for.

The Sampling Distribution. The appropriate sampling distribution for the Wald-Wolfowitz runs test is contained in Table G in Appendix A.

The Region of Rejection. From the sampling distribution we discover that a value (actually the number of runs) of 5 *or less* (or 15 *or more*) is sufficient to reject H_0. These values appear at the intersection of n_1 (8) and n_2 (10).

To compute the test statistic the following steps are recommended:

1. Arrange all scores (n_1 and n_2) in a single ordered series, irrespective of the group. For the data in Table 10.3 this procedure produces the following array:

$$\begin{array}{c}\overline{M}\qquad\qquad\qquad\overline{M}\qquad\quad\ \overline{M}\qquad\quad\ \overline{M}\\ 7\ \overline{8}\ \underline{9\ 10\ 11\ 12}\ \overline{13\ 15\ 16}\ \underline{20\ 21}\ \overline{22\ 23}\ \underline{24}\ \overline{25\ 26\ 27\ 28}\\ \underline{C}\qquad\quad\ \ C\qquad\qquad\ \ C\qquad\qquad C\end{array}$$

2. Determine the number of runs (designated r) by drawing a line *under* all scores from group 1 (civilian = C) and a line *above* all scores from group 2 (military = M). This has been done in the above array. The number of runs is eight, that is, $r = 8$.

3. The method for determining the statistical significance of the data depends upon the two sample sizes. When n_1 and n_2 are ≤ 20, Table G in Appendix A may be used. This table contains the critical values of r for various sample sizes. In this table locate the value of n_1 along the left-hand column and the value of n_2 across the top of the table. The critical value of r appears where these two values (n_1 and n_2) intersect. For our example the critical value is 5. If our observed r is *equal to or less than* the critical value, we conclude that H_0 cannot be accepted. Since our r equals 8 and since $8 > 5$ we cannot reject the null hypothesis. Substantively speaking, we cannot claim a statistically significant difference in civilian and military attitudes toward the U.S.'s involvement in Southeast Asia, that is, $p > .05$ and not statistically significant (N.S.).

When the size of the two samples exceeds 20, a modification of the z test of significance may be employed.

Observations on the Wald-Wolfowitz Runs Test. The test assumes ordinal level data and is useful for detecting *any* differences between two independent samples.[1] It may be used for samples of unequal sizes and is relatively easy to compute. The major disadvantage occurs when there are ties among the scores from the two samples. When there are excessive ties the researcher must decide whether to maximize or minimize the number of runs. In general, a conservative way of dealing with tied scores is to maximize the number of runs.

The Mann-Whitney U Test

The **Mann-Whitney U test** is one of the most powerful nonparametric significance tests. It is often thought of as the nonparametric counterpart to the t test (which will be discussed in the next chapter). This test is used with independently drawn random samples, and we are testing the null hypothesis that the two samples come from the same population or that the two samples have the same distributions. The alternative hypothesis, stated in nondirectional terms, is that the two samples are drawn from different universes.

Assume we have the set of scores (stolen bases) for two baseball leagues shown in Table 10.4.

Let us set up this study in formal statistical terms.

Stating the Null and Alternative Hypotheses. The null hypothesis is that both samples (the number of stolen bases for Leagues X and Y) are drawn from populations with the same distributions. The alternative hypothesis is that the parent populations from which the samples are drawn have different distributions.

The Choice of a Statistical Test. The Mann-Whitney U test is selected since we have randomly selected two independent samples and wish to treat the data as ordinal in nature. Notice that this is a perfectly legitimate maneuver, although one would ordinarily *not* want to reduce interval level data to ordinal level information.

The Level of Significance and Sample Size. Let us set alpha at the .05 level. n_1 = 10 and n_2 = 10.

---

[1] This is probably a good time to point out several things apropos tests of significance. *Nonparametric tests* like those presented in this chapter are designed to detect a difference in the central tendency of two or more distributions along a continuum. However, these tests will "pick up" differences *other than* that of central tendency (for example, variability and/or shape or form). By locating the samples on a single continuum, differences in location may emerge even though the two distributions cannot be accurately placed along their common scale (Mueller, Schuessler, and Costner, 1970: 421). Much of statistical analysis concentrates on differences in central location but differences in variability and shape or form are also important properties, albeit somewhat neglected, of data distributions.

TABLE 10.4

Illustration of Mann-Whitney *U* Test: Hypothetical Number of Stolen Bases in Two Baseball Leagues

Team Member	League X	League Y	R_x	R_y
1	91	81	15	12.5
2	46	51	4.5	6.5
3	108	63	18	9
4	99	51	16	6.5
5	110	46	19	4.5
6	105	45	17	3
7	191	66	20	11
8	57	64	8	10
9	34	90	2	14
10	81	28	12.5	1
	$n_x = 10$	$n_y = 10$	$\Sigma R_x = 132$	$\Sigma R_y = 78$

One- versus Two-Tailed Tests. Since H_1 is nondirectional in nature, a two-tailed test is called for.

The Sampling Distribution. The sampling distribution for U is a function of the n's and the significance level selected. More will be said about this sampling distribution in the next few pages.

The Region of Rejection. The zone of rejection for $n_1 = 10$ and $n_2 = 10$ at the .05 level includes U_1 values of 23 or less *or* U_2 values of 77 or more. How these critical values are obtained will now be set forth.

The following steps are recommended for computing the U statistic.

1. Arrange all scores (stolen bases for both leagues) into a single ordered series, assigning the rank of 1 to the score which is the smallest and proceeding with ranking until all scores are exhausted. If ties occur, assign the tied observations the average of the tied ranks. For example, in Table 10.4 the fewest number of stolen bases occurred in team number 10 in League Y and a rank of 1 is placed in a column labeled R_y (rank of Y for League Y teams). The second fewest stolen bases is for team number 9 in League X and a rank of 2 is placed in a column labeled R_x (rank of X for League X teams). Notice that team number 5 in League Y and team number 2 in League X have an identical number of stolen bases. When ties occur, we assign the average rank to the positions occupied. Since these two teams occupy positions 4 and 5 we assign the average rank of these positions, $4 + 5 = 9/2 = 4.5$, to each.

2. Sum each column of ranks. The sum of the R_x column equals 132, that is, $\Sigma R_x = 132$, while the sum of the R_y column equals 78, that is, $\Sigma R_y = 78$. As a

check, we may employ formula (10.1):

$$\Sigma R_x + \Sigma R_y = \frac{n(n+1)}{2} \tag{10.1}$$

$$132 + 78 = \frac{20(21)}{2}$$

$$210 = \frac{420}{2}$$

$$210 = 210$$

Since our check works out we may proceed to step three.

    3. To obtain the U statistic the computational formulae (10.2) and (10.3) are employed:

$$U_1 = n_1 n_2 + \frac{n_1(n_1+1)}{2} = \Sigma R_x \tag{10.2}$$

and

$$U_2 = n_1 n_2 + \frac{n_2(n_2+1)}{2} = \Sigma R_y \tag{10.3}$$

Substituting our data into formulas (10.2) and (10.3), respectively:

$$U_1 = (10)(10) + \frac{10(11)}{2} - 132$$

$$= 100 + 55 - 132$$

$$= 23$$

and

$$U_2 = (10)(10) + \frac{10(11)}{2} - 78$$

$$= 100 + 55 - 78$$

$$= 77$$

Although we need to use only the smaller U, it is necessary to calculate both in order to determine which is smaller. As a check to see if we have the smaller one we may substitute our obtained value into formula (10.4).

$$U_1 = n_1 n_2 - U_2 \tag{10.4}$$

$$23 = (10)(10) - 77$$

$$23 = 100 - 77$$

$$23 = 23$$

Since our computations are correct we may proceed to assess U's statistical significance.

4. To evaluate U, turn to Table H in Appendix A. Notice that more than one table exists. These tables vary in accordance with sample size and the nature of the test, that is, one- or two-tailed. Table H is comprised of four subtables with alpha values of .005, .01, .025, and .05 for directional tests (one-tailed) and .01, .02, .05, and .10 for nondirectional tests (two-tailed). To illustrate, suppose we wished to determine the critical value for a one-tailed test at the .01 level with $n_1 = 11$ and $n_2 = 13$. Where n_1 and n_2 intersect you will find a value of 31. If the obtained U is *equal to or smaller than* this value, H_0 is rejected. Or, if the computed U_2 value is *equal to or greater than* 112 it is rejected. In the present example $n_1 = 10$ and $n_2 = 10$. Let us use a two-tailed test at the .05 level. The critical U_1 value is 23, and the critical U_2 value is 77. If our computed U_1 is *equal to or smaller than* the table's critical value then we reject H_0, or if U_2 is *equal to or greater than* the critical value we reject H_0. Since our U_1 value is equal to the critical value, that is, $23 = 23$, we can reject the null hypothesis and claim that a statistically significant difference exists between the number of stolen bases in the two different leagues. That is, $p < .05$. When one sample exceeds 20, a modification of the z test may be used.

Observations on the Mann-Whitney U Test. This test assumes at least ordinal level data and is an excellent nonparametric counterpart to the t test. A major advantage of U pertains to tied ranks. Although a correction factor for tied ranks is available, the discussion of it is beyond the scope of this book.

TWO-SAMPLE TESTS OF SIGNIFICANCE: RELATED SAMPLES

Sign Test

The **sign test**, one of the simplest tests for related samples, gets it name from the use of plus (+) and minus (−) signs in analyzing a given data-set. To reiterate a point made before, there are two generic ways that samples can be matched: (1) subjects may act as their own controls in a before-after research design, or (2) the subjects may be matched according to the salient research traits.

Suppose we are interested in the effectiveness of a management training program on managers' social skills with fellow employees. We develop a scale that purportedly measures such skills and administer the instrument both before and after the training program. We focus upon ten managers' scores at the two points in time. Although the scores on the social skills instrument appear to be interval in nature, it is sometimes the case that researchers do not feel comfortable about having met the assumptions for an interval level variable. Consequently, a decision is made to use an ordinal statistic, a perfectly legitimate strategy. Let us set up this study in formal statistical terms to correspond to Table 10.5.

TABLE 10.5

Illustration of Sign Test: Hypothetical Social Skills Scores of Management Trainees

Management Trainee Number	Social Skills Scores		Sign Associated with Change in Social Skills Score
	Before	After	
1	35	38	+
2	41	42	+
3	27	31	+
4	14	24	+
5	15	26	+
6	34	35	+
7	38	38	0
8	39	37	−
9	40	39	−
10	42	51	+
$n = 9$ (see text explanation)			$2 = m$ (sum of less frequent sign)

+ = before score smaller than after score
− = before score larger than after score

Stating the Null and Alternative Hypotheses. The null hypothesis is that there is no difference in management trainees' before-after scores. The alternative hypothesis is that there is a positive change in trainees' scores between the two measurement phases.

The Choice of a Statistical Test. With a matched sample, each subject acting as his or her own control, and with data we prefer to treat ordinally rather than intervally, the sign test is appropriate.

The Level of Significance and Sample Size. Let us set alpha at the .05 level. For computational purposes, n is 9 and not 10 since there is one instance where the score difference equals zero and *such differences are not used in the sign test.*

One- versus Two-Tailed Tests. Since the alternative hypothesis is expressed in a directional fashion, a one-tailed test is called for.

The Sampling Distribution. The binomial distribution for $p = q = \frac{1}{2}$ is appropriate for determining the sign test's significance. Table J in Appendix A is where it can be found. These critical values are for *one-tailed* applications; *for two-tailed tests the table value must be doubled.*

The Region of Rejection. Where $n = 9$ and $m = 2$ intersect the critical value is found to be .090. Notice that decimal points have been eliminated to conserve space.

The following steps are recommended for computing the sign test statistic.

1. Determine the *sign* of the difference between the two measurement scores for each subject (see Table 10.5). Note that we use the before scores as the *base*, that is, if the before score is larger than the after score we place a minus $(-)$ sign in the adjacent column; if the before score is smaller than the corresponding after score we place a plus $(+)$ sign in the adjacent column. Note that there is one instance where there is no difference. In such cases a zero is entered in the "Sign Associated with Change in Social Skills Score" column.

2. Sum the sign $(+ \text{ or } -)$ which occurs less *frequently*. In the present illustration there are only two minus signs. The less frequent sign is labeled m. Consequently, $m = 2$. To determine n, we focus *only* on those persons whose scores at the two different times are different. Since there is one case where no difference was recorded (trainee number 7), we omit this subject from further consideration. Consequently, $n = 9$ rather than 10.

3. To assess the significance of our test statistic we must consult the appropriate sampling distribution, Table J in Appendix A. We locate n along the left-hand column and m along the top of the table. Where these two values intersect, $n = 9$ and $m = 2$, we find the critical value. In this case, it is .090. If this probability is less than or equal to alpha, we can reject H_0. Since this isn't the case, that is, $.090 > .05$, we must retain H_0 and our results cannot be claimed to be significant at the .05 level. Substantively, we have no statistical evidence to claim that the management training program is effective in changing trainees' social skills, that is, $p > .05$.

Observations on the Sign Test. This test assumes the use of correlated samples, each sample having been randomly selected and matched on relevant criteria or consisting of individuals serving as their own controls. This procedure can be used when n is equal to or less than 25. When n is larger than 25 a modification of the z test of significance may be employed. The sign test is a useful measure for determining differences between related samples. Obviously, it does not use the true numerical score values.

The Wilcoxon Matched Pairs—Signed Ranks Test

The Wilcoxon matched pairs—signed ranks test (hereafter referred to as the Wilcoxon test) is a useful one for assessing the significance of differences between two related samples. It is similar to the sign test in that it uses the sign of the difference between the two related samples, but it differs from the sign test in that it uses the *magnitude of the sign differences* as well.

To illustrate, suppose we return to the management trainee illustration in which we measured the same subjects at two points in time, before the training session and after. To employ the Wilcoxon test it is necessary to assume that the social skills scores conform to interval level measurement requirements. Although the original scores conform to interval level measurement, the computations involve summing ranks and ranks by definition are ordinal in nature. The hypothetical before-and-after scores appear in Table 10.6.

TABLE 10.6

Illustration of Wilcoxon Test: Hypothetical Social Skills Scores of Ten Management Trainees

Management Trainee Number	Social Skills Score		Sign Difference (3)	Rank of Absolute Difference (4)	Ranks with Smaller Signs (5)
	Before (1)	After (2)			
1	35	38	+3	5	
2	41	42	+1	2	
3	27	31	+4	6	
4	14	24	+10	8	
5	15	26	+11	9	
6	34	35	+1	2	
7	38	38	0		
8	39	37	−2	−4	4
9	40	39	−1	−2	2
10	42	51	+9	7	
$n = 9$					$\Sigma T = 6$

(see text explanation)

Let us set up this example in formal statistical terms.

Stating the Null and Alternative Hypotheses. The null hypothesis is that there is no difference in trainees' social skills scores before and after management training. The alternative hypothesis is that there will be an increase in social skills scores after the training program.

The Choice of a Statistical Test. The Wilcoxon test is selected because the study uses a matched sample design and it yields scores which may be ranked in order of absolute magnitude.

The Level of Significance and Sample Size. Let us set alpha at the .01 level. The sample size (*n*) equals the *number of trainees* minus any trainee whose difference is zero. Hence, $n = 9$ since one trainee (number 7) had identical scores in the before-after measurement stages.

One- versus Two-Tailed Tests. Since the alternative hypothesis is directional in nature, a one-tailed test is appropriate.

The Sampling Distribution. Table K in Appendix A gives the critical values from the sampling distribution of T. T is defined as the smaller of the sums of the signed ranks.

The Region of Rejection. From a knowledge of the T sampling distribution we find a critical value of *3 or less* is needed to reject H_0. Notice that the ΣT (sum of ranks with the less frequent sign) must be *equal to or less than* the critical value in the table.

To calculate the Wilcoxon test statistic the following steps are recommended:

1. For each trainee find the sign difference (D) between the two measurement periods. If the after score is larger than the before score, attach a + sign; if the after score is smaller, attach a − sign. Of course, if there is no change, attach a zero. This has been done in column 3 (Sign Difference) of Table 10.6.

2. Rank these differences disregarding the sign of the differences, giving the smallest score a rank of 1. If tied ranks occur, assign the average value of the tied ranks. Trainees number 2, 6, and 9 had identical sign differences so each received a rank of 2. This has been done in column 4 (Rank of Absolute Difference) of Table 10.6.

3. For each of the ranks in column 4 attach the sign (+ or −) of the D it represents. This can be easily determined by noting the sign in the sign difference column, column 3. This step is essential since the test statistic is computed using only the ranks of the *less frequent* sign. There are only two cases of minus signs, trainees 8 and 9, and we sum the ranks they occupy. Hence, ranks of 4 and 2 = 6. The symbol $\Sigma T(-)$ means the sum of the less frequently occuring ranks or 2 + 4 = 6. Similarly, there are 7 cases of plus signs but we need not be concerned with them since only the less frequent signed ranks sum is used for computational purposes.

4. Find ΣT, the Wilcoxon test statistic. In our example $T = 6$.

5. To determine T's significance turn to the appropriate sampling distribution, Table K in Appendix A, and locate the n, in this case nine, along the left-hand column at the designated alpha level, in this case .01, for a one-tailed test. The critical value where $n = 9$ and $\alpha = .01$ intersect is 3. For our scores to be significant at the .01 level, we must have a ΣT *equal to or less than* 3. Since our ΣT is larger, that is, $6 > 3$, we cannot reject H_0 and must conclude that there are not significant differences in social skills scores among trainees after a management training program. Again, the data fail to achieve statistical significance since $p > .01$.

Observations on the Wilcoxon Test. When $n > 25$ a modification of the z test of significance may be employed.

To employ the Wilcoxon test we should have interval level data or an equal-appearing interval measurement scale. This technique is an excellent one to use when we have reservations about having met the interval level measurement assumptions of the measured variable(s). For example, in attitudinal scaling there is often a hesitation to employ interval level statistics even though attitude scores appear or are assumed to meet interval level assumptions. Of course, matched samples, too, are essential.

This test is advantageous since it deals not only with the *direction of difference* (+ or −) but also with the *magnitude* of these differences.

k-SAMPLE TEST: INDEPENDENT SAMPLES

Kruskal-Wallis (*H*) One-Way Analysis of Variance Test

The **Kruskal-Wallis** *H* one-way analysis of variance test is used to test whether or not *k* independent samples are from the same or different populations. In short, it permits a test for significant differences among *k* independent samples ranked according to some ordinal characteristic.

Like other tests discussed in this chapter, the *H* test rank orders all scores in one continuous series, disregarding the group from which the observations are drawn. After this has been completed the sums of the ranks for all *k* independent samples are found and the Kruskal-Wallis test enables us to determine whether or not the sums of ranks for these samples are likely to have been selected from the same universe.

Suppose we are interested in the relationship between age (trichotomized into: [1] under 26, [2] 26–39, and [3] 40–65) and sexual permissiveness. We confine our interest to the attitudinal component and administer an instrument explicitly designed to answer this research question. Assume, furthermore, that high scores represent permissive attitudes and low scores, conservative attitudes. We select a random sample from each age group and present their hypothetical scores in Table 10.7.

Let us set up this study in formal statistical terms.

Stating the Null and Alternative Hypotheses. The null hypothesis is that there is no difference among the three age categories with respect to sexual attitudes. This amounts to saying that the three independent samples are from the same population. The alternative hypothesis is that there is a difference among the three age categories in sexual attitudes.

The Choice of a Statistical Test. Since *k* (3) independent samples are under study, a test for *k* independent samples is called for. Because our scores can legitimately be reduced to ranks, the Kruskal-Wallis *H* test is appropriate.

TABLE 10.7

Illustration of Kruskal-Wallis *H* Test: Hypothetical Sexual Attitude Scores for Three Different Age Categories

Under 26	Rank₁	26–39	Rank₂	40–65	Rank₃
12	11	11	10	9	8
17	16	15	14	19	18
13	12	10	9	2	2
18	17	1	1	8	7
7	6	14	13	16	15
6	5	$n_2 = 5$	$\Sigma = 47$	20	19
5	4			$n_3 = 6$	$\Sigma = 69$
3	3				
$n_1 = 8$	$\Sigma = 74$				

The Level of Significance and Sample Size. Let us set alpha at the .10 level. *n*, the sample size, is the number in all samples combined, that is, $n_1 + n_2 + n_3$ in our Table 10.7 example.

One- versus Two-Tailed Tests. We will employ a two-tailed test in light of the nondirectional nature of the alternative hypothesis.

The Sampling Distribution. The appropriate sampling distribution appears in Table L in Appendix A. When the number of observations in three independently selected samples is five or less, Table L provides *exact* probabilities for determining the significance of *H*. To illustrate the use of this table suppose we had three groups with $n_1 = 3$, $n_2 = 2$, and $n_3 = 1$ and we wish to locate the critical value at the .10 level of significance. We locate this particular combination of sample sizes and discover a critical value of 4.2857 or larger is sufficient to reject the null at the .10 level.

    With larger samples (> 5) the chi-square sampling distribution with *k* − 1 degrees of freedom may be used for gauging the statistical significance of the *H* statistic. As is often our custom, if the computed *H* equals or exceeds the critical value, the null hypothesis is rejected.

The Region of Rejection. We determine the critical value by locating the intersection of *k* − 1 degrees of freedom and the preselected alpha level in the chi-square table, Table C in Appendix A.

    To compute *H* the following steps are recommended:

    1. Rank each score *across* the independent samples. That is, rank the scores from 1 to *n*, *irrespective* of the group. Ties are treated in the usual manner by

assigning the tied scores the average rank which they occupy. It does not matter whether the highest score is ranked 1 or the lowest score is ranked 1, as long as this is done consistently. For the present example, let's assign the lowest score a rank of 1. Notice that the lowest score appears in the 26–39 age group and a rank of 1 is located in an adjacent column. The next lowest score appears in the 40–65 age group and receives a rank of 2. Rank all scores in this fashion.

2. Determine the sum of ranks (ΣR_i) for each of the groups. The ΣR_1 for the under 26 category: $11 + 16 + 12 + 17 + 6 + 5 + 4 + 3 = 74$. The ΣR_2 for the 26–39 category is: $10 + 14 + 9 + 1 + 13 = 47$. For the third category, 40–65, ΣR_3 is: $8 + 18 + 2 + 7 + 15 + 19 = 69$.

3. To compute the Kruskal-Wallis H statistic formula (10.5) is used:

$$H = \frac{12}{n(n+1)} \left[\frac{\Sigma R_1^2}{n_1} + \frac{\Sigma R_2^2}{n_2} + \dots + \frac{\Sigma R_k^2}{n_k} \right] - [3(n+1)] \qquad (10.5)$$

where:

H = Kruskal-Wallis statistic
n = the total number of observations (in the k samples)
n_k = the number of observations in the kth sample
ΣR_k^2 = the square of the sum of ranks for the kth sample

Substituting our data into formula (10.5):

$$H = \frac{12}{19(20)} \left[\frac{74^2}{8} + \frac{47^2}{5} + \frac{69^2}{6} \right] - 3(20)$$

$$= \frac{12}{380} \left[\frac{5,476}{8} + \frac{2,209}{5} + \frac{4,761}{6} \right] - 60$$

$$= .03158(684.5 + 441.8 + 793.5) - 60$$

$$= .03158(1,919.8) - 60$$

$$= 60.63 - 60$$

$$= .63$$

What does $H = .63$ mean? We consult the chi-square table with $k - 1$ degrees of freedom at the appropriate alpha level in order to determine the critical value. Since $k - 1$ equals $3 - 1 = 2$ at the .10 level, the critical value is 4.605. Since our value is less than the table value, that is, $.63 < 4.605$, we fail to reject H_0. Substantively speaking, there is not a statistically significant difference in sexual attitudes among the three age categories, that is, $p > .10$ (N.S.).

Observations on the Kruskal-Wallis H Test. H assumes k independent samples in which the observations are (or can be) ranked. A significant H indicates that differences exist *somewhere* in the k independent samples but does not tell the researcher *where* these differences lie.

k-SAMPLE TEST: RELATED SAMPLES

Friedman Two-Way Analysis of Variance Test

With *k* matched samples, the **Friedman two-way analysis of variance test** is a useful ordinal measure of statistical significance. Suppose we are interested in the effect of different leadership styles on individuals' satisfaction in a group. Technically we could match several sets of subjects on those variables deemed relevant and randomly assign them to different treatments. The data would then be cast in a two-way table with *n* rows (in this example matched sets of subjects) and *k* columns (in this example three different leadership styles). After we have ranked the scores in each *row*, the Friedman test enables us to determine if the treatment conditions (leadership styles) have a different effect on the matched subjects' satisfaction scores. In other words, this test enables us to determine if statistically significant differences in rank totals exist. We subject six sets of matched individuals to three different leadership styles: (1) autocratic, (2) laissez-faire, and (3) democratic. These data are arranged in Table 10.8.

TABLE 10.8

Illustration of Friedman Analysis of Variance Test: Hypothetical Satisfaction Scores under Three Different Leadership Styles

Matched Sets of Individuals	Scores by Leadership Style					
	Auto-cratic	Rank	Laissez-Faire	Rank	Demo-cratic	Rank
A	9	1	10	2	14	3
B	13	1	14	2	19	3
C	12	1	18	2	19	3
D	21	3	17	1	19	2
E	7	1	9	2	12	3
F	6	1	9	2	10	3
$n = 6$		$\Sigma = 8$		$\Sigma = 11$		$\Sigma = 17$

Let us set up this study in formal statistical terms.

Stating the Null and Alternative Hypotheses. The null hypothesis is that there is no difference in satisfaction scores under the three different leadership styles. The alternative hypothesis is that satisfaction scores are (or will) differ under the three leadership conditions.

The Choice of a Statistical Test.   The Friedman two-way analysis of variance test is chosen since we have k related samples, matched sets of individuals, in which the scores can be rank ordered.

The Level of Significance and Sample Size.   Let us set alpha at the .10 level. n, the number of k matched individuals, is equal to six and k, the number of different treatment conditions, is equal to three.

One- versus Two-Tailed Tests.   Since the alternative hypothesis is nondirectional, a two-tailed test is called for.

The Sampling Distribution.   The Friedman test approximates the chi-square sampling distribution with $k - 1$ degrees of freedom. Although *exact* probability tables are available we will assess the test statistic's significance by referring to the chi-square sampling distribution, Table C in Appendix A.
Appendix A.

The Region of Rejection.   With $k - 1$ degrees of freedom, and since $k = 3$ in the present example, a value of 4.605 or larger (at .10 level) is necessary to reject H_0.

To calculate the Friedman test statistic the following steps are recommended:

1.   Rank each matched set of individuals' scores under the three leadership styles. For matched individuals A, we note that the scores are 9, 10, and 14 under the different leadership conditions. Assign a rank of 1 to the smallest score, a rank of 2 to the next smallest score, and a rank of 3 to the largest score. This has been done for each individual matched set in an adjacent column labeled Rank. It makes no difference whether the largest or smallest is 1 as long as the scores are consistently ranked in that manner. Do this, as we have done in Table 10.8, for each matched set. Notice that we rank *across* treatment conditions.

2.   Sum the ranks of the scores under each of the leadership conditions, that is, each of the *column* ranks is summed, as shown in Table 10.8.

3.   To test your hypothesis formula (10.6) is employed:

$$\chi_r^2 = \frac{12}{nk(k + 1)}[\Sigma(\Sigma R_i)^2] - [3n(k + 1)] \qquad (10.6)$$

where: χ_r^2 =   Freidman two-way analysis of variance test
             k =   the number of treatment conditions (leadership styles in the present example)
      $(\Sigma R_i)^2$ =   the square of the sum of ranks under each experimental condition (i)
             n =   number of matched sets of individuals in each treatment condition

Substituting our data into formula (10.6):

$$\chi_r^2 = \frac{12}{(6)(3)(3+1)} (8^2 + 11^2 + 17^2) - [3(6)(3+1)]$$

$$= \frac{12}{72} (474) - 72$$

$$= .167(474) - 72$$

$$= 7.158$$

What does $\chi_r^2 = 7.158$ mean? Since the critical value in the chi-square table for 2 *df* and .10 level of significance equals 4.605 and our computed value is larger, that is, $7.158 > 4.605$, we reject the null hypothesis. Substantively speaking, we have reason to believe that satisfaction scores vary significantly at the .10 level from one leadership style to the next. In notation form, $p < .10$ and statistically significant.

Observations on the Friedman Test. The two basic assumptions for using this test are that we have ordinal level data and that the samples are matched. It is a good nonparametric counterpart to the parametric analysis of variance test without having to meet some of the latter's rather stringent assumptions.

SUMMARY

In this chapter a discussion of various ordinal level tests of significance was presented. A couple of one sample tests, the Kolmogorov-Smirnov and runs tests, were considered. A couple of two-sample tests of significance, the sign test and Wilcoxon test, appropriate for related samples were discussed along with a couple of two-sample tests of significance appropriate for use with independent samples, the Wald-Wolfowitz runs test and Mann-Whitney U test. Finally, the Friedman and Kruskal-Wallis tests were discussed with respect to k samples, related and independent samples, respectively. Figure 10.1 depicts the organizational scheme for this chapter.

IMPORTANT CONCEPTS DISCUSSED IN THIS CHAPTER

One, two, and k samples

Independent samples

Related samples

Kolmogorov-Smirnov one-sample test

Observed and theoretical cumulative frequencies

One-sample runs test

Runs (r)

Wald-Wolfowitz runs test

Mann-Whitney U test

Sign test

Wilcoxon matched pairs—signed ranks
    test

Kruskal-Wallis (H) one-way analysis of
    variance test

Friedman two-way analysis of variance
    test

REVIEW QUESTIONS

1. In many universities today, a series of general educational courses must be taken in order
   to secure a bachelor's degree. Students' attitudes toward this requirement range from
   highly opposed to highly in favor. From the data below, determine if there is an equal
   distribution of attitudes over the attitudinal spectrum using the *Kolmogorov-Smirnov test*
   of significance.

   A survey of 50 introductory economics students showed that:

Highly opposed	18%
Opposed	24
Indifferent	20
Favor	22
Highly favor	16

   a. Is this a one-tailed or two-tailed test?
   b. Is there a significant difference at the .05 level?
   c. Is there a significant difference at the .01 level?

2. In the following exercise, a single die was tossed a total of twenty times. The observations were based on whether the die thrown came up even (2, 4, or 6) or odd (1, 3, or
   5) each time. Using the *one-sample runs test*, determine whether or not the distribution of even and odd observations occur in a random sequence.

Toss	1	2	3	4	5	6	7	8	9	10
Number on die	2	6	1	3	3	1	3	5	1	5

Toss	11	12	13	14	15	16	17	18	19	20
Number on die	6	2	2	2	1	1	2	3	5	4

   a. Is this a one or a two-tailed test?
   b. How many runs are in this sample of observations?
   c. Is this distribution random at the .05 level?

3. Suppose you are an industrial sociologist and wish to measure job satisfaction among
   a sample of farmers and coal miners. Assuming you have used some valid indicator
   of job satisfaction, compare the results below to determine if the two samples have

the same distribution of job satisfaction scores. Employ the *Mann-Whitney U test* at the .05 level.

Job Satisfaction Score for Farmers	Job Satisfaction Score for Coal Miners
76	85
89	92
82	81
77	87
80	83
78	90
$n_F = 6$	$n_C = 6$

a. Check the sum of the ranks.
b. Determine U_1 and U_2.
c. Is the difference significant at the .05 level?
d. State the null hypothesis.
e. Do we accept or reject the null hypothesis?

4. Suppose a test is administered to a sample of males and females in an effort to determine their attitudes toward traditional sex role socialization. For the hypothetical data below (high scores represent favorability) determine if there is a significant difference in attitudes at the .05 level using the *Wald-Wolfowitz runs test*.

Females ($n_1 = 8$)	Males ($n_2 = 8$)
95	82
80	65
72	85
91	62
78	70
87	58
90	66
75	71

a. What is the critical value of r in this case?
b. How many runs do we observe?
c. Are there significant differences at the .05 level?

5. Some recent research has been conducted comparing attitudes toward premarital sexual relations of both parents and their children. Suppose an instrument has been developed to measure these attitudes and further assume that we wish to determine if parents' and children's attitudes are different. Using the *sign test* determine if there is a significant difference at the .05 level between the samples (+ = larger parents' score, − = larger children's score).

	Attitudes toward Premarital Sexual Relations	
Family Number	Parents	Children
1	70	79
2	65	80
3	72	64
4	62	75
5*	78	78
6	58	70
7	75	73
8	67	70
9	72	82
10	68	62
11	71	85
12*	70	70
13	64	80
14	61	76
15	73	84

$n = 13$

6. Using the (sign test) data calculate the *Wilcoxon test statistic* and decide if significant differences at the .01 level exist between the attitudes of parents and their children.

	Attitudes	
Family	Parents	Children
1	70	79
2	65	80
3	72	64
4	62	75
5*	78	78
6	58	70
7	75	73
8	67	70
9	72	82
10	68	62
11	71	85
12*	70	70
13	64	80
14	61	76
15	73	84

$n = 13$

7. Assume we are interested in the influence of social class on deviant behavior tendencies. For the hypothetical data below, a high score represents high deviant tendencies, while

a low score represents the opposite. Employ the *Kruskal-Wallis H test* to determine if there are significant differences in deviant behavior inclinations among members of different social class positions. Let alpha = .01.

Lower Class	Middle Class	Upper Class
21	19	16
19	22	15
25	16	24
17	23	18
20	11	14
13	$n_m = 5$	12
18		$n_u = 6$
$n_l = 7$		

8. Suppose we wish to determine if the effectiveness of advertising varies according to the media used. We design an instrument that measures "effectiveness" and have several sets of matched individuals respond to it. For the data below, employ *Friedman's two-way analysis of variance test* to determine whether any statistically significant differences between TV, radio, and the printed page exist. Set alpha at the .10 level.

Matched Individuals	Effectiveness Ratings		
	Television	Radio	Printed Page
White collar	21	20	25
Factory workers	25	24	23
Trade laborers	22	23	20
Housewives	25	24	19
Clerical workers	20	22	21
Farm workers	24	20	22

*

11

INTERVAL/RATIO LEVEL TESTS OF SIGNIFICANCE

In this chapter three of the most commonly used interval/ratio level significance tests will be discussed. Two of these tests, z and t, are employed with one or two samples, although there are certain conditions necessary to assume before using them. The third test, F, is known as the analysis of variance test and is employed with k independent samples. Each of the illustrative test applications will make explicit whether the samples should be *independent* or *related*. It should be clear that this battery of tests uses the quantitative information inherent in the data-set rather than simple classification or ranking as used by nominal and ordinal tests, respectively. Figure 11.1 provides an overview of the interval level tests of significance discussed in this chapter.

FIGURE 11.1

Interval/Ratio Level Tests of Significance

One-Sample Tests		Two-Sample Tests		k-Sample Tests
Large Sample	Small Sample	Independent Samples	Related Samples	Independent Samples
z test	t test	t test $\sigma_1^2 = \sigma_2^2$ $\sigma_1^2 \neq \sigma_2^2$	t test	F test

ONE-SAMPLE TESTS OF SIGNIFICANCE

In this section two single sample tests of significance, z and t, will be discussed along with the criteria used to decide which is more appropriate. Our decision as to which is more suitable is determined by: (1) the size of the sample, and (2) whether the parameters (μ and σ) are known or unknown. In general, if the sample is large ($n > 30$) and the parameters are known, the z test may be used. On the other hand, if the sample is small ($n \leq 30$) and the parameters are unknown, the t test is more pertinent. We will first examine the research conditions under which z is appropriate and, secondly, the conditions under which t should be employed.

z Test for a Single Sample

When the μ and σ of the population are known, the z **test of significance** is an appropriate test statistic. Consider the following example. Suppose that hospital administrators at a large metropolitan medical complex are concerned with the apparent dissatisfaction of patients who are hospitalized for a period of one month and longer. The administrators strongly believe that this dissatisfaction is due to the infrequent visits by the patients' physicians. They feel that more doctor visitations could decrease the number of patients who feel disgruntled. To test their contention, they ask all patients to keep track of the number of times their physicians visit them during their hospital stay. Let us assume that the μ for the entire patient population is 10. That is, on the average, these patients were seen ten times by their physicians. Assume, too, that the σ was calculated to be 4.5. Several months later a random sample of 49 patients expressing dissatisfaction with their hospital tenure is located and asked how many times their doctors had seen them. This random sample of 49 patients has $\overline{X}$ equal to 7. That is, they had been seen, on the average, seven times during their hospital stay.

The research question is this: *Is there reason to believe that the average number of visits among the sample of dissatisfied patients is significantly lower than that of the entire hospital population?* Let us set up this problem in formal statistical terms.

Stating the Null and Alternative Hypotheses. The null hypothesis is that there is no statistically significant difference in the mean number of doctors' visitations to the entire hospital's patients and to the dissatisfied group. Symbolically, $H_0 : \overline{X} = \mu = 10$. The alternative hypothesis is that the dissatisfied sample had fewer visits, on the average, than the entire patient population. Symbolically, $H_1 : \overline{X} < \mu < 10$. It may appear confusing to hypothesize that $\overline{X} = \mu = 10$ when, in fact, we know that $\overline{X}$ (7) and μ (10) are not the same. The reason for this positon reflects the underlying rationale of statistical decision making. The statistical logic is to determine if the difference is a *chance* one. It cannot be denied that there is a difference, but the question is whether this difference could be due to chance factors.

The Choice of a Statistical Test. Since the data are interval/ratio level in nature and the parameters are known, the z test is appropriate. When the μ and σ of the population are known and n is large, the z test of significance is employed.

The Level of Significance and Sample Size. Let us set alpha at the .05 level. The sample size of our dissatisfied group is 49.

One- versus Two-Tailed Tests. Since the alternative hypothesis is stated in directional terms, a one-tailed test is called for.

The Sampling Distribution. The sampling distribution for the z test statistic is the normal curve and appears in Table B in Appendix A. This decision stems from the central limit theorem; that is, if repeated random samples of size n are drawn from a normal population, the sampling distribution of sample means will be normal.

The Region of Rejection. The region of rejection for a one-tailed test includes z values of $|-1.645|$ (critical value)[1] or larger to be significant at the .05 level.

To test these data formula (11.1) is employed:

$$z = \frac{\overline{X} - \mu}{\dfrac{\sigma}{\sqrt{n}}} \tag{11.1}$$

where: z = z tests of significance for a single sample
$\overline{X}$ = sample mean (dissatisfied patients in this case)
μ = population mean (all patients in this case)
$\sigma/\sqrt{n}$ = the standard error of the mean ($\sigma_{\overline{X}}$)

You will recall that the standard error of the mean, symbolized $\sigma_{\overline{X}}$, is the standard deviation of the sampling distribution of means. If you need to refresh your memory on these concepts, Chapters 7 and 8 should be reviewed.

Let us substitute our values into formula (11.1):

$$z = \frac{7 - 10}{\dfrac{4.5}{\sqrt{49}}}$$

$$= \frac{-3}{\dfrac{4.5}{7}}$$

$$= \frac{-3}{.64}$$

$$= -4.69$$

---

[1]You will recall that the vertical lines bounding a number indicate a concern with its *absolute* value only.

What does a $z = -4.69$ mean? To answer this question we must consult the N.C. table, the sampling distribution of z. Using a one-tailed directional test at the .05 level requires a z of $|-1.645|$ or larger to be significant. In this chapter the computed z and t values are to be understood and interpreted in terms of the *deviation from the expected value under the null hypothesis*. To illustrate, a z value of $|-4.69|$ is a more extreme *deviation* than is a deviation of $|-1.645|$. In other words, a z of -4.69 represents a rarer occurrence under the null than a $z = -1.645$. In all instances of computed z and t values be cognizant that the interpretation is in terms of *deviations* from the expected value. Although all values of z shown in the table are positive, a negative sign $(-)$ precedes the critical z value because the alternative hypothesis is a directional one. This operation is permissible since the normal curve is *symmetrical* with one-half the cases *below* the mean. Of course, this procedure assumes a normally distributed set of observations. Since our computed value is larger than the table value, that is, $|-4.69| > |-1.645|$, we conclude that the dissatisfied patients had received fewer physician visits than the entire patient population.[2] Consequently, H_0 is rejected and H_1 tentatively accepted, that is, $p < .05$.

t Test for a Single Sample

In much social research the fact is that the parameters are generally unknown. Furthermore, the sample size is often less than 30. When this is the case, we must estimate the parameter values on the basis of statistics computed from a sample of observations. In order to test hypotheses about the population on the basis of samples when μ and σ are unknown, the t statistic is appropriate. The t test statistic is similar to the z test statistic but with a modification in the denominator of the equation. More specifically, instead of using $\sigma/\sqrt{n}$ to compute the standard error, $s/\sqrt{n-1}$ is employed. Notice that the sample standard deviation, s, is employed instead of σ, and that $\sqrt{n-1}$ rather than $\sqrt{n}$ is used. The expression $\sqrt{n-1}$ is the *correction factor* for the known bias that occurs when the sample standard deviation is used to estimate the population standard deviation. If this is unclear, a re-reading of Chapter 7 should be helpful. In that chapter we demonstrated the biased nature of s as an estimate of σ, that is, $E(s) \neq \sigma$ or $E(s) < \sigma$.

The following example will clarify this. Suppose we are interested in studying the financial aspirations of Appalachian folk. We are interested in the amount of money per month they believe is necessary to assure them a decent and modest living. Through interviews conducted with 75 Appalachian persons we compute the mean income expected to assure them a comfortable living to be $6,000 with a standard deviation equal to $500. Suppose the federal government has specified a

---

[2] Technically speaking, a $z = -4.69$ is *smaller* than a $z = -1.645$. Furthermore, in two-tailed tests there are actually *two* different critical regions, the *upper critical region* (and its corresponding critical values) and the *lower critical region* (and its values). Consequently, if the computed z value is *equal to or greater than* the upper critical z value or *equal to or smaller than* the lower z value, the null hypothesis is rejected. My preference is: if $|$computed $z| \geq$ critical value, reject H_0.

figure of $4,500 to be sufficient to guarantee a decent living, we wish to test if there is a significant difference between the sample's estimate, namely $6,000, and the federal government's proclamation of $4,500, this latter figure having been derived on some theoretical basis.

Let us set up this study in formal statistical terms.

Stating the Null and Alternative Hypotheses. The null hypothesis is that there is not a statistically significant difference between the sample's estimate and the figure determined by the federal government. Symbolically, $H_0: \overline{X} = \mu = \$4,500$. The alternative hypothesis is that there is a significant difference between the two figures. Symbolically, $H_1: \overline{X} \neq \mu \neq \$4,500$.

The Choice of a Statistical Test. Since we have interval/ratio level data and the parameter σ is unknown, the t test is fitting to use.

The Level of Significance and Sample Size. Let us set alpha at the .10 level. The sample size is 75, the number of Appalachians interviewed.

One- versus Two-Tailed Tests. Since the alternative hypothesis is nondirectional in nature, a two-tailed test is called for.

The Sampling Distribution. The t test statistic has the t sampling distribution (Table E in Appendix A) as its model with $n - 1$ degrees of freedom. The t sampling distribution was discussed in Chapter 9 and should be reviewed if you have forgotten it. In the next few pages we will reiterate some major aspects of Student's t.

The Region of Rejection. The critical value of t appropriate to the .10 level (two-tailed test) with 74 degrees of freedom ($n - 1 = 75 - 1 = 74$) is ± 1.671 ($df = 60$).

To compute the t statistic for this problem formula (11.2) is used:

$$t = \frac{\overline{X} - \mu}{\dfrac{s}{\sqrt{n - 1}}} \tag{11.2}$$

where: t = t test of significance for a single sample
  $\overline{X}$ = sample mean
  μ = population mean
  $s/\sqrt{n - 1}$ = standard error of the mean for the t statistic

Substituting our values into formula (11.2):

$$t = \frac{6,000 - 4,500}{\dfrac{500}{\sqrt{75 - 1}}}$$

$$= \frac{1,500}{\frac{500}{8.6023}}$$

$$= \frac{1,500}{58.1240}$$

$$= 25.81$$

What does $t = 25.81$ mean? In order to interpret this value we consult the t sampling distribution in Table E of Appendix A with $n - 1$ degrees of freedom. Notice that various df values (1 to ∞) are located down the far left-hand column. We select the closest df since our value falls between two specified df's. These values are very similar, but if one wants the more conservative critical value one should choose the smaller, in this case 60 df, rather than the larger df (120). This example makes clear that we are sometimes not able to find the *exact* degrees of freedom. When this occasion arises there are several options. We may use the critical value closest to our obtained df. Since the df in the table jump from 60 to 120, we could select the closest one for our sample. Since our $df = 74$ we may choose the critical value at the 60 df juncture. This is the procedure adopted above. A more precise way of calculating the critical value would be to *interpolate*. Only in rare cases would interpolating yield significant substantive differences; consequently, the former procedure is recommended. The critical value of 60 df is more conservative than that for $df = 120$ since a slightly larger computed t is necessary in order to reject H_0. Since our value is larger than the table value, that is, 25.81 > 1.671, we reject H_0 and retain H_1. Substantively speaking, there is a significant difference between our hypothesized value and that of our sample. In short, the federal government's figure is significantly different from the Appalachians' figure. Consequently, $p < .10$ and statistically significant.

Observations on the z and t Single-Sample Tests

The z and t single-sample tests both assume interval/ratio level data and a normal population from which the samples are selected. However, there are different criteria beyond these. For example, z is an appropriate test of significance when the sample size is larger than 30 and the population standard deviation is known. On the other hand, t is useful when small samples ($n \leq 30$) are used and/or when σ is unknown.

However, in much social research single-sample test applications are not applicable because they are impractical. The impracticality surrounds the fact that the population parameters are either unknown or not easily hypothesized or estimated. Consequently, two-sample tests are more frequently used and found in the research act.

TWO-SAMPLE TESTS OF SIGNIFICANCE

In the previous two sections, the applications of the z and t single-sample tests of significance were demonstrated. A moment's reflection will enable you to conclude that these conditions (knowing the parameter values or being able to hypothesize a parameter value) are somewhat uncommon in social research. When interest is focused upon comparisons between samples, it becomes *un*necessary to hypothesize the absolute values for the samples under consideration. Instead, the researcher can test the null hypothesis that there is no significant difference between them. The following illustration will clarify these statements.

t Test

It is conventional to use the z statistic, the ratio of the difference between the means to the standard error of the difference between the means, when n (the sample size) is large. When n is small (usually considered to be 30 or less) a different test statistic is used. This statistic is referred to in a number of ways, such as the t **test,** t **ratio, Student's t,** the **critical ratio,** or the t **statistic.**

This statistic, and its sampling distribution, received its name from the statistician William Sealy Gosset (1876–1937) who published under the pseudonym of *Student*. He noted that the approximation of s to σ was not good for small samples. Consequently, his major contribution to statistics consisted of a description of a whole family of distributions, varying as a function of the degrees of freedom (df), which permit the testing of hypotheses with normally distributed populations when σ is unknown.

The t sampling distribution is both similar to and different from the normal curve. Like the N.C., the t distribution is symmetrical, but unlike the N.C., it is platykurtic in nature. The symmetrical feature means that the proportion of the area between specific positive and negative t values is the same. But, its platykurtic nature means that the t distribution is more spread out than the N.C. Consequently, there is a larger area in the tails of a t distribution than in the tails of a normal one. However, this area decreases as n becomes larger, and when $n = \infty$, t and z are virtually identical.

Several variations of the t test exist. The appropriate formula to use depends upon certain conditions under which it is to be applied. We will demonstrate several generic conditions for which the t test is applicable. The first will deal with a situation in which the σ's (or σ^2's) are *unknown* and presumed to be *unequal* ($\sigma_1^2 \neq \sigma_2^2$). The second concern will be with a situation in which the unknown σ's are considered to be *equal* ($\sigma_1^2 = \sigma_2^2$). Let us now consider the former illustration.

Difference between Means: Independent Samples, Unequal Variances ($\sigma_1^2 \neq \sigma_2^2$)

Let us assume we are interested in comparing male and female attitudes toward the feminist social movement. We develop and administer an instrument in which high scores indicate favorable attitudes and low scores, unfavorable attitudes, to 41 randomly selected males and to 51 randomly selected females. We tabulate the data and find that the male mean score is 120 ($\overline{X}_1 = 120$) with a standard deviation of 15 ($s_1 = 15$), while the female mean score is 125 ($\overline{X}_2 = 125$) and the standard deviation is 10 ($s_2 = 10$).

Let us set up this problem in formal statistical terms.

Since the formula for the t ratio varies according to whether or not the variances are equal (technically called *homoscedasticity*), we must first determine whether they are or are not. To do this we consult the F sampling distribution, Table M in Appendix A.[3] This sampling distribution was first described by R. A. Fisher and must be entered with the df of the larger variance located along the heading and the df of the smaller variance listed down the stub. The critical value of F is where these two df's intersect.

For our example, the variances are 225 ($s_1 = 15; s_1^2 = 225$) and 100 ($s_2 = 10$; $s_2^2 = 100$) and the respective df's are 40 and 50. The critical values where these df's intersect are 1.63 (.05 level of significance) and 2.00 (.01 level of significance). If the F formula (11.3) produces a value *equal to or larger than* the critical one we may reject the null hypothesis that $s_1^2 = s_2^2$.

$$F = \frac{s^2 \text{ (larger variance)}}{s^2 \text{ (smaller variance)}} \tag{11.3}$$

Substituting our values into formula (11.3):

$$F = \frac{225}{100}$$

$$= 2.25$$

Consequently, with alpha equal to .05, we claim that the variances are unequal since 2.25 > 1.63 (or 2.00).

Stating the Null and Alternative Hypotheses. The null hypothesis states that there is no difference in male and female attitudes toward the feminist movement. Symbolically, H_0: $\mu_1 = \mu_2$ or $\mu_1 - \mu_2 = 0$. The alternative hypothesis is that females are more favorable toward the movement than are males. Symbolically, H_1: μ_2 (females) > μ_1 (males).

The Choice of a Statistical Test. The t statistic is selected since we have interval/ratio level data, independent samples, and unequal variances.

---

[3]The concept *mean square* appears in Table M and is used synonymously with *variance*.

The Level of Significance and Sample Size. Let us set alpha at the .10 level. The sample sizes are 41 (n_1) and 51 (n_2) for the males and females, respectively.

One- versus Two-Tailed Tests. Due to the directional nature of the alternative hypothesis, a one-tailed test is called for.

The Sampling Distribution. Table E in Appendix A provides the appropriate sampling distribution for the t test statistic with df equal to $(n_1 - 1) + (n_2 - 1)$ or $(41 - 1) + (51 - 1) = 90$. The sampling distribution in this case is one of the differences between means and technically called the *sampling distribution of the differences between means.* To conceptualize this distribution we will extend and modify the logic of sampling distributions developed in Chapter 7. Instead of drawing a large number of *single* random samples of a fixed size from a given universe and computing some statistic, for example, mean, imagine drawing *pairs* of samples, calculating the means for each pair and finding the differences between the means of each pair. A distribution of these differences would produce a sampling distribution of the differences between means. The sampling distribution would take on the shape of the normal curve and would enable us to use the N.C. as a mathematical model against which to compare our results. However, when the parameters are unknown (as is the case here) the t rather than the normal curve is the appropriate sampling distribution.

Why would this sampling distribution of the differences between means be normal? From the now familiar central limit theorem we may derive another theorem: if independent random samples of sizes n_1 and n_2 are drawn from normal populations, then the sampling distribution of the difference between two sample means will be normal with the difference between means ($\mu_{\bar{x}_1 - \bar{x}_2}$) equal to $\mu_1 - \mu_2$ and the standard error of the differences between the means ($\sigma_{\bar{x}_1 - \bar{x}_2}$) equal to $\sqrt{\sigma_1^2/n_1 + \sigma_2^2/n_2}$.

We may symbolically express the standard error of the difference as $\sigma_{\bar{x}_1 - \bar{x}_2}$. With independent samples and *unequal* variances we may compute it via formula (11.4).

$$\sigma_{\bar{x}_1 - \bar{x}_2} = \sqrt{\frac{\sigma_1^2}{n_1} + \frac{\sigma_2^2}{n_2}} \tag{11.4}$$

where: σ_1^2 and σ_2^2 = the respective population variances[4]

Formula (11.4) can be expressed in a different way. That is, with independent samples and *equal* variances, the standard error of the difference between means becomes:

---

[4] It may come as a surprise that the standard error of the *difference* between means is obtained by *adding* or *summing* the variances. A moment's reflection should convince you that subtracting the variances could not be used since it would then be possible to obtain a negative variance.

$$\sigma_{\bar{X}_1 - \bar{X}_2} = \sqrt{\sigma^2 \left(\frac{1}{n_1} + \frac{1}{n_2} \right)} \qquad (11.5)$$

where: $\sigma_{\bar{X}_1 - \bar{X}_2}$ = standard error of the difference between means
σ^2 = pooled population variance
n = number of observations, subscripts indicating which sample

Notice that formulas (11.4) and (11.5) are expressed in terms of parameters. It is rare when the universe parameters are known and, as a consequence, they must be estimated from the sample statistics. Since we do calculate the *sample* variances (or standard deviations) to estimate the population values formulae (11.4) and (11.5) are modified and become (11.6) and (11.7), respectively:

$$s_{\bar{X}_1 - \bar{X}_2} = \sqrt{\frac{s_1^2}{n_1 - 1} + \frac{s_2^2}{n_2 - 1}} \qquad (11.6)$$

$$s_{\bar{X}_1 - \bar{X}_2} = \sqrt{s^2 \left(\frac{1}{n_1} + \frac{1}{n_2} \right)} \qquad (11.7)$$

where: $s^2 = \dfrac{\Sigma x_1^2 + \Sigma x_2^2}{n_1 + n_2 - 2}$ or $\dfrac{(n_1 - 1)(s_1^2) + (n_2 - 1)(s_2^2)}{n_1 + n_2 - 2}$

The Region of Rejection. As is the custom, we enter the t table at the preselected alpha level (in this case .10) with df equal to $(n_1 - 1) + (n_2 - 1)$ for a one-tailed test.

For this problem, t formula (11.8) will be employed:

$$t = \frac{\bar{X}_1 - \bar{X}_2}{s_{\bar{X}_1 - \bar{X}_2}} \qquad (11.8)$$

where: t = t test statistic for independent samples with unequal variances
$\bar{X}_1, \bar{X}_2$ = the two sample means, one and two, respectively
$s_{\bar{X}_1 - \bar{X}_2}$ = the standard error of the difference between the two means

where: $s_{\bar{X}_1 - \bar{X}_2} = \sqrt{\dfrac{s_1^2}{n_1 - 1} + \dfrac{s_2^2}{n_2 - 1}}$

where: s_1^2, s_2^2 = the variances for the first and second samples, respectively
n_1, n_2 = the sample sizes for the first and second samples, respectively

In this formula the denominator involves a procedure known as *pooling the variances*. This pooling or combining of the respective variances takes into account (1) the difference in n's, and (2) the difference in variances.

Let us now substitute our computed data into formula (11.8):

$$t = \frac{120 - 125}{\sqrt{\dfrac{(15)^2}{40} + \dfrac{(10)^2}{50}}}$$

$$= \frac{-5}{\sqrt{\dfrac{225}{40} + \dfrac{100}{50}}}$$

$$= \frac{-5}{\sqrt{5.625 + 2.000}}$$

$$= \frac{-5}{\sqrt{7.625}}$$

$$= \frac{-5}{2.76}$$

$$= -1.81$$

What does $t = -1.81$ mean? We must consult the t sampling distribution, Table E in Appendix A, at the .10 level of significance according to the df determined as follows:

$$df = (n_1 - 1) + (n_2 - 1)$$
$$= (41 - 1) + (51 - 1)$$
$$= 40 + 50$$
$$= 90$$

For our particular data-set, $df = 90$. We now turn to the t table and locate the critical value where alpha $= .10$ and $df = 90$ intersect (for a one-tailed test). The critical value is between -1.296 (60 df) and -1.289 (120 df). Since our value is larger than the table value, that is, $|-1.81| > |-1.289|$ (or $|-1.296|$), we reject the null and accept the alternative hypothesis. Substantively speaking, there's a statistically significant difference between male and female attitudes toward the feminist movement. Specifically, females are more favorable to the movement than are males. Therefore, $p < .10$.

Difference between Means: Independent Samples, Equal Variances ($\sigma_1^2 = \sigma_2^2$)

In much social research it is more reasonable to assume that the variances are unequal. Nevertheless, there are occasions when the variances are equal, or can be assumed to be so for all practical purposes. In this section we will illustrate the use of the t test statistic under the latter condition.

Suppose we're interested in comparing working-class and middle-class attitudes toward the need for family planning. We design an equal interval scale[5] in which high scores are indicative of favorable attitudes toward family planning and low scores are indicative of unfavorable attitudes. We randomly select 18 working-class persons and 24 middle-class persons. We tabulate the results of the survey and find that the working-class sample has a mean of 11 ($\bar{X}_1 = 11$) with a standard deviation of 4.3 ($s_1 = 4.3$), whereas the middle-class sample has a mean of 15 ($\bar{X}_2 = 15$) and a standard deviation of 3.5 ($s_2 = 3.5$).

Let us set up this problem in formal statistical terms.

To demonstrate that the variances are equal, formula (11.3) may be employed. For our data:

$$F = \frac{18.49}{12.25}$$

$$= 1.51$$

Turning to Table M in Appendix A, the sampling distribution of the F statistic, we locate the critical value at the intersection of 17 and 23 df's. The exact df's are not available but the intersection of the closest df's (16 and 23) produces a critical value of 2.10, alpha = .05. Since $1.51 < 2.10$ we cannot reject the null hypothesis of equal variances. Apparently, the variances are close enough to be considered equal.

Stating the Null and Alternative Hypotheses. The null hypothesis is that there is no difference in working-class and middle-class attitudes toward family planning. Symbolically, $H_0: \mu_1 = \mu_2$ or $\mu_1 - \mu_2 = 0$. The alternative hypothesis is that there is a difference between working-class and middle-class attitudes toward family planning. Symbolically, $H_1: \mu_1 \neq \mu_2$ or $\mu_1 - \mu_2 \neq 0$.

The Choice of a Statistical Test. For these interval/ratio level data, with relatively small n's, the t test statistic is appropriate.

The Level of Significance and Sample Size. Let us set alpha at the .05 level. The n's for the working- and middle-class samples are 18 (n_1) and 24 (n_2), respectively.

One- versus Two-Tailed Tests. Since the alternative hypothesis is stated in non-directional fashion, a two-tailed test is called for.

The Sampling Distribution. Once again, the t statistic uses the t sampling distribution, Table E in Appendix A, with $n_1 + n_2 - 2$ degrees of freedom or, for our illustration, $18 + 24 - 2 = 40$.

---

[5] An equal-appearing interval scale (e.g., a Likert scale) contains a series of items each of which is located along an attitudinal continuum from, for example, most favorable, favorable, unfavorable, most unfavorable, and so forth. The scale receives its name from the fact that the interval distances between the various points along the continuum are assumed to be equal.

The Region of Rejection. As is customary, we locate the critical value at the intersection of the selected alpha level (.05 in this example) and the *df* determined by $n_1 + n_2 - 2$.

When researchers have drawn two random samples and assume or determine that the variances are equal, formula (11.9) is applicable:

$$t = \frac{\overline{X}_1 - \overline{X}_2}{\sqrt{(s^2) \dfrac{n_1 + n_2}{n_1 n_2}}}$$

(11.9)

where: $t = t$ test statistic for independent samples with equal variances.

$$s^2 = \frac{(n_1 - 1)s_1^2 + (n_2 - 1)s_2^2}{n_1 + n_2 - 2}$$

where: s_1^2, s_2^2 =   variance of samples one and two, respectively
         n_1, n_2 =   size of samples one and two, respectively

Notice that the denominator in formula (11.8) is different from the demoninator in formula (11.9). Instead of having two separate sample variances as we did in the difference between means test assuming unequal variances, we now have a single variance (which is an estimate of the population variance). With the difference of means test assuming equal variances we actually have a better estimate since it is based on $n_1 + n_2$ cases rather than two separate ones, each based on a smaller number of cases. Again we combine the two separate sample variances into a single pooled variance, symbolized s^2 in the formula. However, we pool the variances differently than we did formerly.

Let us substitute our values into formula (11.9):

$$t = \frac{11 - 15}{s^2}$$

$$s^2 = \frac{(18 - 1)(4.3)^2 + (24 - 1)(3.5)^2}{18 + 24 - 2}$$

$$= \frac{17(18.49) + 23(12.25)}{42 - 2}$$

$$= \frac{314.33 + 218.75}{40}$$

$$= \frac{533.08}{40}$$

$$= 13.33$$

Substituting s^2 into formula (11.9):

$$t = \frac{11 - 15}{\sqrt{13.33 \left[\frac{18 + 24}{(18)(24)} \right]}}$$

$$= \frac{-4}{\sqrt{13.33 \left(\frac{42}{432} \right)}}$$

$$= \frac{-4}{\sqrt{13.33 \, (.1)}}$$

$$= \frac{-4}{\sqrt{1.333}}$$

$$= \frac{-4}{1.15}$$

$$= -3.48$$

What does $t = -3.48$ mean? We enter the t table at the .05 level (two-tailed test) with $df = n_1 + n_2 - 2 = 18 + 24 - 2 = 40$. The critical value where these figures intersect is 2.021. Since our computed value is larger than the table value, that is, $|-3.48| > |-2.021|$, we must reject the null hypothesis. Substantively speaking, we have statistical support for claiming a difference between middle- and working-class attitudes toward family planning. By examining the direction of the differences we can see that the middle-class sample is more favorable to family planning than is the working-class sample. In notation form, $p < .05$ and statistically significant.

Two-Sample Test of Significance: Related Samples

As with other level (nominal and ordinal) tests of significance, a distinction is made between independent and matched samples. The previous sections have discussed the t test for independent samples. We now turn to the t test for related or matched samples. You will recall that there are two basic procedures for arriving at cor-related samples. One way is to use a *matched group design* in which individuals in two different groups, perhaps experimental and control, are matched or related on some variable known to be correlated with the dependent variable. The second generic way is to study the *same* subjects at different points in time as in a *before-after* research design.

   With correlated or matched samples it probably seems reasonable to assume that the magnitude of sampling error as found in the denominator of the t ratio (the standard error of the difference between means) is smaller than it is with independent samples. While this is more likely to be the case, it still remains an empirical question. The general formula for the standard error of the difference between means is formula (11.10):

$$\sigma_{\overline{X}_1 - \overline{X}_2} = \sqrt{\sigma_{\overline{X}_1}^2 + \sigma_{\overline{X}_2}^2 - (2r_{X_1 X_2})(\sigma_{\overline{X}_1}\, \sigma_{\overline{X}_2})} \qquad (11.10)$$

Notice the correlation term (r) in the expression. For independent samples, this term drops out of the formula, and the previous t test computational formulae reflected this. That is, for uncorrelated measures, $r_{X_1 X_2} = 0$.

Interestingly, even for matched samples it is *not* necessary to calculate the correlation between samples. Instead, we may use a procedure which enables a direct calculation of the standard error and call it by its conventional name, the **direct difference method**.

This technique consists of finding the difference between the subjects' scores (each subject in this case being used as his or her own control) at two points in time and treating these differences as raw scores. In effect the null hypothesis is that the mean difference, symbolized $\overline{D}$, is zero.

Assume a new teaching method for teaching sociological methodology has been developed. This new technique involves the use of visual aids to convey the understanding of some very important methodological concepts. The comprehension of eight students is assessed before and after the presentation of these visual aids. It is anticipated that greater understanding (higher scores) will result from such exposure.

Let us set up this problem in formal statistical terms.

Stating the Null and Alternative Hypotheses. The null hypothesis is that there is no difference in the comprehension of methodological concepts before and after exposure to these visual aids. Symbolically, $\overline{D} = 0$ (where $\overline{D}$ equals the mean difference). The alternative hypothesis is that there will be greater comprehension of the concepts after exposure. Symbolically, $\overline{D} > 0$.

The Choice of a Statistical Test. Since we have related samples, specifically a before-after research design in which students are used as their own controls, the t statistic for correlated samples may be employed.

The Level of Significance and Sample Size. Let alpha equal .01. The sample size consists of eight students, each being used as his or her own control.

One- versus Two-Tailed Tests. Since the alternative hypothesis is directional in nature, a one-tailed test is called for.

The Sampling Distribution. The t test statistic's sampling distribution is found in Table E of Appendix A. Degrees of freedom in this case $= n - 1$ or $8 - 1 = 7$.

The Region of Rejection. The region of rejection includes all values equal to or greater than 2.998 for a one-tailed test at the .01 level.

To compute the t statistic, formula (11.11) must be applied to the data in Table 11.1.

$$t = \frac{\bar{D}}{\sqrt{s_{\bar{X}_1 - \bar{X}_2}}}$$ (11.11)

where: t = t test statistic for matched samples

   $\bar{D}$ =   the mean difference between scores where $\bar{D} = \Sigma D / n$

   $s_{\bar{X}_1 - \bar{X}_2}$ =   the standard error of the difference between means

where: $s_{\bar{X}_1 - \bar{X}_2}$ = $\sqrt{\dfrac{\Sigma D^2 - \dfrac{(\Sigma D)^2}{n}}{n(n-1)}}$

where: D =   difference between individual scores

   n =   number of subjects

TABLE 11.1

Illustration of Computations of the t Statistic: Hypothetical Before-After Test Scores

			Differences	
Student (1)	Before Score (2)	After Score (3)	D (4)	D² (5)
A	75	78	3	9
B	59	62	3	9
C	83	85	2	4
D	54	59	5	25
E	67	71	4	16
F	68	70	2	4
G	72	73	1	1
H	80	84	4	16
			$\Sigma D = 24$	$\Sigma D^2 = 84$

$$\bar{D} = \frac{\Sigma D}{n} = \frac{24}{8} = 3$$

The following steps are recommended for computing the t statistic for correlated samples using the direct difference method.

1. Determine the differences in before-after scores and locate these differences in the D column. See column 4 in Table 11.1.

2. Square these differences and place these values in the D^2 column. See column 5 in Table 11.1.

3. Sum the D column and divide this sum by n to obtain $\overline{D}$, that is, $24/8 = 3$.

4. Sum the D^2 column. In column 5, $\Sigma D^2 = 84$.

5. Substitute these values into the t computational formula (11.11).

$$t = \frac{3}{\sqrt{\dfrac{84 - 576/8}{8(7)}}}$$

$$= \frac{3}{\sqrt{\dfrac{84 - 72}{56}}}$$

$$= \frac{3}{\sqrt{\dfrac{12}{56}}}$$

$$= \frac{3}{\sqrt{.214}}$$

$$= \frac{3}{.46}$$

$$= 6.52$$

What does $t = 6.52$ mean? We must consult the t table with $n - 1$ degrees of freedom for a one-tailed test at the .01 level. The critical value is 2.998. The t statistic is significant if the computed value is equal to or greater than the table value. Since $6.52 > 2.998$ we reject H_0 and accept H_1. Substantively speaking, we conclude that there is greater comprehension of methodological concepts after exposure to the visual aids than before. Moreover, $p < .01$ and statistically significant.

k-SAMPLE TEST OF SIGNIFICANCE

F Test (Analysis of Variance)

There are several varieties of the **analysis of variance** (ANOVA) test. In addition to the *simple* or *one-way* type, which will be discussed here, there exist two-way and *N*-way (called factorial) ANOVA tests. This technique is often referred to as the *F* test in honor of its development by Sir R. A. Fisher, who reported on it in the mid-1920s. Although ANOVA is a test of differences in means, it is based upon the comparison of variances, from which it gets its name.

Let us introduce ANOVA by considering why the test is an important statistical tool. Assume we have computed the means for eight different samples and wish to determine if there are significant differences among them. How many comparisons or tests would have to be made, taking two samples at a time (as was done in the case of the t or z test)? The number of comparisons, taking two samples at a time, can be determined by formula (11.12):

$$\frac{n(n - 1)}{2} \qquad (11.12)$$

where: $n =$ the number of samples

This means that for eight different samples, the number of possible comparisons between any two is, without repetition, $8(8 - 1)/2 = 28$. Working through formula (11.12) indicates that twenty-eight t or z tests would have to be run on the data-sets. With the analysis of variance test, rather than make twenty-eight separate tests, we could make *one* test, the ANOVA, and the results would inform us of whether or not there are significant differences among our eight independent samples.

If we were to calculate twenty-eight different t tests for eight different samples, the various tests would not all be independent comparisons and the resulting probabilities would overlap. For illustrative purposes suppose we wished to compare three different mean scores. If we compare $\bar{X}_1$ (mean of group one) with $\bar{X}_2$ (mean of group two) and then compare $\bar{X}_1$ or $\bar{X}_2$ with $\bar{X}_3$ (mean of group three), this latter comparison would not be independent of the former comparisons. Consequently, the F sampling distribution, which assumes independent comparisons, would not be applicable. In comparing k independent samples' means as we do with ANOVA, this problem is avoided.

The *major advantage* of the ANOVA test is that it is a parsimonious procedure by which a single test can be used in place of several. The purpose of the ANOVA test, which is related to the major advantage, is to determine the significance between the means of two or more independent samples. While it is possible and permissible to use the ANOVA test with *two* independent samples, its major advantage and saving in computational time occur when the researcher has three or more independent samples and wishes to know if there are significant differences among them. ANOVA is an extension of the difference of means test but it does involve some new mathematical principles as we will now see.

The discussion above conveys the idea that ANOVA is a statistical test like chi-square, Mann-Whitney U, and z. However, it is much more than a statistical test; it is a research design as well. Let us elaborate this.

Suppose, for example, that we wish to determine the effectiveness of different class structures on students' performances. We pose the question: *Do students learn better by lecture, project, or discussion methods?* To answer this query we would have to develop a criterion measure, perhaps grade in the course or score on a standardized test, and compare the average performance of students taught under the three different instructional modes. But to eliminate the problem of self-selection, that is, students choosing their own class structure, the researcher would have to intervene and *randomly* allocate persons to the different experimental conditions. ANOVA, as a research design, assumes such a random distribution of cases.

Let us extend the logic behind ANOVA. To begin with, assume that all students, regardless of class structure, make the same score on the criterion measure. If this unusual outcome were to occur, we would be dubious that the experimental conditions have any measurable influence on students' performances. However, this outcome is not likely to occur since there are numerous factors that would contribute to bringing about differential student performances. For example, some students are brighter than others, some study more than others, and so forth. Consequently, these individual differences would probably be reflected on the criterion measure. Nevertheless, in the long run these individual differences would tend to cancel each other out if the students were originally randomly assigned to different treatments.

But there is another source of influence, the three different teaching modes. Specifically, the lecture, project, and discussion formats may contribute to performance on the criterion measure. The analysis of variance design permits us to answer the question: *Is it reasonable to claim that one teaching method is better* (on the criterion measure) *than another?* How do we do this?

To determine the effect of the three different experimental conditions it would be necessary to sum the individual performances in each group and divide by the number of students in each group to find the respective group means. Having done this we would know the average performance in each group. Secondly, it would be necessary to determine the overall average performance, the average performance of all subjects in all treatments. By subtracting the individual group averages from the overall average we would be in a position to assess the differential effects, if any, of the different instructional modes. But the reasoning is a bit more complicated.

If there were no significant individual differences within the treatment conditions, it would be easy to answer the question of whether one teaching method is better than another by computing the ratio between the group averages to some standard error. But we can never be assured that there are no significant individual differences. However, if subjects have been randomly allocated, any variations that occur between groups that are due to individual differences can be measured in terms of random sampling error. If there are treatment effects and individual difference effects the group means will reflect this. Consequently, if the group means differ by an amount that is greater than would be expected by chance alone, we are in a position to assert that the different modes of instruction—the group effects— are significantly different. Before turning to a specific problem, a brief exposition of the general notation and statistical theory is in order.

General Notation and Statistical Theory for One-Way ANOVA. For illustrative purposes, consider the notational scheme presented in Table 11.2. Notice that we have obtained measurements for three different independent samples or groups and have indicated the scores by an X and two subscripts. In this scheme, a system of double subscripts is used. The first column entry is X_{11}: the first subscript identifies the individual in the group and the second subscript identifies the group. Consequently, X_{11} refers to the score (or measurement) of the first person in the first group. Similarly, X_{32} refers to the score of the third individual in the second group. All other entries are identified in this manner.

TABLE 11.2

General Statistical Notation for Simple ANOVA

Sample 1	Sample 2	. . .	Sample k
X_{11}	X_{12}		X_{1k}
X_{21}	X_{22}		X_{2k}
X_{31}	X_{32}		X_{3k}
.	.		.
.	.		.
.	.		.
$\dfrac{X_{n_1}}{\Sigma X_1} =$	$\dfrac{X_{n_2}}{\Sigma X_2} =$		$\dfrac{X_{n_k}}{\Sigma X_k} =$
$\bar{X}_1 =$	$\bar{X}_2 =$		$\bar{X}_k =$
$n_1 =$	$n_2 =$		$n_k =$

In the ANOVA test we determine whether or not the means of the k independent samples can be considered to have been selected from the same population. In other words, $H_0: \mu_1 = \mu_2 = \mu_k$.

This test is called the analysis of variance test because variances rather than standard deviations or standard errors are used to arrive at the final statistical value which is compared to the known sampling distribution. The basic rationale is that the total sum of squares (or *total variation*) of a data-set composed of two or more independent samples can be divided into specific components, each component being identified with a given source of variation. Accordingly, the **total sum of squares** (symbolized TSS) can be analyzed and divided into two parts: (1) a **within sum of squares** (symbolized WSS) or within k groups variation, and (2) a **between sum of squares** (symbolized BSS) or a between k groups variation. In short, we have the following identity: $TSS = WSS + BSS$. Let us partition the three sums of squares for computational purposes.

Consider the formula (11.13):

$$\Sigma(X_{ij} - \bar{X}_{..})^2 = \Sigma(X_{ij} - \bar{X}_{.j})^2 + \Sigma(\bar{X}_{.j} - \bar{X}_{..})^2 \qquad (11.13)$$

where: $\Sigma(X_{ij} - \bar{X}_{..})^2$ refers to the *total sum of squares* obtained by subtracting the grand mean $(\bar{X}_{..})$ from each score (X_{ij}), squaring the difference and summing these squared differences. This operation is performed for all individual scores in all *k* independent groups.

$\Sigma(X_{ij} - \bar{X}_{.j})^2$ refers to the *within sum of squares* (sometimes called the residual or unexplained variation) obtained by subtracting the group mean $(\bar{X}_{.j})$ from each score (X_{ij}) in that given group, squaring the differences and then summing these squared differences.

$\Sigma(\bar{X}_{.j} - \bar{X}_{..})^2$ refers to the *between sum of squares* (sometimes called the explained variation) obtained by subtracting the grand mean $(\bar{X}_{..})$ from each group mean $(\bar{X}_{.j})$, squaring these differences and then summing these squared differences.

By dropping the summation signs, the mathematical identity expressed in formula (11.13) states that the deviation of any given score from the grand mean is comprised of two parts: (1) a deviation of the given score from the group mean to which it belongs, and (2) a deviation of the group mean (to which the score belongs) from the grand mean. That is, $(X_{ij} - \bar{X}_{..}) = (X_{ij} - \bar{X}_{.j}) + (\bar{X}_{.j} - \bar{X}_{..})$.

Earlier we stated that the ANOVA test works with variances. Now we will make this statement operational. A sum of squares quantity is technically referred to as *variation*. In order to calculate a *variance* we must divide the sum of squares by an appropriate denominator.[6] Each of the sum of squares has an associated number of degrees of freedom (*df*) which are determined as follows:

1. *The df for the total sum of square equals n* − 1 (the total number of observations minus 1) because one *df* is lost by taking deviations from the grand mean.

2. *The df for the between sum of squares equals k* − 1 (the number of groups or samples minus 1) because we have *k* sample means and 1 *df* is lost by expressing the group means as deviations from the grand mean.

3. *The df for the within sum of squares equals k* (*n* − 1) because there are *k* groups and 1 *df* is lost in each group.

Consequently, when the within sum of squares and between sum of squares are divided by their corresponding *df*'s we obtain a within and between groups'

---

[6]You may recall that in discussing measures of dispersion (Chapter 5) we symbolized the variance computation as:

$$s^2 = \frac{\Sigma(X_i - \bar{X})^2}{N}$$

The numerator alone is called *variation* or *sum of squares*. When this numerator was divided by *N* we referred to the quotient as the *variance*. If this is not understood a rereading of interval/ratio measures of dispersion in Chapter 5 should refresh your memory.

variance estimate, respectively. These two independent computations are estimates of the common population variance. These variance estimates are commonly spoken of as *mean squares*.

It should be apparent that the sums of squares are *additive* (that is, $TSS = WSS + BSS$) as are the degrees of freedom, that is, $n - 1$ (total df) $= k(n - 1)$ (within df) $+ k - 1$ (between df). However, the variance estimates are *not* additive. The final computation, called the F *statistic*, is obtained by dividing the between variance estimate by the within variance estimate or

$$\frac{\dfrac{BSS}{k - 1}}{\dfrac{WSS}{k(n - 1)}} = F \text{ ratio}$$

Let us illustrate these principles with an actual problem. Assume you are interested in the sociology of education. More particularly, you are concerned with the effect of different modes of instruction on achievement test scores. You design an experiment in which students are taught by three different instructional modes and you wish to determine whether there are significant differences in test scores of students taught by: (1) the conventional lecture approach, (2) the project method, and (3) the discussion method. The hypothetical data appear in Table 11.3.

The proper application of the F test makes the following assumptions: (1) the individuals (students in this case) in the (three) groups have been randomly selected from normally distributed populations; (2) the (three) group variances are equal, that is, they are homoscedastic ($\sigma_1^2 = \sigma_2^2 = \sigma_3^2$); (3) the factors affect the total variation in an additive fashion; (4) the samples are independent in nature. It has been shown, however, that certain violations of these assumptions do not necessarily affect the data analysis. This feature attests to the *robust* nature of ANOVA.

Let us set up this problem to formal statistical terms.

Stating the Null and Alternative Hypotheses. The null hypothesis is that there is no difference among the mean achievement test scores of students taught by three different modes of instruction. Symbolically, H_0: $\mu_1 = \mu_2 = \mu_3$. The alternative hypothesis is that there are differences among the mean achievement test scores of students taught by three different modes. Symbolically, H_1: $\mu \neq \mu_2 \neq \mu_3$.

The Choice of a Statistical Test. With interval/ratio level data secured from k independent samples (three in this case) the analysis of variance test is appropriate.

The Level of Significance and Sample Size. Let us set alpha at the .01 level. The total n equals 15 and the individual group sizes $= 5$.

One- versus Two-Tailed Tests. Since the alternative hypothesis is nondirectional, a two-tailed test is called for.

The Sampling Distribution. The ANOVA test has a sampling distribution known as F. The F sampling distribution, like chi-square and t, is actually a family of distributions that is a function of the degrees of freedom for the between and within sums of squares. In testing the null hypothesis that $\mu_1 = \mu_2 = \mu_3$, the ratio of the two sample variances, between and within groups, is distributed as F. Table M in Appendix A is the F sampling distribution. Notice that the table contains entries for two different df's, one along the heading (top) and the other down the stub (side). The df for the between sum of squares is located *across* the table and the df for the within sum of squares is located *down* the table. The critical F value is located where these df's intersect. The critical F value at the .05 level is listed first, and below it, the critical value at the .01 level.

Like t and chi-square, the F distribution's shape varies according to different df values. In general, the F sampling distribution is skewed to the right. Figure 11.2 illustrates the sampling distributions of F for selected df combinations. In fact, the critical region (and values) of F appear only in the right-hand tail. The F formula (11.3) always places the between-groups variance estimate in the numerator and the within-groups variance estimate in the denominator. Only when the numerator is larger than the denominator is it possible to reject the null statement. The rationale for this decision is this: if the numerator (between groups variance) is smaller than the denominator (within groups variance), you encounter a situation where individual differences exceed between group differences. Hence, the null hypothesis is retained.

FIGURE 11.2

Sampling Distributions of F for Selected df Combinations

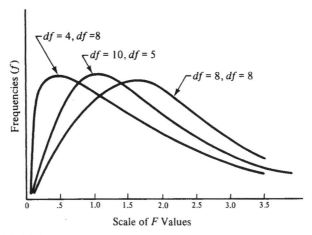

The Region of Rejection. To determine the critical value, as well as the entire region of rejection, we enter the F table at the appropriate alpha level according to the between and within groups' degrees of freedom. In this table we locate the larger mean square's (variance estimate) df along the top of the table and the lesser mean square's df along the left-hand column. Again, where these two df's intersect, the critical value is found. For our data, the critical F value at the .01 level is 6.93. Had we selected the .05 level, the critical F would have been 3.88.

Assume we've collected the data in Table 11.3.

TABLE 11.3

Illustration of ANOVA: Hypothetical Achievement Test Scores of Students Taught by Three Different Instructional Methods

Lecture (Group 1)		Project (Group 2)		Discussion (Group 3)	
X	X^2	X	X^2	X	X^2
17	289	14	196	12	144
20	400	16	256	12	144
20	400	17	289	13	169
21	441	19	361	17	289
22	484	19	361	16	256
$\Sigma X = 100$ $\Sigma X^2 = 2{,}014$		$\Sigma X = 85$ $\Sigma X^2 = 1{,}463$		$\Sigma X = 70$ $\Sigma X^2 = 1{,}002$	

The following steps are recommended for computing the F statistic.

1. Sum each group's X values (X values are individual scores) as has been done in Table 11.3. The sum for the lecture method is: $17 + 20 + 20 + 21 + 22 = 100$. The sum for the project method is: $14 + 16 + 17 + 19 + 19 = 85$. The sum for the discussion method is: $12 + 12 + 13 + 17 + 16 = 70$.

2. Square each X value in the respective groups and sum these squared values as has been done in Table 11.3. The sums of the squared X values are 2,014, 1,463, and 1,002 in the lecture, project, and discussion methods, respectively.

The following computational formula may be used for determining the three sums of squares. The **total sum of squares** (*TSS*) or total variation may be computed with formula (11.14):

$$TSS = \Sigma X^2 - \frac{(\Sigma X)^2}{n} \tag{11.14}$$

Substituting our data:

$\Sigma X^2 = 2{,}014 \text{ (Group 1)} + 1{,}463 \text{ (Group 2)} + 1{,}002 \text{ (Group 3)} = 4{,}479$

$(\Sigma X)^2 = 100$ (Group 1) $+ 85$ (Group 2) $+ 70$ (Group 3) $= 255^2 = 65{,}025$

$n = 15$

$$\frac{(\Sigma X)^2}{n} = \frac{65{,}025}{15} = 4{,}335$$

Hence, $TSS = 4{,}479 - 4{,}335 = 144$

The **within sum of squares** (*WSS*) or within variation may be computed by using the same formula (11.14) for *each* group and summing the separate results. Therefore, for the lecture method (group 1) we have:

$$2{,}014 - \frac{(100)^2}{5} = 14$$

For the project method (Group 2):

$$1{,}463 - \frac{(85)^2}{5} = 18$$

And for the discussion method (Group 3):

$$1{,}002 - \frac{(70)^2}{5} = 22$$

To obtain the within sum of squares we must add the sum of squares computed for each group. Hence,

$$14 \text{ (Group 1)} + 18 \text{ (Group 2)} + 22 \text{ (Group 3)} = 54$$

Our *WSS* value equals 54.

Since the total sum of squares can be partitioned into two parts, the *WSS* and the *BSS*, we need not calculate the **between sum of squares** (*BSS*). Instead, we can obtain this quantity by substituting the proper value in the identity: $TSS = WSS + BSS$. Therefore, $144 = 54 + ?$ (90). However, as a check let us compute *BSS* using formula (11.15).

$$BSS = \frac{(\Sigma X_1)^2}{n_1} + \frac{(\Sigma X_2)^2}{n_2} + \frac{(\Sigma X_3)^2}{n_3} + \frac{(\Sigma X_{total})^2}{n_1 + n_2 + n_3} \qquad (11.15)$$

where: subscripts indicate the respective groups

$$BSS = \frac{(100)^2}{5} + \frac{(85)^2}{5} + \frac{(70)^2}{5} - \frac{(255)^2}{15}$$

$$= 2{,}000 + 1{,}445 + 980 - 4{,}335$$

$$= 4{,}425 - 4{,}335$$

$$= 90$$

Obviously, our check corroborates the value produced by $TSS = WSS + BSS$ or $144 = 54 + 90$.

To obtain the *variance* or *mean square* estimates we must divide each sum of squares by its corresponding *df*. The *TSS* has a *df* equal to $n - 1$. Since $n = 15$, $n - 1 = 15 - 1 = 14$ (for *TSS*). For the *WSS* the *df* equals $k(n - 1)$ or $3(4) = 12$ (in the computation for *WSS*, *n* means the *group* size rather than the total number of observations). Finally, the *BSS* has a *df* equal to $k - 1$ or $3 - 1 = 2$ (for *BSS*). It is conventional to place this information in tabular form in such a way that the source of variation, sum of squares, *df*, and variance estimates can easily be identified. Such an arrangement is called an *ANOVA summary table*. Let us do this for our problem in Table 11.3 and construct a new table (11.4):

TABLE 11.4

An ANOVA Summary Table for Table 11.3

Source of Variation	Sum of Squares	df	Variance Estimate*	F
Between groups	90	2	45.0	10.000
Within groups	54	12	4.5	
Total	144	14		

*Sometimes called *mean square*.

Notice again that the sums of squares and the *df*'s are additive but, of course, the variance estimates are not.

With the data in AVOVA summary form we may compute the *F* ratio directly with formula (11.16):

$$F = \frac{\text{between variance estimate}}{\text{within variance estimate}} = \frac{\dfrac{BSS}{k - 1}}{\dfrac{WSS}{k(n - 1)}} \qquad (11.16)$$

Substituting our values into formula (11.16):

$$F = \frac{45}{4.5} = 10.000$$

What does $F = 10.000$ mean? We enter the *F* table, Table M in Appendix A, and locate the *df* for the between mean square (variance estimate) along the top and the *df* for the within mean square down the left-hand column. Setting alpha at the .01 level with 2 and 12 *df*'s we find the critical value to be 6.93. Since $10.000 > 6.93$ we reject H_0 and conclude that there are significant differences in achievement test scores among students taught by different modes of instruction. That is, $p < .01$.

Observations on ANOVA. The analysis of variance test is an extremely useful one in social research that involves comparisons of more than two independent samples. With multigroup comparisons it avoids the overlapping probability dilemma that occurs when the separate comparisons are not independent in nature. Probably the major disadvantage of *F* surrounds its *lack of specificity*. That is, if *F* is statistically significant we may conclude that there is a significant difference between the largest and smallest means. But we do not know where the other differences, if any, are. The Newman-Keuls procedure, a technique for determining where the specific differences can be found, is recommended for such considerations. Additional discussions of how to find where the significant differences lie can be found in Norusis (1995).

SUMMARY

In this chapter three interval/ratio level tests, *t*, *z*, and *F*, were discussed along with the conditions under which they can be appropriately applied. It was shown that the *t* and *z* tests can be used in both one- and two-sample situations. In general, *t* is the appropriate test statistic when the parameters are unknown and *n* is small ($\leq$ 30) and *z* is appropriate when the parameters are known and *n* is large (> 30). The analysis of variance test (*F*) is useful in dealing with the multigroup comparisons of independent samples. Figure 11.1 contains a summary of these statistics.

IMPORTANT CONCEPTS DISCUSSED IN THIS CHAPTER

z test of significance

t test (*t* ratio, Students's *t*, critical ratio,
   t statistic)

Direct difference method

F test (analysis of variance)

Total sum of squares

Within sum of squares

Between sum of squares

REVIEW QUESTIONS

1. Assume that a particular community college the average graduating senior is 26 years of age, with a standard deviation (σ) of 4.8. For several reasons age at the time of

graduation can vary (military service, financial difficulties, marriage, etc.). Suppose we take a random sample of 100 graduating seniors from the upper quarter (in terms of GPA) of the class. The mean age of the sample is calculated to be 27. Using the *z single-sample test*, determine whether or not there is a significant age difference between the sample of students from the upper quarter and the entire graduating class. Answer this question letting alpha = .05 and .01.

2. Assume that corporation "MBI" permits its salespeople 100 miles per day for deducting the cost of gasoline. A sample of five salespersons shows that the mean number of miles traveled per diem is 85 with a standard deviation of 20 miles. Using the *t single-sample test*, determine whether there is a significant difference between the corporation's allowance and the sample's figure. Set alpha at the .05 level.

3. Suppose we wish to compare the tips of cab drivers in Chicago and New York City. A hypothetical sample of 26 Chicago cab drivers yields a mean income of $28 in tips per night with a standard deviation of $4. Likewise, a hypothetical sample of 25 cab drivers in New York reveals a mean of $25 in tips with a standard deviation of $6.
   a. Determine whether the variances are equal or unequal at the .05 level (two-tailed).
   b. Apply the appropriate two independent sample *t test* to determine if any significant differences exist.
   c. Interpret the meaning of *t* setting alpha at the .05 level.

4. For the data in question 3:
   a. Determine whether the variances are equal or unequal at the .01 level (two-tailed).
   b. Then, apply the appropriate *t test*.
   c. Interpret *t*'s statistical significance setting alpha = .01.

5. Suppose we wish to assess the effectiveness of a remedial driver education program on persons who have already been driving for several years. Assume each participant receives a competency skill score before and after taking the course. Test these data to see if there is a significant difference between the pre- and post-test course scores with alpha = .05. Employ the *t test for matched samples*.

Driver	Before Score	After Score
A	87	88
B	75	79
C	68	73
D	85	87
E	77	80

6. Suppose that the military wants to test the effect of three different training programs on the socialization into the Army. Ten recruits are randomly assigned to three different training programs. "Effective military socialization scores" are determined at the end of the training period. The hypothetical results are below. For these data, follow the steps listed in completing Fisher's *analysis of variance test* for k independent samples.

Training Programs		
Type I	*Type II*	*Type III*
X	X	X
8	8	8
7	7	8
6	9	6
7	8	5
5	10	4
9	6	9
8	8	5
7	8	4
6	9	5
7	7	6

a. Sum each group's X values.
b. Square each X value and sum these squared values for each training program.
c. Calculate the total sum of squares.
d. Compute the within sum of squares.
e. Calculate the between sum of squares.
f. Determine df for TSS, BSS and WSS.
g. Determine the variance estimates for BSS and WSS.
h. Compute the F ratio.
i. Is there a significant difference at the .01 level?
j. Is there a significant difference at the .05 level?

*

4

DESCRIPTIVE STATISTICS: BIVARIATE DISTRIBUTIONS

CHAPTER 12

MEASURES OF ASSOCIATION (CORRELATION): NOMINAL LEVEL COEFFICIENTS

In the preceding descriptive statistics chapters (3–6) our major interest was in calculating various statistics which permitted us to describe the values of a single variable. When concern is with a *single* variable we are dealing with what is technically known as a **univariate distribution.** However, many of the more interesting issues and problems in the behavioral sciences go beyond the description of a single variable; in other words, social research often centers on the relationship between *two variables* technically called **bivariate distributions,** or *more than two variables,* referred to as **multivariate distributions.** In this chapter we will begin with a brief discussion of the **concept of relationship** and several illustrations of the type of research problem with which measures of association are equipped to deal. Then we will move on to some general considerations of the different types of correlation coefficients and some of their common characteristics. Finally, an exposition of some very popular nominal level measures of association and their underlying rationale will be presented.

THE CONCEPT OF RELATIONSHIP

From a philosophy of science standpoint there is no more important idea than that of the **relationship** between variables or events. The methodology (the logic of discovery) of the behavioral sciences assumes that events don't just happen; instead, these events are cloaked in a cause-effect framework. The goal of the empirical researcher is to ferret out this causal nexus, and one partial way of doing this is to determine the relationship between events. However, establishment of an association is *not* sufficient to prove cause-effect; instead, it is a necessary condition.[1] In short, the scientist assumes that events don't just happen randomly but occur under specified conditions. By examining different circumstances and conditions one is in a position to posit when events are and/or are not likely to occur. Since an event is often the result of numerous factors, some known and some unknown, as well as some factors being amenable to quantification procedures and others more elusive, our understanding is grounded in the **principle of contingency** (Mueller, Schuessler, and Costner, 1970: 239–240).

The principle of contingency can be illustrated by taking a familiar example, that of a college or professional basketball player. The number of points that the person scores is associated with one's natural ability as a shooter coupled with such factors as the teamwork of the ballclub, the defensive prowess of the opposing players, whether the court is at home or away, fatigue, and so forth. The point is that one's offensive ability is affected both positively and negatively by a host of other factors which the sport sociologist may attempt to disentangle. A social researcher proceeds in the same way. However, it must be conceded that dealing with *bivariate* relationships is but the foundation for more elaborate statistical analysis. The more elegant techniques in which several variables are systematically studied fall under the rubric of *multivariate* analysis. In this book our attention will center upon the basic building block of bivariate associations.

Let's consider three *bivariate* examples. First, college counselors and recruiters are perennially interested in the relationship between high school grades and success in college. This concern is one that deals with the relationship between two variables: high school grades on the one hand, and college success, however defined, on the other. Secondly, Freud was concerned with the effect of child-rearing techniques on adult personality development. In essence, he wished to establish a relationship between specific socialization practices and the personality of the adult. Finally, one might be interested in the relationship between the size of a graduate department and scholarly productivity. While these examples are but a few from the infinite universe of relationships, they all have in common a concern with the relationship between two variables.

A variety of statistical techniques have been devised to provide us with a *numerical* or *quantitative* description of such relationships. These techniques are commonly called **measures of association** or **correlation coefficients.** The terms *relationship* and *co-variation* may also be used.

---

[1] Methodologists maintain that to establish causality, four criteria must be met. In addition to (1) an association or relationship between variables; (2) the presumed causal variable must precede the effect variable in a temporal (time) sequence; (3) the original relationship must not be spurious, that is, it must not disappear when examined in the context of additional variables; and (4) there should be a theoretical rationale for linking the variables together. These criteria allow us to distinguish *necessary* from *sufficient* conditions. Each condition separately is necessary in the sense that it must be present, but any one, two, or three, is not enough to claim a cause-effect relationship. When all four conditions are present we have the sufficient conditions for claiming a causal connection between the variables.

TYPES OF CORRELATION COEFFICIENTS[2]

Since there are many different strains of coefficients of correlation, the decision of which one, or ones, to employ in the context of a given situation is influenced by several factors. Let's consider some of the questions one should ask in order to select the most appropriate measure(s) of relationship.

The *first* query deals with the *level of measurement* of the data. In other words, do the data best meet the assumptions of a nominal, ordinal, or interval/ratio measurement scale? In the discussion that follows, measures of association will be categorized in terms of the theory of measurement paradigm outlined in Chapter 2.

The *second* question asks, *What is the nature of the underlying distribution?* Specifically, we are concerned with whether our variables are *continuous,* for example, height, age, weight, or *discrete,* for example, family size, "head counts," and so forth. You will recall (from Chapter 3) that any value, theoretically, is possible with a continuous variable. In other words, with a perfect measuring instrument it is possible to imagine an infinite division of the values of the variable(s). Discrete variables, on the other hand, come only in whole number or integer form.

The *third* inquiry asks, *What is/are the characteristic(s) of the distribution of scores?* That is, are the data *linear* or *nonlinear* in nature? In general, as we will see shortly, data that can be described by a straight line are said to be linearly related. On the other hand, if the data cannot be described by a straight line they are said to be nonlinear in character. All measures of association to be discussed subsequently will assume linearity.

CHARACTERISTICS OF A RELATIONSHIP

There are *four* characteristics of a relationship to which social statisticians and social researchers are generally attuned (Loether and McTavish, 1993: 176). These will now be discussed commencing with a rhetorical question for each.

1. *How do we determine whether or not an association exists?* Stated a different way, *what criteria are used to establish the existence of a relationship?* There are two broad ways of answering these questions (Mueller, Schuessler, and Costner, 1970: 241–242). The first is called the **principle of the joint occurrence of**

---

[2]Some statisticians prefer to distinguish *association* coefficients from *correlation* coefficients. When this is done, the former refer to nominal and ordinal measures whereas the latter refer to interval/ratio techniques. Instead of making this distinction, this writer will use the two concepts interchangeably. In mathematics a *coefficient* is a number or quantity generally placed before and multiplying another quantity, for example, 15 in the expression $15W$. However, in the context of correlation it refers to the value produced by the numerous statistical techniques that permit one to compute the degree of association between variables.

attributes and applies to nominal level data. For example, if homosexuality is more often found among males than females, we conclude that homosexuality is associated with males. Or, if "health consciousness" occurs more often among middle-class individuals than among upper-, working-, or lower-class persons, we say that "health consciousness" is associated with the middle class. The second response to these questions is referred to as the **principle of covariation** and applies to interval/ratio level data. In this instance we notice a change in two types of *quantitative* data such as when annual income increases, family size decreases. Again, we say that an association, inverse in this case, exists between income and family size. With ordinal level data in which ranks are assigned to the observations we ordinarily discover a more rudimentary application of the covariation principle.

Aside from these verbal analogues let us review some general considerations for understanding the principle of the joint occurrence of attributes. To do this it will be instructive to review **contingency tables** and their structure. In Chapter 9, nominal level tests of significance, a preview of this more extensive exposition can be found. A contingency table is a cross-classification of variables containing rows and columns. It can take on many different *dimensions*, that is, it may have any number of rows (designated r) and columns (designated c), but we will focus on the simplest type, called a **2 × 2** or **fourfold table**. The "2 × 2" means it contains two rows and two columns and the "fourfold" means it is made up of four cells. Table 12.1 depicts, again, the arrangement of a 2 × 2 contingency table.

TABLE 12.1

Arrangement of a 2 × 2 Contingency Table

Variable Y (Stub)	Variable X (Heading)		Marginal Totals (Rows)
	Column 1	Column 2	
Row 1 Row 2	A (cell frequency) C (cell frequency)	B (cell frequency) D (cell frequency)	A + B C + D
Marginal totals (columns)	A + C	B + D	A + B + C + D Grand Total or N

Let us reiterate the generic features of Table 12.1.[3] It is a 2 × 2 table since

---

[3] Sometimes a system of double subscripts, i and j, are used to label the cell frequencies in a bivariate table. When this nomenclature is employed i identifies the row in which the cell is located and j the column in which it is located. In general, f_{ij} or n_{ij} would be the frequency (number of cases) in the ith row and jth column of the table. Using this system cells A, B, C, and D in Table 12.1 would be designated n_{11} (f_{11}), n_{12} (f_{12}), n_{21} (f_{21}), and n_{22} (f_{22}), respectively.

each variable (X and Y) has been dichotomized or has two subdivisions (two columns and two rows). It is customary to locate the independent variable (X) along the top and the dependent variable (Y) along the side. Technically the categories of the dependent variable are placed down the **stub** (side) and the independent variable categories across the **heading** (top). The letter designations of A, B, C, and D are called **cells** and the number of cases the cells contain are known as **cell frequencies.** At the bottom of each column and at the side of each row are marginal totals, **column marginal totals** and **row marginal totals,** respectively. Finally, the table contains a summation of all cell frequencies, $A + B + C + D$, and is labeled the **grand total.**

To demonstrate how we determine whether or not an association exists let us look at some actual data. In Table 12.2 males and females have been classified into high or low cognitive dissonance groups. To arrive at this classification scheme this writer modified an index that purportedly measured dissonance and then categorized male and female responses accordingly.

TABLE 12.2

Dissonance Group by Gender of Student

	Sex (Gender)					
	Male			Female		
Dissonance Group	f	%	$\lvert \epsilon \rvert$	f	%	
Low	39	61	20	39	41	78
High	25	39	20	56	59	81
	64	100		95	100	159

If we disregard the percentages in Table 12.2, we would have what is called a **bivariate frequency distribution** because the cell frequencies are shown. The cell frequencies indicate the number of cases that simultaneously fall into two categories. Each of the cell frequencies is called a **conditional frequency** or **joint frequency** (from which the principle of the joint occurrence of attributes gets its name). These cell frequencies represent the joint occurrence of a particular gender category and a particular dissonance category. Using sex as our independent variable we will examine the distribution of dissonance scores (collapsed into the two categories of low and high).

The row and column marginal totals are nothing more than the univariate totals for each variable. For example, the column marginal totals of 64 and 95 represent the total number of males and females, respectively, in our sample. The row marginal totals of 78 and 81 represent the number in the low and high dissonance groups, respectively. The grand total of 159 indicates the total number of persons in the sample.

Absolute frequencies are difficult to deal with because the number of male and female students is unequal. Since this often turns out to be the case, a more efficient way to assess the data is to convert the bivariate frequency distribution into a **bivariate percentage distribution**. In doing this we can more easily compare the percentage distribution of our dependent variable (dissonance group) within the categories of our independent variable (gender of student).

Percentaging Tables

Any contingency table can be percentaged in three ways, the three ways being determined by what marginal total is used as the percentage base. One way would be to use the grand total, in this case 159. Ordinarily we do not use the total number of cases since it does not permit us to compare conditional distributions. A second way would be to use the row totals, 78 and 81 in our example, and the third way would be to use the column totals, 64 and 95 in our illustration. The **basic rule**[4] for computing **percentages** in a contingency table is: *compute percentages using the independent variable totals as the base.*

Since our dependent variable is down the stub, the proper way to determine if there are differences between males and females is to use the column marginal totals as the base for percentaging. In other words, we want to compare and contrast the distribution of dissonance scores for men and women and the way to do this is to remove the effect of unequal n's by percentaging down (in the direction of the independent variable). Had we not followed the convention of locating the independent variable along the heading, that is, had we placed it along the stub, we would have used the row marginal totals as the percentage base.

After correctly percentaging the table in the direction of the independent variable we **compare across**. Comparisons are made in the *opposite* direction from that in which the percentages are computed. In general, *we percentage down and compare across* as Figure 12.1 shows.

The percentage difference between males and females in the low dissonance group is 20. The percentage difference between men and women in the high dissonance group is 20, too. Each of these values is technically called **epsilon** (symbolized by the lowercase Greek letter ϵ) and represents the percentage difference between the categories in the contingency table. In a fourfold table the (absolute value) epsilons will be identical so that determining one rather than two would be sufficient to answer the original inquiry.

With this discussion we can now directly answer the query: *How do we determine whether or not an association exists?* If, after percentaging the table correctly, there is *any* difference between the percentaged distributions, we have evidence that an association exists. In our example an association does exist by

---

[4]There may be occasions when the researcher may have to percentage in the direction of the "nonrepresentative" variable (see Loether and McTavish, 1993: 170).

virtue of the fact that a percentage difference of 20 is found. If all epsilons are zero, no association exists. On the other hand, if any epsilon is not zero, there is an association, although it may be extremely small and/or lack *statistical significance*.

FIGURE 12.1

Illustration of Directions in Percentaging and Comparing Conditional Distributions

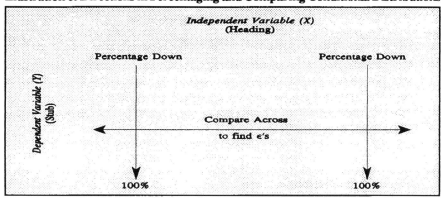

Another way of determining whether or not an association exists is to compare the **observed frequencies** (O_f) in a table with the **expected frequencies** (E_f), the latter generated assuming no association between the variables. This exposition, important in its own right, will also serve as a preview for the logic behind more specific techniques that measure association (delta or chi-square based measures) and a review of a popular test of statistical significance (chi-square) discussed in Chapter 9.

To establish a mathematical *model of no association* we start with the categorized data and then specify the pattern of cell frequencies in the body of the table that would be expected if there were no relationship between the variables. Returning to Table 12.2 the reasoning is this. If there were no association between sex and dissonance we would expect the same proportion of males and females to be in the low (and high) dissonance group. Since 64 of the total sample of 159 are men, the expectation would be that 64/159 × 78 men would be found in cell *A*. This figure comes to 31.4. For the females, since 95 of the total sample of 159 are women, the expectation would be that 95/159 × 78 would be found in cell *B*. This figure comes to 46.6. The same reasoning is applied to determining the expected distribution of males and females in the high dissonance group. For the males it would be 64/159 × 81 or 32.6; for the females it would be 95/159 × 81 or 48.4. This logic boils down to the following operation for generating the expected frequencies in any contingency table: *Multiply the marginal frequencies common to a given cell and divide by the grand total.* Employing this rule for our data the expected cell frequencies would be:

Cell	Expected Cell Frequencies (E_f)
A	$(78 \times 64)/159 = 31.4$
B	$(78 \times 95)/159 = 46.6$
C	$(81 \times 64)/159 = 32.6$
D	$(81 \times 95)/159 = 48.4$

In notation form,

$$E_f = \frac{\text{(row marginal total)(column marginal total)}}{\text{grand total}}$$

where: E_f = expected frequency (of any cell)

Having computed the expected cell frequencies under the assumption of no association, we systematically compare and contrast the observed (obtained) frequencies with the expected frequencies for each cell. We do this by subtracting the two values in order to obtain a difference known as **delta** (symbolized by the uppercase Greek letter Δ[5]). For any cell,

$$\Delta = O_f - E_f$$

where: Δ = difference between
O_f = observed frequency
E_f = expected frequency

The deltas for the data in Table 12.2 are:

Cell	O_f	E_f	Δ
A	39	31.4	7.6
B	39	46.6	−7.6
C	25	32.6	−7.6
D	56	48.4	7.6

With deltas, like epsilons, *any* nonzero difference is indicative of some association. Similarly, when all deltas are zero no association exists. Although epsilons and/or deltas greater than zero indicate some association, this fact does *not* mean, necessarily, that the association is statistically significant.

In summary, an association exists in a table if any epsilon and/or delta value is not zero. On the other hand, if either of these two computations produces all zero values, there is no association between the variables and a state of **statistical independence** has been achieved.

2. *How do we determine the strength or degree of association between variables?* Coefficients of association indicate the *degree* or *magnitude* to which two (or more) variables are associated with each other. They do *not*, prima facie, imply a causal connection between the variables. This statement, philosophically speaking,

---

[5]Sometimes the lowercase Greek letter delta δ is used.

is true even though the existence of a relationship is a *necessary*, not sufficient, condition for determining a cause-effect relationship. Some ridiculous examples may convince you that this is so. Each time the price of tomatoes increases, the rice crop in China increases as well. Each time you go to your 8:00 class, the weather is inclement. The point is that it is unlikely that a causal nexus exists between these variables. In statistical jargon these relationships are said to be **spurious** in nature.

From the above discussion you know that when all epsilons and/or deltas are not zero, *some* association exists. Intuitively you might surmise that the larger the epsilons and/or deltas, the stronger the degree of association. But here is where ϵ's and Δ's limitations come out. They are *crude* indicators of association because: (1) there are more than one epsilon and/or delta in a table, (2) they are influenced by marginal totals, (3) they don't permit us to describe the association in the entire table clearly, and (4) they lack standardization in the sense that ϵ and Δ can vary from zero to some indeterminate upper limit.

At this point we reach a very important junction in statistical analysis. Ideally, we would like to have a measure of association that circumvents the liabilities of epsilon and delta. In statistical vernacular, the need for **standardized** or **normed measures of association** becomes apparent. A standardized technique is one that has fixed limits so that its interpretation is not ambiguous. Often, but not always as we will see, the theoretical limits vary between -1.00 and $+1.00$. The former value (-1.00) represents a perfect negative association and the latter value $(+1.00)$ a perfect positive association. A value of .00 would indicate the complete absence of a linear relationship.

Statisticians have developed measures of association that avoid some of the problems intrinsic to epsilon and delta. Before turning to some of these (partial) remedies for nominal level data, let us answer two more questions about a relationship.

3. *How do we determine the direction of an association?* The *direction* of an association is expressed as either **positive** or **negative** and is determined by the *sign* of the coefficient. Before defining and illustrating each of these it is necessary to point out that *direction is only applicable to at least ordinally defined variables*. For nominal level variables the sign of the coefficient does *not* make sense and the researcher is obliged to study the data in the table to infer what the sign means. Furthermore, many nominal level measures of association only take on values from .00 to $+1.0$ (or some defined or restricted upper limit).

The values of coefficients of correlation are generally normed to vary between $+1.00$ and -1.00. However, there are some measures of association, for example, C (contingency coefficient) and ϕ (phi), whose upper limits are restricted so that it's impossible to obtain a perfect relationship. In addition, there are some measures that can only be positive. These considerations will be made explicit in later sections. Both of these extremes ($+1.00$ and -1.00) represent perfect relationships, perfect positive and perfect negative, respectively, but are very, very rare. A coefficient of .00, likewise very uncommon, represents the absence of a linear relationship. If a *nonlinear* relationship is found, the unbiased *correlation ratio*, *eta*, is an appropriate measure of association. Nonlinear relationships preclude the use of association coefficients in this text. In virtually all cases, the correlation value will be somewhere between ±1.00.

What is a *positive*, sometimes referred to as a *direct*, relationship? There are two ways of viewing this. First of all, if individuals who obtain high grade point averages in high school are also highly successful in college, we say there's a positive relationship between the two variables. Secondly, the converse is also true, that is, if individuals who obtain low grade point averages in high school are not successful in higher education. In other words, if high scores on one variable occur along with high scores on another variable and if low scores on one variable are associated with low scores on another variable, we have evidence of a positive association.

What is a *negative*, sometimes called an *indirect* or *inverse*, relationship? When an individual scores high on one variable, for example, high school grades, and low on another, for example, college grades, or low in high school and high in college, we have an illustration of a negative relationship. Empirical studies have frequently confirmed an inverse relationship between socioeconomic status and authoritarianism. This means that high social class positions are related to low authoritarianism scores and low social class positions are associated with high scores on authoritarianism.

The absence of a relationship, indicated by a zero (or near zero) coefficient of association, means that no statistical relationship between (or among) the variables can be established.

4. *How do we determine the **nature or pattern of an association**?* With nominal and ordinal level data we may gain insight into the pattern of the data by examining the cell percentages and how they are concentrated in the table. To discover a pattern to contingency table data it is recommended that at least three categories of the variable be maintained. With only two categories it is not possible to determine the nature of an association. With interval/ratio level data the construction of a scattergram permits an approximate determination of whether the nature of the relationship is linear or nonlinear.

Having discussed the four characteristics of an association that concern statisticians, let us return to an extension of what can be done to overcome the limitations of epsilon and delta for nominally defined variables.

There are two generic breeds of nominal measures of association. They are (1) *delta or chi-square based measures* and (2) *proportional reduction in error techniques*. These two types are *not* mutually exclusive. The difference resides basically in their interpretation. We will examine five delta based techniques: (1) the contingency coefficient (C), (2) Yule's Q, (3) phi coefficient, (4) Tschruprow's T, and (5) Cramér's V. As we will see, C, ϕ, T, and V have identical numerators and make only a minor change in the denominator. The alteration in these denominators is but an attempt to refine and standardize the meaning of the statistic.

DELTA (CHI-SQUARE) BASED MEASURES OF ASSOCIATION

Contingency Coefficient (C)

The **contingency coefficient** (C), being delta based, deals with the difference between observed and expected frequencies. Earlier it was noted that the larger the Δ's, the stronger the association. In order to compute a single index number for an *entire table*, rather than a single cell, it seems logical to sum all delta values. But several problems arise. If this were done, that is, $\Sigma\Delta = \Sigma(O_f - E_f)$, the algebraic summation would always equal zero since positive and negative differences would always balance each other out. To see this, refer to the discussion in which Δ's for cells A, B, C, and D in Table 12.2 were +7.6, −7.6, −7.6, and +7.6, respectively. One way of skirting this problem of the sum equaling zero is to square the differences (as we did with the standard deviation), and divide this squared difference by the respective expected cell frequencies to handle the differential number of cases in the row and column totals. Dividing the squared difference by the expected frequency (for each cell) results in a *margin-free* statistic, that is, different marginal totals are adjusted and taken into account. The end result of these operations is the *chi-square* statistic,[6] expressed in formula (12.1):

$$\chi^2 = \Sigma \frac{(O_f - E_f)^2}{E_f} \tag{12.1}$$

where: χ^2 = chi-square statistic
O_f = observed frequency
E_f = expected frequency

Several nominal measures of association, all of which are delta based, use the computed χ^2 value in the formula. For example:

$$C = \sqrt{\frac{\chi^2}{\chi^2 + n}} \tag{12.2}$$

where: C = contingency coefficient
n = total number of cases

$$T = \sqrt{\frac{\chi^2}{n(df)}} \tag{12.3}$$

[6] Chi-square is *not* a measure of association even though it is used in the calculation of several measures of association. The reason this is so stems from the fact that its upper limit is restricted by the structure of the contingency table. More specifically, the upper limit of chi-square can be obtained using the formula: $n(k - 1)$ where n = size of the sample and k = the number of rows or columns in a table, whichever is smaller. In Table 12.2 the maximum value of chi-square would be 159 (that is, 159(2 − 1) = 159). Chi-square is used in inferential statistics (refer to Chapter 9) as a *test of significance*. To repeat, it is *not* a coefficient of association.

where: T = Tschruprow's T
$\qquad$ n = total number of cases
$\qquad$ df = degrees of freedom where $df = (r - 1)(c - 1)$

$$V = \sqrt{\frac{\chi^2}{nt}}$$

(12.4)

where: V = Cramér's V
$\qquad$ n = total number of cases
$\qquad$ t = smaller of the two quantities, $(r - 1)(c - 1)$

$$\phi = \sqrt{\frac{\chi^2}{n}}$$

(12.5)

where: ϕ = phi
$\qquad$ χ^2 = chi-square statistic
$\qquad$ n = total number of cases

Let us compute C, T, V, and ϕ for the data in Table 12.2:

Cell	O_f	E_f	$(O_f - E_f)^2$	$(O_f - E_f)^2 / E_f$
A	39	31.4	$(7.6)^2 = 57.76$	1.84
B	39	46.4	$(-7.6)^2 = 57.76$	1.24
C	25	32.6	$(-7.6)^2 = 57.76$	1.77
D	56	48.4	$(7.6)^2 = 57.76$	1.19
				$\Sigma = \chi^2 = 6.04$

Substituting into formula (12.2):

$$C = \sqrt{\frac{6.04}{6.04 + 159}}$$

$$= .1913$$

Substituting into formula (12.3):

$$T = \sqrt{\frac{6.04}{159(1)}} \qquad \begin{aligned} df &= (r - 1)(c - 1) \\ &= (2 - 1)(2 - 1) \\ &= 1 \end{aligned}$$

$$= .1949$$

Substituting into formula (12.4):

$$V = \sqrt{\frac{6.04}{159(1)}} \qquad \begin{aligned} t &= \text{smaller of two quantities, } (r - 1) \text{ or } (c - 1) \\ &= (2 - 1) \text{ or } (2 - 1) \\ &= 1 \end{aligned}$$

$$= .1949$$

Substituting into formula (12.5):

$$\phi = \sqrt{\frac{6.04}{159}}$$

$$= .1949$$

Some General Comments on C, T, V, and φ

Comparing and contrasting the four delta based nominal measures of association illustrates, in an informative fashion, the pursuit of refined or standardized statistics of association. Examining C's formula (12.2), notice that χ^2 appears in both the numerator and denominator. Practically speaking, this means that C can never reach 1.0 regardless of a table's dimensions. Further on we will see that the maximum value C can attain is a function of the number of rows and columns.

Tschuprow's T (see formula [12.3]) alters the denominator so that the number of cells, not χ^2, is taken into account. What this means is that the upper limit can be 1.0 but this can only occur in square ($r = c$) tables, for example, 2×2, 3×3, 4×4, and so forth.

Cramér's V (formula [12.4]) solves the problem with T by introducing a different quantity, t, in the denominator. This added dimension is defined as the smaller of the two quantities $(r - 1)$ or $(c - 1)$. It can attain 1.0 even in $r \neq c$ tables.

Lastly, ϕ (see formula [12.5]) has an upper limit of 1.0 but this can only occur in 2×2 tables. In other words, its value can exceed 1.0 in tables larger than 2×2.

In general, C, T, V, and ϕ have .00 as their lower limit when there is no association between the variables and different upper limits. Of these four nominal measures, Cramér's V is generally the best to use, particularly for tables that have more than two categories for each variable. The reason this is true is that it does not have the restrictions and limitations of C, T, and ϕ. A discussion of Yule's Q has been deferred for two reasons: (1) it has a proportional reduction in error interpretation whereas C, T, and V do not; and (2) it is restricted to 2×2 contingency tables whereas C, T, and V are not.

PROPORTIONAL REDUCTION IN ERROR (*PRE*) MEASURES OF ASSOCIATION

Let us say that a hypothetical Gallup poll reports that 75 percent of respondents sampled favored the Republican candidate over the Democratic candidate for President. Obviously, 25 percent of the respondents preferred the unnamed Democratic aspirant. If you were asked to guess a respondent's preference, you would make fewer errors in the long run by guessing the modal response or, in this case, the Republican candidate. Now let us say that we know the relationship between respondents' presidential choices and their political affiliation. If 90 percent of Republicans favored the Republican candidate and 40 percent of Democrats did and prior to your guess you were told the person's political affiliation, you would modify your guess in light of this added information. In other words, by having additional knowledge we can reduce our prediction error by using the known empirical relationship between our variables.

The *logic* underlying all *PRE* measures is the same but the particular computational procedure varies from one level of measurement to another. The common denominators of proportional reduction in error measures are these:

(1) predicting the outcome of a dependent variable based on knowledge of that variable's marginal totals only;

(2) predicting the outcome of a dependent variable by knowing the empirical relationship between it and the independent variable (or another variable):

(3) defining and measuring error; and

(4) a measure of association that takes this form:

$$PRE \text{ association measure} = \frac{\text{error by (1)} - \text{error by (2)}}{\text{error by (1)}}$$

Shortly we will demonstrate the computation of Yule's Q and lambda, two nominal measures of association with a *PRE* interpretation.

The above discussion provides a background for understanding the logic of delta based and proportional reduction in error nominal measures of association. There are several very important additional features of these statistics that must be discussed. In the following pages we will highlight the interpretation, limitations and assets, and the testing for significance of these association coefficients. To do this a research problem will be presented along with the procedure by which an investigator would systematically tackle the problem. Figure 12.2 will be helpful in organizing your thinking about the nominal level measures of association reported in this chapter.

FIGURE 12.2

Nominal Level Measures of Association*

Symmetric		Asymmetric	
Non-PRE	PRE	Non-PRE	PRE
C, T, V	Q, ϕ, λ_n	ϵ	λ

*A distinction between *symmetric* and *asymmetric* measures of association will be made explicit in the discussion of lambda toward the end of the chapter.

NOMINAL MEASURES OF ASSOCIATION

Six nominal measures will be discussed: (1) C (the contingency coefficient), (2) T, (3) V, (4) ϕ (the phi coefficient), (5) Yule's Q, and (6) lambda.

Contingency Coefficient (C)

The **coefficient of contingency**, sometimes called *Pearson's contingency coefficient* and symbolized C, is a measure of association appropriate to use with attribute data. Its relationship to chi-square has been illustrated and can be seen in formula (12.2).

To illustrate the computation of C consider Table 12.3 taken from M. F. Nimkoff's book entitled *Comparative Family Systems* (1965). In this book a series of tables is presented to show the cause-effect relationships between the family and other societal subsystems. This writer critiqued this presentation on the grounds that no measure of association was included. In any event, the computed chi-square value was 55.97 and with 9 df it was statistically significant at the .001 level. To determine the *degree* of association between the variables in Table 12.3 this writer made the appropriate substitutions into formula (12.2):

TABLE 12.3*

Dominant Subsistence Patterns and Principal Descent Systems

Subsistence Patterns	Patrilineal Descent		Matrilineal Descent		Bilateral Descent		Double Descent	
	N	%	N	%	N	%	N	%
Agriculture	164	46.7	56	15.9	117	33.3	14	04.1
Hunting-gathering	14	18.9	7	09.4	47	63.5	6	09.2
Animal husbandry	32	71.1	2	04.4	9	20.1	2	04.4
Fishing	7	17.5	8	20.0	23	57.5	2	05.0

Chi-square = 55.97, df = 9, $p < .001$

*From Nimkoff (1965: 41). Reprinted by permission of the publisher. Notice that the percentages are computed using the row totals and that the values in the fourth column are "off" due to rounding errors. Also, $p < .001$ not $p > .001$.

$$C = \sqrt{\frac{55.97}{55.97 + 510}}$$

$$= .314$$

Because of the affinities between the delta based measures, the values of T (formula [12.3]), V (formula [12.4]), and ϕ (formula [12.5]) are also presented for comparative purposes. Notice that these four nominal measures of association produce different values. Interestingly, in 2 $\times$ 2 tables it is often the case that the values of these coefficients are the same. For example, the fourfold table (Table 12.2) yielded virtually identical numerical values. Hence, for 2 $\times$ 2 tables, $T = V = \phi = r$. Pearson's r is an interval/ratio based association measure that will be discussed in the next chapter.

$$T = \sqrt{\frac{55.97}{510(9)}} = .110$$

$$V = \sqrt{\frac{55.97}{510(3)}} = .191$$

$$\phi = \sqrt{\frac{55.97}{510}} = .331$$

Interpretation of the Contingency Coefficient. What does a C of .314 mean? Interpreting the contingency coefficient is not easy. C is simply an *index number*. The major problem in interpreting C surrounds the restrictions on its upper limit. That is, unlike some other measures of association, the maximum C is always less than 1.00 and, furthermore, it can only take on positive values as an examination of the equation makes obvious. In symmetrical tables, that is, tables with an even number of rows and columns, C_{max} (the largest possible value C can attain) is determined by formula (12.6):

$$C_{max} = \sqrt{\frac{r-1}{r}} \qquad\qquad (12.6)$$

where: r = the number of rows

For Table 12.3 C_{max} would be $\sqrt{3/4}$ = .866. In other words, the correction factor enables the investigator to make a more systematic appraisal of the strength of the relationship between the variables in question. To do this formula (12.7) may be employed:

$$\bar{C} = \frac{C}{C_{max}} \qquad\qquad (12.7)$$

where: $\bar{C}$ = corrected contingency coefficient

C = computed contingency coefficient
C_{max} = maximum value C can attain with a given data-set

If we substitute our values into formula (12.7):

$$\bar{C} = \frac{.314}{.866}$$

$$= .362$$

Applying this correction gives the reader a more realistic picture of the correlation since 1.00 is *not* its upper limit.

Table 12.4 presents the correction factors (C_{max}) for both symmetrical ($r = c$) and asymmetrical ($r \neq c$) tables up to and including a 10 × 10 table to be used with the contingency coefficient. When tables are larger than 10 × 10 the correction factor turns out to be negligible and generally unnecessary. These values will be the divisors in the $\bar{C}$ formula (12.7).

TABLE 12.4

Correction Factors for Coefficient of Contingency

Table Size	(Divisor) Correction	Table Size	(Divisor) Correction	Table Size	(Divisor) Correction
2 × 2	.707	3 × 9	.843	6 × 6	.913
2 × 3	.685	3 × 10	.846	6 × 7	.930
2 × 4	.730	4 × 4	.866	6 × 8	.936
2 × 5	.752	4 × 5	.863	6 × 9	.941
2 × 6	.765	4 × 6	.877	6 × 10	.945
2 × 7	.774	4 × 7	.888	7 × 7	.926
2 × 8	.779	4 × 8	.893	7 × 8	.947
2 × 9	.783	4 × 9	.898	7 × 9	.952
2 × 10	.786	4 × 10	.901	7 × 10	.955
3 × 3	.816	5 × 5	.894	8 × 8	.935
3 × 4	.786	5 × 6	.904	8 × 9	.957
3 × 5	.810	5 × 7	.915	8 × 10	.961
3 × 6	.824	5 × 8	.920	9 × 9	.943
3 × 7	.833	5 × 9	.925	9 × 10	.966
3 × 8	.838	5 × 10	.929	10 × 10	.949

Testing C for Significance

After computing a measure of association one should adopt the practice of testing it for significance. As with any test of significance, we are interested in generalizing from our sample to some larger population from which our sample was selected. We test the null hypothesis that the computed association $= 0$ against the alternative that the *absolute* value of the computed association > 0. Ordinarily, tests of significance for association coefficients are *directional* (one-tailed) since we already have obtained a specific value that we wish to test for statistical significance.

To test C for significance, simply determine if the calculated chi-square value is significant with the appropriate degrees of freedom. The significance level for a given contingency coefficient (C) is taken to be the same as that associated with the chi-square from which it is calculated. In our example, χ^2 is significant at the .001 level. Consequently, C is too. This means that, for our data, only 1 time in 1,000 could chance factors have produced our C of .314 or our $\overline{C}$ of .362. In effect we are testing:

$$H_0 : C = 0$$
$$H_1 : C > 0$$

If we reject H_0 we can retain the alternative hypothesis at the selected level of significance. Since our C is significant we are assured that in the larger population from which the sample was selected $C > 0$ at the .001 level.

Observations on C. As we indicated above, the coefficient of contingency is used in conjunction with chi-square. It is important to remember that $C = 0$ when there is no association between the variables, but it *cannot* attain unity (1.00) due to the restrictions on its upper limit. The upper limit in symmetrical tables is a function of the number of categories, for example, $\sqrt{r - 1/r} = C_{max}$, and consequently, will vary according to the dimensions of the particular contingency table. Consider the following illustrations of C_{max}. In a 2 X 2 table $C_{max} = \sqrt{(2-1)/2} = .707$; in a 3 X 3 table $C_{max} = \sqrt{(3-1)/3} = .816$; in a 4 X 4 table $C_{max} = \sqrt{(4-1)/4} = .866$; and in a 5 X 5 table $C_{max} = \sqrt{(5-1)/5} = .894$. Note that as the number of rows increases so, too, does the maximum value C can attain.

Unfortunately, C is not directly comparable to other measures of association such as the Pearsonian product-moment correlation coefficient, Spearman's rho, or Kendall's tau. Even with the correction factor applied, C's from different data-sets cannot, necessarily, be compared. This is why it's referred to as an *index number*. Ideally C's should only be compared, and then cautiously, when they are computed from identical tables in terms of (1) the degrees of freedom (*df*), (2) sample size (*n*), and (3) identical marginal frequencies.

C has no sign, that is, it will always be positive as the computational formula (12.2) denotes. But an inspection of the tabled data will enable one to intuitively grasp the "*direction*" of the relationship between the variables.

Despite these disadvantages, with nominal level data the alternatives are few in number. Furthermore, given the popularity of chi-square as a test of significance, C is a logical and practical measure of relationship to employ.

Yule's Q

Q is defined as *the ratio of the differences between the products of the diagonal cell frequencies to the sum of the products of the diagonal cell frequencies*. This verbal expression can be visualized in formula (12.8):

$$Q = \frac{AD - BC}{AD + BC} \tag{12.8}$$

where: Q = Yule's Q
       A, B, C, D = cell frequencies

Let's assume that we are interested in the relationship between attitudes toward abortion, dichotomized into pro and anti, and gender, dichotomized, of course, into male and female, and the contingency Table 12.5 is produced.

TABLE 12.5

Illustration of Computation of Yule's Q from a Contingency Table

Attitudes toward Abortion	Gender		
	Male	Female	
Pro	20 (A)	40 (B)	60
Anti	30 (C)	10 (D)	40
	50	50	100

Substituting the values of Table 12.5 into formula (12.8) we have:

$$Q = \frac{(20)(10) - (40)(30)}{(20)(10) + (40)(30)}$$

$$= \frac{200 - 1,200}{200 + 1,200}$$

$$= \frac{-1,000}{1,400}$$

$$= -.71$$

Interpretation of Yule's Q. A Q of $-.71$ indicates a relatively high association between gender and attitudes. Remember that *the sign of a nominal measure of association has no meaning.* Examining the table's layout reveals that males tend to be more opposed ("anti") whereas females tend to be more favorable ("pro").

Yule's Q also has a proportional reduction in error interpretation. To employ it, we take the *absolute* value of Q, in this case .71, and say that the independent variable, in this case gender, explains or accounts for so much of the variation in the dependent variable, in this case attitudes. In our example, approximately 71 percent of the variation in attitudes is attributed to or accounted for by sex. Or, saying it a different way, 71 percent of the error in predicting attitudes has been reduced by knowing a person's gender.

Testing Q for Significance. Since Q is a special case of gamma, we will make use of the procedure developed by Goodman and Kruskal for testing the significance of gamma. This technique is a normal approximation of gamma's sampling distribution and permits a test of the null hypothesis, H_0: $\Gamma = 0$. Formula (12.9) is employed for converting gamma to a z score.

$$z = (\gamma - \Gamma) \sqrt{\frac{N_s + N_d}{N(1 - \gamma^2)}} \qquad (12.9)$$

where: $\gamma = Q$ statistic (gamma)
$N_s = AD$, where A, B, C, D = cell frequencies
$N_d = BC$, where A, B, C, D = cell frequencies

Let us substitute our data into formula (12.9):

$$z = (-.71 - 0) \sqrt{\frac{200 + 1,200}{100(1 - .5041)}}$$

$$= (-.71) \sqrt{\frac{1,400}{100(.4959)}}$$

$$= (-.71) \sqrt{\frac{1,400}{49.59}}$$

$$= -3.77$$

Suppose we had set alpha equal to .01. The critical value of z is -2.33.[7] Again recall that a test of significance for a correlation coefficient is virtually always one-tailed since we know the statistic's value *before* applying the significance test. Since our computed z value (in absolute terms) exceeds the critical value we conclude that the population from which our sample was selected actually has an association significantly greater than zero.

---

[7]If you have forgotten how to find critical z values at different levels of significance review that discussion in Chapter 8.

Observations on Yule's Q. Q is used exclusively with 2 X 2 tables, that is, each variable must be expressed in a dichotomous fashion. This should be clear from the definition of Q as well as from the computational formula (12.8).

The advantages of Q over C are that it can be directly computed from a table without the necessity for an intermediate calculation (e.g., chi-square), no correction factor need be applied to its interpretation, and it has a proportional reduction in error interpretation not available when using the contingency coefficient. The fact that it has a PRE interpretation links it to the Pearsonian r and contributes to uniformity in the interpretation of association coefficients.

The disadvantage of Q resides in its limitation to 2 X 2 tables. However, with larger tables gamma, a statistic to be discussed later, may be used with ordinal data. Yule's Q is a special case of gamma and it can be demonstrated that Q is gamma for fourfold tables. The continued use of the two terms, Yule's Q and gamma, when one would suffice is traditional.

Phi Coefficient (ϕ)

The **phi coefficient** sometimes called the *fourfold coefficient*, *mean square contingency*, or *fourfold point coefficient* is a nominal level alternative to C and Q. It is like C and Q in a number of respects. Formula (12.10) for ϕ is expressed as follows:

$$\phi = \frac{AD - BC}{\sqrt{(A + B)(C + D)(A + C)(B + D)}} \qquad (12.10)$$

where: ϕ = phi coefficient
        A, B, C, D = cell frequencies

Let's say we were interested in the relationship between year in school, dichotomized into upper and under-classpersons, and satisfaction with a class, dichotomized into much and little. The hypothetical data for analysis appear in contingency Table 12.6:

TABLE 12.6

Illustration of Computation of Phi from a Contingency Table

Satisfaction	Year in School		
	Underclasspersons	*Upperclasspersons*	
Much	10 (A)	30 (B)	40 (row 1)
Little	35 (C)	20 (D)	55 (row 2)
	45 (column 1)	50 (column 2)	95 (n)

Substituting our values from Table 12.6 into formula (12.10):

$$\phi = \frac{(10)\,(20) - (30)\,(35)}{\sqrt{(10 + 30)\,(35 + 20)\,(10 + 35)\,(30 + 20)}}$$

$$= \frac{200 - 1{,}050}{\sqrt{(40)\,(55)\,(45)\,(50)}}$$

$$= \frac{-850}{2{,}224.86}$$

$$= -.38$$

Interpretation of Phi. Phi, like Pearson's *C*, has a restriction on its upper limit. The maximum value phi can obtain is called *phi maximum* (ϕ_{max}) and varies according to the following dimensions. The marginal totals, both row and column, must be converted to proportions of the total number of observations. For Table 12.6 this operation is accomplished as follows:

$$\text{row 1 total} = 40; \frac{40}{95} = .42$$

$$\text{row 2 total} = 55; \frac{55}{95} = .58$$

$$\text{column 1 total} = 45; \frac{45}{95} = .47$$

$$\text{column 2 total} = 50; \frac{50}{95} = .53$$

These calculations result in four proportions, two for the columns and two for the rows. The *larger* proportion for rows and columns is designated *p* and the smaller proportion is designated *q*. In our case, $p_{row} = .58$, $q_{row} = .42$, $p_{column} = .53$, and $q_{column} = .47$.

Phi maximum is then calculated using formula (12.11):

$$\phi_{max} = \sqrt{\left(\frac{q_{row}}{p_{row}}\right)\left(\frac{p_{column}}{q_{column}}\right)} \qquad (12.11)$$

Substituting our values into formula (12.11):

$$\phi_{max} = \sqrt{\left(\frac{.42}{.58}\right)\left(\frac{.53}{.47}\right)}$$

$$= .90$$

ϕ_{max} for Table 12.6 is .90. Like C_{max}, our computed ϕ value is interpreted in relation to its maximum which, of course, is not 1.00.

What does a phi coefficient of $-.38$ mean? One way of interpreting phi is in terms of the proportional reduction in error notion. In other words, if we *square* phi, that is, $\phi^2 = .38^2 = .14$, we can say that so much of the error, in this case a meager 14 percent, has been accounted for. Substantively speaking, in using year in school as the independent variable we have accounted for 14 percent of the error in predicting class satisfaction.

Testing Phi for Significance. There are two options available in testing the significance of phi. Since phi is a member of the chi-square family, the significance level of . . . ϕ is most easily determined by inference from the significance level of the associated chi square. To employ this option for our problem, the chi-square value would have to be computed since we don't have it. Like C, if chi square is significant at a certain level so, too, is phi.

A second way of determining phi's significance is expressed in formula (12.12):

$$\chi^2 = n\phi^2 \qquad\qquad (12.12)$$

where: χ^2 = chi-square
$\quad\quad\quad n$ = number of observations
$\quad\quad\quad \phi^2$ = phi squared

Since we haven't computed chi-square for our table, we will use the second approach because it involves substituting values we've already obtained. Hence, substituting into formula (12.12):

$$\chi^2 = 95(.14)$$
$$= 13.30$$

Next, we consult the chi-square sampling distribution (Table C in Appendix A) and with the *df* clearly in mind, determine at what level a $\chi^2 = 13.30$ is significant. In our example we have one degree of freedom. For χ^2 to be significant at the .001 level a value of 10.827 or larger is required. Since $13.30 > 10.827$ we can conclude that phi (as well as chi-square) is statistically significant at the .001 level.

An Alternative Method for Computing Phi. Since phi is a close relative of the chi-square test statistic, we can easily obtain ϕ if (and when) chi-square has already been obtained by utilizing formula (12.5). If we wanted to know phi in our previous example (Table 12.3), we would merely substitute the appropriate values into formula (12.5). Hence:

$$\phi = \sqrt{\frac{55.97}{510}}$$
$$= .331$$

Observations on Phi. Phi, like Q, is geared to be used with naturally dichotomous variables. This means that it is only appropriate when data can be construed in a 2 X 2 table. If one is dealing with a situation that deals with larger dimensions, and if the data can be legitimately collapsed, phi may be calculated.

One nice feature of phi is its susceptibility to a proportional reduction in error interpretation which relates it to the Pearsonian r. However, the coefficient must be *squared*, that is, ϕ^2, instead of using the absolute coefficient as was done in the case of Q. With tables larger than 2 X 2 the statistic lambda is appropriate.

Lambda (λ)

One of the more recently developed nominal measures of association is *Guttman's coefficient of predictability* or simply **lambda** (symbolized λ). This coefficient measures the degree to which one variable may be predicted from a knowledge of another. Whereas all the preceeding nominal association coefficients were of the symmetrical type, lambda has both a **symmetric** (nondirectional) and an **asymmetric** (directional) computational equation.

What is the difference between a symmetric and asymmetric statistic? A symmetric statistic provides an index of *mutual association* or *mutual predictability* between the variables under examination. In other words, no distinction is made between the presumed independent and dependent variables. When an asymmetric statistic is employed, the researcher conceptualizes the variables in cause-effect terms, that is, in terms of independent and dependent variables, and consequently, different values are rendered depending upon how the variables are viewed. An example will make this clear.

In social psychology attitudes are often considered to have three dimensions: (1) an affective, (2) a cognitive, and (3) a behavioral component. In a paper by this writer, the concern was with whether what a person believes (technically, one's cognitions) is a better predictor of how one feels (technically, one's affect) about an attitude object than vice versa. In short, interest focused upon the relationship between cognition (independent variable) and affect (dependent variable) and affect (independent variable) and cognition (dependent variable). To determine which arrangement of the variables was the better predictor, Guttman's coefficient of predictability was employed. The lambda computational formula (12.13) is this:

$$\lambda = \frac{\Sigma f_i - F_d}{n - F_d} \tag{12.13}$$

where: λ = lambda (Guttman's coefficient of predictability)

Σf_i = the sum of the largest frequencies occurring within *each* subclass of the independent variable

F_d = the (single) largest frequency found within the dependent variable totals

n = total number of observations

Table 12.7 will be used for computing lambda.

TABLE 12.7

The Relationship between the President's Policy of Military versus Domestic Spending and Feelings about the President: Illustrating the Computation of λ (Lambda)

| Affect: Sentiments toward President | Cognition: Belief that the President Favors | | | | Total n |
| | Military Spending | | Domestic Spending | | |
	n	%	n	%	
Like	81	31.3	113	75.8	194
Dislike	178	68.7	36	24.2	214
	n = 259	100	n = 149	100	408

To compute lambda the following steps are recommended:

1. Determine the largest frequencies within *each* subclass of the independent variable, and sum them. In Table 12.7 the largest frequencies are 178 and 113, and 178 + 113 = 291.

2. Determine the single largest frequency within the dependent variable marginal *totals*. In Table 12.7 it is 214.

3. Determine *n*. In Table 12.7 $n = 408$.

4. Now substitute these values into the lambda formula (12.13):

$$\lambda = \frac{291 - 214}{408 - 214}$$

$$= \frac{77}{194}$$

$$= .397$$

Interpretation of Lambda. As an asymmetrical proportional reduction in error nominal measure of association, lambda indicates the reduction of prediction error as one shifts from one independent variable to another. The nice feature of λ is that it may vary from .00 to +1.00 regardless of the table's dimensions or the marginal totals. Negative values are impossible. A value of zero indicates no reduction in prediction error while a value of unity indicates that 100 percent of the error in prediction is reduced, that is, the dependent variable could be predicted from knowledge of the independent variable without any error whatsoever. Values inbetween 0 and 1.0 indicate the extent to which prediction errors can be reduced by altering the independent-dependent variable arrangement.

What does a lambda = .397 mean? Since it has an *absolute* proportional reduction in error interpretation we can say that by knowing what a person believes (cognition), 40 percent (.397) of the error in predicting affect (liking or disliking the attitude object) is eliminated.

Now let us turn the causal order of the variables around. In other words, let's use affect as the independent variable and cognition as the dependent one. Table 12.7 contains this arrangement of the independent and dependent variables, too. While the same table can be used it is very important to keep clear the presumed causal connection since the appropriate quantities will vary in accordance with which is the dependent and which is the independent variable.

All we need to do is calculate the quantities the four steps above call for: the largest frequency within each subclass of the independent variable is 113 and 178 = 291. F_d = 259. n, once again, is 408. Now substitute into formula (12.13):

$$\lambda = \frac{291 - 259}{408 - 259}$$

$$= \frac{32}{149}$$

$$= .215$$

A lambda of .215 indicates that 22 percent (.215) of the error in predicting cognition is eliminated by knowing how the person feels. In short, by altering the cause-effect connection we discover that cognition is a better predictor of affect (since 40 percent of the error was reduced) than affect is of cognition (since 22 percent of the error was reduced).

Because of the asymmetric nature of lambda some statisticians prefer to use subscripts such as λ_r, λ_c, λ_{yx}, or λ_{xy}. When the row variable is the dependent or predicted one, λ_r or λ_{yx} is used; when the column variable is the dependent one the symbolic notation of λ_c or λ_{xy} is employed.

The Symmetrical Lambda. The nondirectional or symmetric lambda formula (12.14) is:

$$\lambda_s = \frac{\Sigma f_r + \Sigma f_c - (F_r + F_c)}{2n - (F_r + F_c)} \qquad (12.14)$$

where: λ_s = nondirectional (symmetrical) lambda
Σf_r = sum of largest row frequencies
Σf_c = sum of largest column frequencies
F_r = the largest row marginal frequency
F_c = the largest column marginal frequency
n = total number of observations

Substituting the data in Table 12.7 into formula (12.14):

$$\lambda_s = \frac{113 + 178) + (178 + 113) - (214 + 259)}{2(408) - (214 + 259)}$$

$$= \frac{(291 + 291) - 473}{816 - 473}$$

$$= \frac{109}{343}$$

$$= .32$$

With a $\lambda_s = .32$ we have an index of the mutual predictability between attitudinal cognition and affect.

Testing Lambda for Significance.   At present it does not appear that a specific test of lambda's significance is available. One statistician has suggested that chi-square may be cautiously employed as a significance test for this measure of association. According to this rationale, if chi-square is statistically significant, so, too, is lambda.

Observations on Lambda. Guttman's coefficient of predictability (λ) is a very useful statistic since it enables the researcher to garner some insight into the cause-effect relationship between the variables being examined. Although there exists a · symmetrical formula, we've concentrated here on the asymmetrical one. It is valuable, too, since it may be used on tables of any size whereas some of the other measures of association, for example, phi and Yule's Q, are confined to 2×2 tables. Finally, it has an *absolute* proportional reduction in error interpretation which makes it somewhat comparable to Q, phi, and the product-moment correlation coefficient. Furthermore, it requires no correction factors as was necessary in the cases of C and ϕ.

Despite these assets of lambda, it does have one major liability. There are occasions when the lambda formula "breaks down," that is, it will yield a coefficient of .00 when, in fact, there *may* be a relationship between the variables. This occurs when the frequency maxima are all in the same column/row. The lambda coefficient is explicitly designed to yield a value of 1.00 in the following instance:

f_{11}	0	0
0	f_{22}	0
0	0	f_{33}

When all the maximum frequencies are in the diagonal cells, for example, f_{11}, f_{22}, f_{33}, lambda will equal 1.00. On the other hand, lambda will equal .00 when the maximum frequencies are in one row or column as the illustration demonstrates.

$$
\begin{array}{ccc}
0 & 0 & 0 \\
f_{21} & f_{22} & f_{23} \\
0 & 0 & 0
\end{array}
$$

In this case, lambda will equal zero. The important feature is that while the asymmetrical lambda formula can "break down" and it appears that the association is zero, this *may not* be the case at all.

For the data in Table 12.3 this writer computed lambda to be zero when subsistence patterns was used as the dependent variable and descent systems as the independent variable. When the four steps for computing lambda were completed the following frequency arrangement was uncovered using formula (12.13):

$$
\lambda_s = \frac{(164 + 56 + 117 + 14) - (164 + 56 + 117 + 14)}{510 - (164 + 56 + 117 + 14)}
$$

$$
= 0
$$

Since the numerator is zero, and any number divided into zero is zero, the lambda coefficient equaled zero.

SUMMARY

In this chapter we began with a brief discussion of the concept of relationship and several illustrations of the type of research problem with which measures of association are equipped to deal. Then we moved into a discussion of the different types of correlation coefficients and some of their common characteristics.

An exposition of some very popular nominal level measures of association and their underlying rationale was presented. This led us into a discussion of the two breeds of nominal measures of association: (1) the delta or chi-square based statistics, and (2) the proportional reduction in error (*PRE*) interpretation. Another useful distinction pointed out was between symmetric and asymmetric association coefficients.

Figure 12.2 provides a model for organizing your thinking about the specific coefficients treated in this chapter. In Chapter 13 we will extend the measures of association to ordinal and interval/ratio level variables.

IMPORTANT CONCEPTS DISCUSSED IN THIS CHAPTER

Measures of association, relationship, covariation (correlation coefficients)

Univariate distributions

Bivariate distributions

Multivariate distributions

Concept of relationship

Principle of contingency

Yule's Q

Principle of the joint occurrence of attributes

Principle of covariation

Contingency tables

2×2 or fourfold table

Stub

Heading

Cells

Cell frequencies

Marginal totals (column and row)

Grand total

Bivariate frequency distribution

Conditional frequency

Joint frequency

Bivariate percentage distribution

Percentaging table rule

Comparing (percentages) table rule

Epsilon (ϵ)

Observed frequency (O_f)

Expected frequency (E_f)

Delta (Δ)

Statistical independence

Degree of association

Spurious association

Standardized or normed measures of associations

Direction of an association

Negative association

Positive association

Nature or pattern of an association

Lambda

Asymmetric measures of association

Symmetric measures of association

Proportional reduction in error (PRE)

C (contingency coefficient), $\overline{C}$, C_{max}

χ^2 (chi-square)

T (Tschruprow's T)

V (Cramér's V)

ϕ (phi coefficient), ϕ^2

REVIEW QUESTIONS

1. Suppose we wish to examine sexual permissiveness of males and females. For the following data construct (in a 2×2 table):

   a. A bivariate frequency distribution.

   b. A bivariate percentage distribution.

Hypothetical Data

Nonpermissiveness, male = 37
Nonpermissiveness, female = 48
Permissiveness, male = 43
Permissiveness, female = 12

c. Determine the E_f (expected frequency) for each cell.
d. Compute C, T, V, and ϕ for the preceding data.
e. What is C_{max} and $\overline{C}$ (the corrected contingency coefficient)?
f. Is the C value statistically significant?

2. Assume we wish to study the association between the credibility of executive board members and promotion. For the following data, compute the phi coefficient.

Promotional Pattern	Board Members Credibility		
	Low Credibility	High Credibility	
Promoted	3	9	12
Not promoted	7	2	9
	10	11	21

a. Determine ϕ_{max}.

3. Suppose we are interested in the relationship between vocabulary and the amount of formal education one has achieved. Both variables have been dichotomized into high and low categories. From the contingency table below, compute Yule's Q to determine the degree of association.

Vocabulary	Education		
	Low	High	
High	20	35	55
Low	40	15	55
	60	50	110

a. Test to see if Q is statistically significant at the .01 level.

4. Assume we are interested in the relationship between occupation and income. From the hypothetical data below, determine which variable is a better predictor of the other using Guttman's coefficient of predictability (lambda).

Occupational Prestige	Yearly Income		
	Low	High	
High	46	89	135
Low	79	51	130
	125	140	265

5. For the above data, calculate a nondirectional or symmetrical lambda.

CHAPTER 13

MEASURES OF ASSOCIATION (CORRELATION): ORDINAL AND INTERVAL/RATIO COEFFICIENTS

FIGURE 13.1

Ordinal and Interval/Ratio Measures of Association

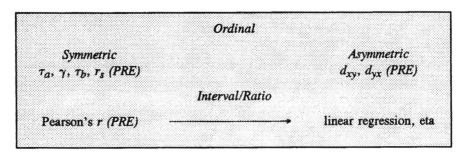

In this chapter you will see that ordinal and interval/ratio measures of association are computed on the basis of different mathematical properties inherent in the assigning of numbers to the data. Specifically, ordinal level association coefficients correlate *ranks* or positions, whereas interval/ratio level association coefficients correlate *magnitudes*. Before we turn to association measures for ordinal level data, Figure 13.1 will be presented as an aid for organizing your thinking about the ordinal and interval/ratio statistics discussed in this chapter. Two features of Figure 13.1 are important: (1) the distinction between symmetric and asymmetric statistics and (2) the "PRE" interpretation. You will recall from Chapter 12 that those statistical techniques that do not make a conceptual and/or computational distinction between independent and dependent variables are referred to as *symmetrical*

whereas those that do are termed *asymmetrical*. Secondly, the numerical value of a *PRE* measure may be interpreted as the proportion (or percent when multiplied by 100) by which prediction errors can be reduced by using your knowledge of the second variable. Review the appropriate sections in Chapter 12 if you are unclear on the meaning of these concepts.

ORDINAL MEASURES OF ASSOCIATION

Association measures for ordinal level data are based upon different mathematical principles than those for nominal level variables. With ordinal level variables we're interested in *ranking* data and it becomes necessary to think in terms of *pairs* of observations rather than in terms of individual cases. For the concept of rank to become meaningful, a minimum of two scores is necessary. With ordinal measures of association interest centers on the ranks of pairs of cases since we are concerned with whether or not knowledge of the rank ordering of pairs on one variable is useful in predicting the rank order on another ordinal variable.

Since thinking in terms of pairs of observations is relatively unfamiliar, a couple of examples will be considered. Suppose two students take two exams with the following results:

	Exam 1 (X Variable)	Exam 2 (Y Variable)
Student one	B	A
Student two	C	B

Student one received the higher grade on both exams and we say that the students stand in the *same order* with respect to their two exam scores. Suppose a different arrangement had occurred:

	Exam 1 (X Variable)	Exam 2 (Y Variable)
Student one	A	B
Student two	B	A

This time student one received the higher grade on the first test but student two received the higher grade on the second. Now the students stand in the *opposite* or *different order* on exam scores. When the order of scores (grades in our example) on the two variables (X and Y) is the same, as in the former illustration, there is a positive relationship. However, when the order of scores on the two variables is different, as in the latter example, a negative relationship exists. When variables are not related it is not possible to predict or tell anything about the second variable on the basis of our knowledge of the first one.

The logic of the above discussion is the foundation for a host of ordinal level association statistics. What must be done is to consider *all of the possible pairs* and *the different types of pairs* that can be generated from a data-set. It can be demonstrated mathematically that the total number of possible unique pairs from a data-set is:[1]

$$\text{total number of possible unique pairs} = \frac{N(N-1)}{2} \tag{13.1}$$

where: N = total number of paired observations or cases

With N's equal to 5, 10, 20, and 100, the total number of possible unique pairs, using formula (13.1), would be 10, 45, 190, and 4,950, respectively.

You should be aware that the total number of pairs is obtained by counting recurrent pairs only once. For example, the arrangement A and B and B and A is considered only a single pair by the mathematician. This is called the number of **combinations** as opposed to the number of **permutations**. Permutations count the number of different arrangements so that there would be two permutations of A and B but only one combination. The equation for the total number of possible unique pairs is called the *combinatorial* formula and consists of the number of combinations of N things taken two at a time.

In addition to the total number of possible unique pairs there are five other types of pairs:

1. **Concordant** or **same-ordered pairs.** In the computational formula to be presented the number of pairs which are ranked in the same order, concordant pairs, is symbolized n_s.

2. **Discordant** or **reverse-ordered pairs.** The number of pairs ranked in the opposite order, discordant pairs, will be symbolized by n_d.

3. **Pairs tied on the X (independent) variable** but not on the Y (dependent) variable and symbolized t_x.

4. **Pairs tied on the Y (dependent) variable** but not on the X (independent) variable and symbolized t_y.

5. **Pairs tied on the X and Y variables** and symbolized t_{xy}.

These five different types of pairs exhaust all possibilities and must, when added together, equal the **total number of possible unique pairs**, that is:

$$\text{total number of possible unique pairs} = \frac{N(N-1)}{2} = n_s + n_d + t_x + t_y + t_{xy}$$

All ordinal measures of association to be subsequently examined consist of a ratio between the different pair-types discussed above. All of them will use $n_s - n_d$ (the difference between the number of same—concordant—and reverse—discordant—ordered pairs) in the numerator and some combination of the five different types of pairs in the denominator. Each of these ordinal level statistics has a *PRE* interpretation achieved by using either a same-order or reverse-order prediction rule

---

[1]Another way to symbolize formula (13.1), the *combinatorial* formula, is to write: $\binom{N}{2}$ since $\binom{N}{2} = N(N-1)/2$.

as compared to a random guess or prediction about the rankings of pairs of observations. Since these statistics are ordinarily computed from a contingency table, a contingency table format will be assumed in discussing computational procedures.

Computing Procedures

Table 13.1 will be used for demonstrating the logic behind several ordinal measures of association.

TABLE 13.1
Illustrating Computation of Ordinal Measures of Association from a Contingency Table

Y Variable	X Variable		
	Low	Moderate	High
High	n_{11}	n_{12}	n_{13}
Moderate	n_{21}	n_{22}	n_{23}
Low	n_{31}	n_{32}	n_{33}

positive diagonal $n_{31} \longrightarrow n_{13}$ negative diagonal $n_{11} \longrightarrow n_{33}$

In Table 13.1 double subscripts are employed: the first indicates the row and the second denotes the column. For example, n_{23} represents the frequency of the cell where row two and column three intersect. The *positive diagonal*, the one that proceeds from low-low (n_{31}) to high-high (n_{13}) is located, and the *negative diagonal*, the one that proceeds from high-low (n_{11}) to low-high (n_{33}) is located. Locating the positive and negative diagonals assures us of computing the various pairs properly. The particular arrangement of each variable's subcategories is important since the sense of direction is the same as in correlation, particularly, scattergram construction.

To compute the number of *same-ordered pairs*, n_s, we multiply each cell frequency by the sum of frequencies in those cells that are higher on both dimensions and sum their products. That is,

$$n_s = n_{31}(n_{22} + n_{23} + n_{12} + n_{13}) + n_{32}(n_{23} + n_{13}) + n_{21}(n_{12} + n_{13}) + n_{22}(n_{13})$$

When a contingency table is laid out in the same manner as Table 13.1, n_s is computed by multiplying each cell frequency, beginning with the lower left-hand one (n_{31}), by all cell frequencies *above and to the right*.

To compute the number of *reverse-ordered pairs*, n_d, we multiply each cell frequency by the sum of frequencies that are higher on one and lower on the other variable and sum their products. That is,

$$n_d = n_{11}(n_{22} + n_{23} + n_{32} + n_{33}) + n_{12}(n_{23} + n_{33}) + n_{21}(n_{32} + n_{33}) + n_{22}(n_{33})$$

Given the Table 13.1 format, n_d is computed by multiplying each cell frequency, beginning with the upper left-hand one (n_{11}), by all cell frequencies *below and to the right*.

To compute the number of *pairs tied on* X, t_x, we multiply the frequency of the top cell in *each* column by the sum of cell frequencies immediately below. That is,

$$t_x = n_{11}(n_{21} + n_{31}) + n_{21}(n_{31}) + n_{12}(n_{22} + n_{32}) + n_{22}(n_{32}) + n_{13}(n_{23} + n_{33})$$
$$+ n_{23}(n_{33})$$

In a similar vein, to compute the number of *pairs tied on* Y, t_y, we begin by multiplying the frequency of the side row entries by the sum of cell frequencies in adjacent columns. That is,

$$t_y = n_{11}(n_{12} + n_{13}) + n_{12}(n_{13}) + n_{21}(n_{22} + n_{23}) + n_{22}(n_{23}) + n_{31}(n_{32} + n_{33})$$
$$+ n_{32}(n_{33})$$

Finally, for *pairs tied on both* X *and* Y, t_{xy} is computed as $n_i(n_i - 1)/2$ (where n_i = cell frequency) for *each* cell. That is,

$$t_{xy} = n_{11}(n_{11} - 1)/2$$
$$n_{12}(n_{12} - 1)/2$$
$$\cdot$$
$$\cdot$$
$$\cdot$$
$$n_{33}(n_{33} - 1)/2$$

or simply obtain t_{xy} by subtracting, that is:

$$\frac{N(N-1)}{2} = n_s + n_d + t_x + t_y + ? \, (t_{xy})$$

or

$$t_{xy} = \frac{N(N-1)}{2} - (n_s + n_d + t_x + t_y)$$

With this computing format a variety of ordinal measures of association can be computed. The data in Table 13.2 will be used to illustrate these computational procedures.

TABLE 13.2

Social Class of Spouses

Social Class of Wife (Y)	Social Class of Husband (X)			Totals
	Working	Middle	Upper	
Upper	30 negative	10 diagonal	15	55
Middle	20	30	10	60
Working	10 positive	25 diagonal	50	85
Totals	60	65	75	200

Computing the Number of Concordant Pairs. To calculate n_s, first determine which diagonal in the contingency table is positive and then which is negative. In Table 13.2 the diagonal proceeding from the upper left to the lower right is negative and the diagonal proceeding from the lower left to the upper right is positive. Again, this step assures us of computing the n_s and n_d properly.

To compute the number of same-ordered pairs we multiply each frequency beginning with the lower left-hand cell (n_{31}) by the sum of all cell frequencies that are higher on both variables (to the right and above). Consequently,

$$n_s = 10(30 + 10 + 10 + 15) + 25(10 + 15) + 20(10 + 15) + 30(15)$$
$$= 2,225$$

Computing the Number of Discordant Pairs. To calculate n_d multiply each frequency beginning with the upper left-hand (n_{11}) cell by the sum of all cell frequencies that are higher on one variable and lower on another (to the right and below). Therefore,

$$n_d = 30(30 + 10 + 25 + 50) + 10(10 + 50) + 20(25 + 50) + 30(50)$$
$$= 7,050$$

Computing the Number of Pairs Tied on X. To compute t_x we want only those pairs tied on X. To do this we select pairs from the same column but different rows. For example,

$$t_x = 30(20 + 10) + 20(10) + 10(30 + 25) + 30(25) + 15(10 + 50) + 10(50)$$
$$= 3,800$$

Computing the Number of Pairs Tied on Y. To compute t_y we want only those pairs tied on Y. To do this we select pairs from the same row but different columns. Hence,

$$t_y = 30(10 + 15) + 10(15) + 20(30 + 10) + 30(10) + 10(25 + 50) + 25(50)$$
$$= 4,000$$

Computing the Number of Pairs Tied on Both X and Y. To calculate t_{xy} our concern is with the number of pairs that have identical values on X and Y. These are computed for each cell as follows:

$$\frac{n_i(n_i - 1)}{2}$$

where: n_i = cell frequency

These values are then summed over all cells to equal t_{xy}. For our data:

$$
\begin{aligned}
n_{11} &= 30(30 - 1)/2 = 435 \\
n_{21} &= 20(20 - 1)/2 = 190 \\
n_{31} &= 10(10 - 1)/2 = 45 \\
n_{12} &= 10(10 - 1)/2 = 45 \\
n_{22} &= 30(30 - 1)/2 = 435 \\
n_{32} &= 25(25 - 1)/2 = 300 \\
n_{13} &= 15(15 - 1)/2 = 105 \\
n_{23} &= 10(10 - 1)/2 = 45 \\
n_{33} &= 50(50 - 1)/2 = 1{,}225 \\
t_{xy} &= \overline{2{,}825}
\end{aligned}
$$

Computing the Total Number of Unique Pairs. Use formula (13.1) and substitute the appropriate N. Thus,

$$\text{total number of possible unique pairs} = \frac{200(199)}{2}$$

$$= 19{,}900$$

Notice that if we sum n_s, n_d, t_x, t_y, and t_{xy}, the total number of possible unique pairs is produced. For our data:

$$
\begin{aligned}
n_s &= 2{,}225 \\
n_d &= 7{,}050 \\
t_x &= 3{,}800 \\
t_y &= 4{,}000 \\
t_{xy} &= \underline{2{,}825} \\
& 19{,}900 = \text{total number of possible unique pairs}
\end{aligned}
$$

From this discussion we will discover it is relatively easy to compute the following ordinal measures of association.

Tau-a (τ_a)

Tau-a (τ_a) is a measure of ordinal association that consists of a ratio of the preponderance of concordant (or discordant) pairs to the total number of possible unique pairs. Formula (13.2) symbolizes this verbal expression:

$$\tau_a = \frac{n_s - n_d}{\text{total number of possible unique pairs or } \dfrac{N(N-1)}{2}} \tag{13.2}$$

For the data in Table 13.2, tau-a is computed like this:

$$\tau_a = \frac{2{,}225 - 7{,}050}{19{,}900}$$

$$= \frac{-4{,}825}{19{,}900}$$

$$= -.242$$

Tau-a has limits between −1.00 (which indicates that all pairs are discordant) and +1.00 (which indicates that all pairs are concordant). A coefficient of zero (.00) would indicate an equal split between concordant and discordant pairs and would suggest that the reduction in predictive error would not be better than a random guess. The disadvantage of tau-a occurs when ties are present. Under these circumstances its upper and lower limits are not ±1.00. This occurs because the denominator includes the total number of pairs and will always be greater than n_s or n_d. To avoid this limitation, gamma (γ) may be used.

Gamma (γ)

Gamma, symbolized by the lowercase Greek letter γ, is a remedy for the disadvantage of tau-a.[2] To enable unity to be the upper limit it removes the number of ties from the denominator. That is, it consists of $n_s - n_d$ in the numerator but uses only the sum of *untied* pairs in the denominator. Formula (13.3) for gamma is:

$$\gamma = \frac{n_s - n_d}{n_s + n_d} \tag{13.3}$$

For the data in Table 13.2 gamma is computed to be:

[2]Sometimes gamma is symbolized by the uppercase Greek letter (Γ). The use of untied pairs in gamma will produce an inflated coefficient. To see this for yourself compare the magnitude of the various ordinal measures of association for the same data (Table 13.2).

$$\gamma = \frac{2,225 - 7,050}{2,225 + 7,050}$$

$$= \frac{-4,825}{9,275}$$

$$= -.520$$

Unlike tau-a, gamma has an upper limit and lower limit of +1.00 and −1.00, respectively, regardless of the number of ties. Gamma, as well as tau-a, can be used in any size table. Yule's Q, discussed in Chapter 12, is a special case of gamma in fourfold tables. Both tau-a and gamma are symmetrical statistics in the sense that no distinction is made between independent and dependent variables in the computation. When an asymmetrical ordinal statistic is called for, Somer's d is useful.

Somer's d

As an asymmetrical measure of association, **Somer's d** makes a computational and conceptual distinction between independent and dependent variables. More particularly, it takes into account the number of tied pairs on the *dependent* variable. When X is used as the independent variable, we include not only n_s and n_d in the denominator, but also t_y, the number of ties on the dependent variable. Consequently, computational formula (13.4) is:

$$d_{yx} = \frac{n_s - n_d}{n_s + n_d + t_y} \tag{13.4}$$

where: d_{yx} = asymmetrical measure of association for predicting dependent variable (Y) from independent variable (X)

For the data in Table 13.2 d_{yx} is computed as follows:

$$d_{yx} = \frac{2,225 - 7,050}{2,225 + 7,050 + 4,000}$$

$$= \frac{-4,825}{13,275}$$

$$= -.363$$

If Y is the independent variable, the number of ties on the dependent variable, now X, is included. In other words, the formula is:

$$d_{xy} = \frac{n_s - n_d}{n_s + n_d + t_x} \tag{13.5}$$

where: d_{xy} = asymmetrical measure of association for predicting X (which is now the dependent variable) from Y (which is now the independent variable)

Leonard–Basic Social Stats.—21

For our data, d_{xy} would equal:

$$d_{xy} = \frac{2,225 - 7,050}{2,225 + 7,050 + 3,800}$$

$$= \frac{-4,825}{13,075}$$

$$= -.369$$

Somer's d is an asymmetric association coefficient which has -1.00 and $+1.00$ as its lower and upper limits, respectively. It takes into account the number of ties on the *predicted* variable but excludes the number of ties for the predictor variable. It can be computed on any $r \times c$ table and is interpreted as the proportional reduction in error in predicting the rank on the dependent variable from knowledge of the independent variable over chance guessing.

Tau-b (τ_b)

Sometimes a social researcher may wish to account for ties on one or the other variable but not for ties on both (t_{xy}). In effect, **tau-b** is similar to tau-a but includes the number of tied pairs on the X and Y variables. In formula form tau-b is a kind of average of the two Somer's d's, that is:

$$\tau_b = \frac{n_s - n_d}{\sqrt{(n_s + n_d + t_y)(n_s + n_d + t_x)}} \qquad (13.6)$$

In fact, tau-b can be expressed as:

$$\tau_b = \sqrt{(d_{yx})(d_{xy})}$$

Substituting our data into formula (13.6):

$$\tau_b = \frac{2,225 - 7,050}{\sqrt{(2,225 + 7,050 + 4,000)(2,225 + 7,050 + 3,800)}}$$

$$= \frac{-4,825}{\sqrt{(13,275)(13,075)}}$$

$$= \frac{-4,825}{13,174.62}$$

$$= -.366$$

Tau-b takes on clearly defined upper ($+1.00$) and lower (-1.00) limits depending upon the direction of the association. It turns out to be an extremely useful coefficient since it takes ties into account in expressing the degree of association between variables.

These four measures of association, tau-*a*, gamma, Somer's *d*, and tau-*b*, are based upon the mathematical principle of ordinality. In addition, they all use some combination of n_s, n_d, t_x, t_y, and the total number of possible unique pairs in computing their values. They are simple ratios of the preponderance of concordant or discordant pairs to one of the other pair-types discussed.

Testing Tau-*a*, Gamma, Somer's *d*, and Tau-*b* for Significance

As we saw in Chapter 12, the practice of testing the significance of an association coefficient is recommended when one wants to generalize from the sample to the population. Tests of significance for association coefficients enable the researcher to reject or retain the null hypothesis that the association is equal to zero, that is, H_0: association = 0, in the universe from which the sample was selected.

When $n \geq 10$ *tau-a* may be tested for significance with formula (13.7).

$$z = \frac{T_a}{S_{\tau_a}} \qquad (13.7)$$

where: z =   standard score interpreted in terms of the properties and areas of the normal curve

T_a =   computed tau-*a* coefficient

S_{τ_a} =   standard error of tau defined as

$$\sqrt{\frac{2(2n + 5)}{9n(n - 1)}}$$

Substituting our τ_a value computed from Table 13.2 into formula (13.7):

$$z = \frac{-.242}{\sqrt{\frac{2(400 + 5)}{1,800(199)}}}$$

$$= \frac{-.242}{\sqrt{\frac{810}{358,200}}}$$

$$= \frac{-.242}{.048}$$

$$= -5.04$$

Suppose we had decided to test tau-*a* at the .01 level of significance. Turning to the normal curve table, Table B in Appendix A, we discover that a z value of $|-2.33|$ or larger (one-tailed test) is needed to reject the null hypothesis. Since $|-5.04| > |-2.33|$ we reject H_0 and conclude that there is a real association in the population from which the sample was selected.

To test *gamma* for significance, formula (12.9) may be employed.[3] Substituting our data into formula (12.9):

$$z = (-.52)\sqrt{\frac{2{,}225 + 7{,}050}{200[1 - (-.52^2)]}}$$

$$= (-.52)\sqrt{\frac{9{,}275}{200(1 - .2704)}}$$

$$= (-.52)\sqrt{\frac{9{,}275}{145.92}}$$

$$= (-.52)\sqrt{63.56}$$

$$= (-.52)(7.97)$$

$$= -4.14$$

Suppose we had decided to test gamma at the .05 level of significance. The normal curve table indicates that a value of $|-1.645|$ (one-tailed) or larger is needed to reject H_0. Since $|-4.14| > |-1.645|$ we reject the null hypothesis.

To test *Somer's d* for significance, formula (12.9) may be used. Substituting our data into formula (12.9) for d_{yx} and d_{xy}, respectively:

$$d_{yx}: \quad z = (-.363)\sqrt{\frac{2{,}225 + 7{,}050}{200[1 - (-.363^2)]}}$$

$$= (-.363)\sqrt{\frac{9{,}275}{200(1.00 - .1318)}}$$

$$= (-.363)\sqrt{\frac{9{,}275}{200(.8682)}}$$

$$= (-.363)\sqrt{\frac{9{,}275}{173.64}}$$

$$= (-.363)(7.308)$$

$$= -2.65$$

and

$$d_{xy}: \quad z = (-.369)\sqrt{\frac{2{,}225 + 7{,}050}{200[1 - (-.369^2)]}}$$

$$= -2.70$$

[3]You will recall from the discussion of Yule's Q that it is but a special case of gamma. Consequently, the test of significance is the same for both.

Suppose we had tested d_{yx} and d_{xy} for significance at the .01 level. The critical z value in the N.C. table is -2.33. Since both values exceed that, that is, $|-2.65|$ and $|-2.70| > |-2.33|$, we may reject the null hypothesis and conclude that there exists a significant association in the larger population from which the samples were selected.

To test *tau-b* for significance we may employ formula (13.8).

$$z = \frac{S}{\sigma_s} \tag{13.8}$$

where:
z = standard score interpreted in terms of the properties and areas of the normal curve

S = statistic of disarray = $n_s - n_d$

σ_s = standard error of S defined as $\sqrt{1/18 \, n(n-1)(2n+5)}$

Substituting our τ_b value computed from Table 13.2 into formula (13.8):

$$z = \frac{2{,}225 - 7{,}050}{\sqrt{\dfrac{1}{18} 200(199)(400+5)}}$$

$$= \frac{-4{,}825}{\sqrt{\dfrac{1}{18}(200)(199)(405)}}$$

$$= \frac{-4{,}825}{\sqrt{.06(16{,}119{,}000)}}$$

$$= \frac{-4{,}825}{\sqrt{967{,}140}}$$

$$= \frac{-4{,}825}{983.43}$$

$$= -4.91$$

Suppose we had set alpha at the .01 level. Consulting the normal curve table, we find a z value of $|-2.33|$ (one-tailed) or larger is needed to reject the null hypothesis. Since $|-4.91| > |-2.33|$ we reject H_0 and conclude that there's a statistically significant association in the population from which the sample was selected.

Before discussing the Pearsonian r, an interval/ratio level measure of association, one final popular ordinal measure will be discussed.

Spearman's Rank Order Correlation Coefficient (r_s)

Historically, **Spearman's rho** has been the most widely used ordinal measure of relationship. It assists us in answering the query, *How well can we predict one set of* *ranks from another set of ranks?* As an ordinal level statistic, rho correlates ranks, not magnitudes. Spearman's rank order correlation coefficient requires obtaining the differences between the ranks of the variables under examination, squaring and summing the squared differences, and substituting into formula (13.9).

$$r_s = 1 - \frac{6(\Sigma D^2)}{n(n^2 - 1)} \qquad (13.9)$$

where: r_s =   Spearman's rank order correlation coefficient
          ΣD^2 =   the sum of the squared difference between paired ranks
          n =   the number of paired observations

If there are no differences between ranks, the sum of the squared differences will equal zero and rho will equal 1.00. To illustrate, the data below display no differences between the ranks:

Observation	Rank X	Rank Y	D	D²
A	2	2	0	0
B	4	4	0	0
C	3	3	0	0
D	1	1	0	0
E	5	5	0	0
			$\Sigma D = 0$	$\Sigma D^2 = 0$

Substituting into formula (13.9):

$$r_s = 1 - \frac{6(0)}{5(5^2 - 1)}$$

$$= 1 - \frac{0}{120}$$

$$= 1 - 0$$

$$= +1$$

On the other hand, the sum of the squared differences will produce a maximum negative value if the ranks are arranged like this:

Observation	Rank X	Rank Y	D	D²
A	1	5	−4	16
B	2	4	−2	4
C	3	3	0	0
D	4	2	2	4
E	5	1	0	16
			$\Sigma D = 0$	$\Sigma D^2 = 40$

Substituting these values into formula (13.9):

$$r_s = 1 - \frac{6(40)}{5(5^2 - 1)}$$

$$= 1 - \frac{240}{120}$$

$$= 1 - 2$$

$$= -1$$

Notice that both no difference ($\Sigma D^2 = 0$) and maximum differences ($\Sigma D^2 =$ maximum) produced a value of one. However, the *sign* clearly tells us what direction the difference is in as well as aiding us in interpreting rho's substantive meaning.

We have seen that a rho value of $+1.00$ is obtained when the difference between each ranked pair is equal to zero and $\Sigma D^2 = 0$. Similarly, when the rho value is -1.00, the difference between ranks is maximum and ΣD^2 is maximum. The sum of the squared differences (ΣD^2) is a function, in part, of the number of observations ranked. To interpret the meaning of ΣD^2 we could norm on the maximum D^2 or $\Sigma D^2 / \Sigma D^2_{max}$. This latter expression reflects the ratio of the obtained sum of squared differences to the maximum possible squared differences.

It can be shown mathematically that $\Sigma D^2_{max} = n(n^2 - 1)/3$. For our data $5(25 - 1)/3 = 40$. Consequently, rho can vary between $+1.00$ and -1.00, the former depicting a perfect match of ranks and the latter an opposite match of ranks.

Let us compute Spearman's rho for the following research problem.

Assume you are a small group researcher interested in the relationship between pupils' popularity in school and their participation in class activities. Imagine that you have eleven students who have been ranked ordered on the two variables and you wish to know how closely the two rankings correspond. In social research the term rank order means to employ a comparative rating scale whereby the elements under examination are placed into a hierarchy from most to least (or vice versa). A rank of 1 would be assigned to the element having the most of the characteristic being studied, and a rank of N to the element having the least of the characteristic. To do this, the following steps are recommended.

1. Each pupil's popularity rank is placed in a column labeled R_x (rank on variable X).
2. Each pupil's corresponding class participation rank is placed in a column labeled R_y (rank on variable Y).
3. Determine the difference between the two rankings and place the differences in a column labeled D. Even though the D column is not used in the computation, it is useful to sum this column algebraically because the sum must equal zero. If any other value is obtained you should double-check the preceding steps.
4. Square the differences, that is $(D)^2$, and sum these quantities.
5. Substitute these values into formula (13.9).

Table 13.3 provides a worked example.

TABLE 13.3

Illustration of Computation of Spearman's Rho

Pupil	R_x (Popularity Rank)	R_y (Participation Rank)	D	D^2
A	8	10	−2	4
B	3	3	0	0
C	4	4	0	0
D	2	1	1	1
E	1	2	−1	1
F	11	11	0	0
G	6	6	0	0
H	9	8	1	1
I	10	9	1	1
J	7	5	2	4
K	5	7	−2	4
			$\Sigma D = 0$	$\Sigma D^2 = 16$

Substituting the values of Table 13.3 into formula (13.9):

$$r_s = 1 - \frac{6(16)}{11(11^2 - 1)}$$

$$= 1 - \frac{96}{11(121 - 1)}$$

$$= 1 - \frac{96}{1{,}320}$$

$$= .93$$

Interpretation of Spearman's Rho. Rho is a product-moment correlation coefficient for ranked data. For all practical purposes, it may be interpreted the same as *r*. Therefore, rho may be interpreted in several ways. First of all, one may consult **Guilford's Table,** presented in Table 13.5 later in this chapter. Doing this, we can say that the association between popularity and class participation is *very high and dependable.* In other words, there is a very high *degree* of relationship between the two variables. Furthermore, it is *positive* or *direct* in nature, meaning that there is a strong tendency for popular students to be actively involved in class activities and for unpopular students to be relatively uninvolved.

Spearman's rho also has a proportional reduction in error interpretation. However, for mathematical reasons beyond the scope of this book, it is r_s^2, not r_s, that indicates the reduction in prediction errors. In our illustration $r_s = .93$ and to use the *PRE* interpretation we would have to square that value; hence, $r_s^2 = .8649$.

Note that the *PRE* interpretation will always produce positive values. This means that one must examine the r_s sign to determine whether like or unlike ranks go together.

Testing Rho for Significance. When the number of paired observations is thirty or less ($n \leq 30$), Table N in Appendix A is provided for direct testing at the .05 and .01 levels of significance. This table is one-tailed and may be used for both positive and negative values. If the computed value exceeds that table value we may claim a significant association. Remember, we are concerned with the absolute value of the statistic.

In Table N the column labeled n refers to the number of *paired* observations, and the critical values for the .05 and .01 levels are found where n and the significance level intersect. The obtained r_s must be *equal to or larger than* the critical value. For our example in which $n = 11$ and $r_s = .93$ we discover that for $n = 10$ (since no $n = 11$ is found), r_s must be equal to or larger than .564 or .746 to be statistically significant at the .05 and .01 levels, respectively. Since our r_s of .93 is larger than .746, that is, .93 > .746, we may claim a statistically significant association between popularity and class participation in the population from which the sample was selected.

When Table N is not adequate, the t statistic may be employed to test for *rho*'s significance. This formula is as follows:

$$t = r_s \sqrt{\frac{n - 2}{1 - r_s^2}} \qquad (13.10)$$

where: t = t test statistic
$\quad\quad\quad r_s$ = Spearman's rho (coefficient)
$\quad\quad\quad n$ = number of paired observations
$\quad\quad n - 2$ = degrees of freedom

Substituting our values into formula (13.10):

$$t = .93 \sqrt{\frac{11 - 2}{1 - .8649}}$$

$$= .93 \sqrt{\frac{9}{.1351}}$$

$$= .93 \sqrt{66.62}$$

$$= .93(8.16)$$

$$= 7.59$$

What does a $t = 7.59$ mean? To answer this question we consult the t table, Table E in Appendix A, according to our degrees of freedom. Since our t value of 7.59 with 9 df is larger than the table value, that is, 7.59 > 4.781 at the .0005 level of significance (one-tailed), we conclude the rho is statistically significant at the .0005 level.

Observations on Spearman's Rho.   Rho has been the most widely used nonparametric correlational technique. It is the product-moment correlation coefficient (Pearsonian *r*) for ranked data. This means that, for all practical purposes, it is susceptible to the same interpretive procedures as *r*.

Although we haven't dealt with *tied ranks*, when such occur assign to each observation the average rank which the tied observations occupy. To illustrate, suppose we had the following scores: 80, 70, 50, 50, 50, 40, 30. The ranks assigned to these scores would be 1, 2, 4, 4, 4, 6, and 7, respectively. The three scores of 50 would occupy ranks of 3, 4, and 5 and the average of these ranks would be 4 (3 + 4 + 5 = 12/3 = 4). The existence of a few ties is not particularly problematic; however, when a large number of ties occur they can have the effect of exaggerating the magnitude of rho. When a large number of ties occur, it is probably better to substitute another statistic, such as tau, for rho.

INTERVAL/RATIO MEASURE OF ASSOCIATION

We have seen that at least *two sets of measurements* must be obtained on the same phenomenon, for example, individuals, events, and so forth, or on pairs of individuals or events that have been matched on some basis for the concept of correlation to have meaning. To compute a measure of relationship requires at least a bivariate distribution, although a multivariate distribution may also be used. In this section we will demonstrate the graphic display as well as the statistical computations for interval/ratio level bivariate data.

Graphic Representation of Bivariate Data

In Chapter 3 we saw how to portray a frequency distribution *visually*. As you know, graphic devices have been devised to make the characteristics of data-sets easier to grasp. In this section we will show how the statistician graphs *bivariate* data, whereas in Chapter 3 techniques for portraying *univariate* data were examined. To do this, an understanding of *scattergrams* is essential.

Scattergram. The **scattergram**, sometimes called a *scatter plot diagram*, is a graph that, upon inspection, produces an intuitive appreciation of the *existence, direction, nature,* and *degree* of the relationship between two variables. In Figures 13.2 to 13.5 that follow, positive, negative, zero, and curvilinear relationships will be depicted, along with some hypothetical scores that provide the foundation for the scattergrams' constructions. Bear in mind that each point in the scattergram actually represents the intersection of a *pair* of observations.

Perfect Positive Relationship (r = +1.00). Assume we have the following sets of measurements on two variables, labeled X and Y, for ten individuals (A through J):

Individual	X	Y
A	20	40
B	18	36
C	16	32
D	14	28
E	12	24
F	10	20
G	8	16
H	6	12
I	4	8
J	2	4

It is customary to locate values of the Y variable along the ordinate and X values along the abscissa. Let's list the Y values first. Begin at the origin (where the two axes intersect at right angles) listing the values from 0 to 40. Then, along the abscissa, list the X values from 0 to 20. Performing this operation produces the scattergram in Figure 13.2. Notice that points (dots) are plotted where the corresponding X and Y observations intersect, for example, 20 and 40, 18 and 36, 16 and 32, 14 and 28, 12 and 24, 10 and 20, 8 and 16, 6 and 12, 4 and 8, and 2 and 4. The sequence of the series of dots forms a straight line (sometimes referred to in geometric terms as an *ellipse*) from the lower left to the upper right revealing the existence of a *perfect positive relationship*. Conceptually, low scores on X are associated with low scores on Y and high scores on X are associated with high scores on Y. Furthermore, for each unit increase in X, Y increases by two units. Notice that this relationship is constant for the entire data-set.

FIGURE 13.2

Scattergram Illustrating a Perfect Positive Correlation (r = +1.00)

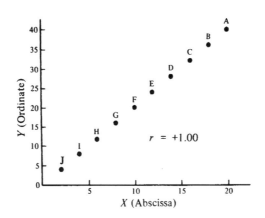

Perfect Negative Relationship ($r = -1.00$).   Assume we have the following bivariate distribution of scores for ten individuals:

Individual	X	Y
A	10	0
B	9	1
C	8	2
D	7	3
E	6	4
F	5	5
G	4	6
H	3	7
I	2	8
J	1	9

Once again, plot a dot at the intersection of the corresponding scores, that is, 10 and 0, 9 and 1, 8 and 2, 7 and 3, 6 and 4, 5 and 5, 4 and 6, 3 and 7, 2 and 8, and 1 and 9. Performing this operation produces the scattergram in Figure 13.3:

FIGURE 13.3

Scattergram Illustrating a Perfect Negative Correlation ($r = -1.00$)

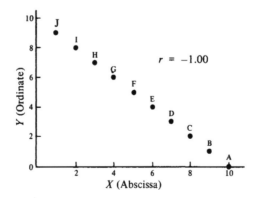

The sequence of the series of dots in Figure 13.3, forming a straight line from the upper left to the bottom right, reveals the existence of a *perfect negative relationship*. Substantively, low scores on X are associated with high scores on Y, and high scores on X are associated with low scores on Y. Notice, again, the constant relationship between the variables. For each unit increase in X, Y decreases by unity.

No Relationship ($r \approx .00$). If there is absolutely no association between the variables, the scatter plot diagram will have little or no order or patterning to it. Such a random arrangement of dots is presented in the scattergram in Figure 13.4.

FIGURE 13.4

Scattergram Illustrating a Correlation of Zero ($r \approx .00$)

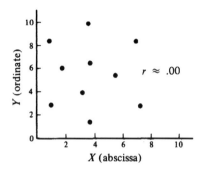

Curvilinear Relationship. A *curvilinear relationship* is an example of a *nonlinear* association between variables. In other words, the dots in Figure 13.5 initially appear to display a positive relationship, then reach a plateau, and finally appear to show a truncated negative relationship. Assume we have the following scores for ten individuals:

Individual	X	Y
A	20	2
B	18	4
C	16	6
D	14	8
E	12	9
F	10	9
G	8	8
H	6	6
I	4	4
J	2	2

Once again, if we plot a point where the corresponding X and Y observations intersect, for example, 20 and 2, 18 and 4, 16 and 6, 14 and 8, 12 and 9, 10 and 9, 8 and 8, 6 and 6, 4 and 4, and 2 and 2, the scattergram in Figure 13.5 is produced.

FIGURE 13.5

Scattergram Illustrating a Curvilinear Relationship

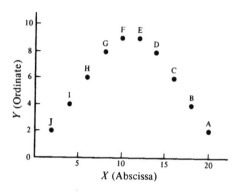

Note that the sequence of dots forms a kind of bell-shaped curve indicating a curvilinear relationship between the variables.

In this section we have constructed scattergrams for four different types of relationships: (1) perfect positive, (2) perfect negative, (3) zero or no relationship, and (4) curvilinear. These are *ideal types* and rarely discovered in this *exact* form in actual research. However, many bivariate distributions will *approximate* one or another of these and provide the investigator with a picture of the data. Furthermore, scattergram construction is recommended since it provides a means of comparing the computed statistical value with the graphic portrayal of the same data. Obviously, there should be a correspondence between the two and this correspondence is a built-in check when calculating the appropriate correlational measure. Finally, since most correlation coefficients assume linearity, the scattergram will provide you with a visual test of whether or not this assumption is met.

Pearson's Product-Moment Correlation Coefficient (r)

Pearson's r is probably the most widely used correlation coefficient for interval/ratio level data. Like other association coefficients, it measures the extent to which the same individuals (objects, events, etc.) have the same relative scores on two variables. This statement will become meaningful when the z score formula for computing r is presented. Unlike ordinal association coefficients, r uses *magnitudes* and not ranks for computational purposes.

The proper use of r makes several assumptions. Firstly, it requires data that conform to at least the *interval* level of measurement. Secondly, it assumes *linear or rectilinear regression*. The two terms, linear and rectilinear, are synonymous. This means that if you construct a scattergram, the line that would best describe the scores would be straight or linear, rather than curvilinear. Linearity can also be determined mathematically rather than graphically.[4] Thirdly, it assumes homoscedasticity or equality of variances in the different sets of measurement.

Before presenting a formula for the computation of the Pearsonian r, let's consider the following problem. Leonard and Schmitt were concerned with the relationship between sociology departments' participation at two annual meetings of the American Sociological Association. To determine the frequency of participation of various universities for these two years, the final programs were used as the source material. Basically, the operation involved systematically counting the number of participants from various sociology departments for these two conclaves. Table 13.4 presents a much abbreviated version of this study and will be used for illustrative purposes. Notice the arrangement of this table. The names of the respective institutions (unit of analysis) are listed to the far left (column 1). The X column (2) contains a frequency count of participation for the initial year for the respective institutions and the Y column (3) a frequency count of participation for the subsequent year. The following steps are recommended for computing the Pearsonian coefficient.

TABLE 13.4

Frequency of Participation of Selected Academic Departments at the Annual Meetings of the American Sociological Association

Academic Departments (1)	(X) (2)	(Y) (3)	X^2 (4)	Y^2 (5)	XY (6)
California (Berkeley)	26	22	676	484	572
Wisconsin	26	18	676	324	468
Columbia	23	18	529	324	414
Yale	23	25	529	625	575
Chicago	20	17	400	289	340
	$\Sigma X = 118$	$\Sigma Y = 100$	$\Sigma X^2 = 2,810$	$\Sigma Y^2 = 2,046$	$\Sigma XY = 2,369$

1. To assure that our data meet the linearity assumption one should construct a scattergram. For the study being reported this was done and linearity was displayed. This could also be done for our five cases, but, as this writer discovered, the abbreviated version failed to produce a clear-cut pattern. With a small number

---

[4] When data are not linearly related, the unbiased *correlation ratio (eta)* should be used. See Mueller, Schuessler, and Costner (1970) and Loether and McTavish (1993), among others, for a description of eta.

of observations this is frequently the case. Linearity exists when the dots lie roughly on a straight line. In other cases, this aspect is not so easily visualized. Under these ambiguous conditions, one may mathematically test for linearity. Since this test of linearity is beyond the purview of this book, those who wish to explore this procedure should consult Dixon and Massey (1957: 197–198) or Walker and Lev (1953: 245–246) for a good discussion. Since our data are linear in nature we may proceed with the calculation of r.

2. In a fourth column labeled X^2 the squared values of X are entered. For example, Berkeley had a frequency of 26 and 26^2 or 676 is entered in the X^2 column. For Wisconsin we enter 676 (since $26^2 = 676$) in the X^2 column. This operation is continued until all cases are exhausted.

3. In a fifth column labeled Y^2 the squared Y values are entered. To illustrate, Berkeley had a frequency of 22 and 22^2 or 484 is entered in the Y^2 column. For Wisconsin we enter 324 (since $18^2 = 324$) in the Y^2 column. Once again, this operation is continued until all cases are exhausted.

4. In a sixth column we enter the *XY cross products*. For example, Berkeley had an X of 26 and a Y of 22 and 572 (26 × 22 = 572) is entered in the XY column. Wisconsin had 26 and 18 in the X and Y columns, respectively. Therefore, 468 (26 × 18 = 468) is entered in the XY column. This operation is continued until all cases are exhausted.

5. The sums of the X, Y, X^2, Y^2, and XY columns are obtained. In the present example, $\Sigma X = 118$, $\Sigma Y = 100$, $\Sigma X^2 = 2,810$, $\Sigma Y^2 = 2,046$, and $\Sigma XY = 2,369$. The only additional value we need is the number of observations (academic departments in this case) to be correlated. In the original study 70 universities were considered, but the illustrative version has been reduced to 5.

6. With these quantities direct substitutions may be made into formula (13.11):

$$r = \frac{N\Sigma XY - (\Sigma X)(\Sigma Y)}{\sqrt{[N\Sigma X^2 - (\Sigma X)^2][N\Sigma Y^2 - (\Sigma Y)^2]}} \qquad (13.11)[5]$$

where: r = Pearson product-moment correlation coefficient
N = total number of paired observations
ΣXY = sum of the XY cross products
ΣX = sum of X column
ΣY = sum of Y column
$(\Sigma X)^2$ = sum of X's, quantity squared (the sum of the X's, quantity squared)

---

[5] This equation is a correct computational, sometimes called a *machine* (useful when a desk or hand calculator is available) one. Unfortunately, it disguises the theoretical basis of r. Pearson's r is the ratio of the covariance of X and Y over the product of the standard deviations of X and Y. Statistically speaking (Loether and McTavish, 1993: 273),

$$r = \Sigma XY - \frac{(\Sigma X)(\Sigma Y)}{N} \Bigg/ \sqrt{\left[\frac{\Sigma X^2 - (\Sigma X)^2/N}{N}\right]\left[\frac{\Sigma Y^2 - (\Sigma Y)^2/N}{N}\right]}$$

$(\Sigma Y)^2$ = sum of Y's, quantity squared (the sum of the Y's, quantity squared)

ΣX^2 = sum of the squared X values (the sum of the squared X values)

ΣY^2 = sum of the squared Y values (the sum of the squared Y values)

Substituting these values into formula (13.11):

$$r = \frac{5(2,369) - (118)(100)}{\sqrt{[5(2,810) - (118)^2]\,[5(2,046) - (100)^2]}}$$

$$= \frac{11,845 - 11,800}{\sqrt{(14,050 - 13,924)\,(10,230 - 10,000)}}$$

$$= \frac{45}{\sqrt{(126)\,(230)}}$$

$$= \frac{45}{\sqrt{28,980}}$$

$$= \frac{45}{170.24}$$

$$= .264$$

Before interpreting r, let us look at an alternative procedure for computing the product-moment correlation coefficient.

Computing the Pearsonian r from Standard Scores. You will recall from Chapter 6 that scores from different distributions may be compared when they are reduced to a common standard. Transforming raw scores to z scores is one very important way to standardize the meaning of scores taken from different distributions. Intuitively we know that if the academic departments listed in Table 13.4 had the exact same z scores for the two years, the relationship, expressed as a correlation coefficient, would equal $+1.00$. On the other hand, if each department had the same z score for the two years but with opposite signs, the correlation would be -1.00. When we express observations in standard score form, z_X and z_Y for the respective observations, rather than in raw score form (X and Y), the Pearsonian r is the arithmetic mean of the sum of the cross products of z scores or a sort of standardized covariance. That is,

$$r = \frac{\Sigma z_X z_Y}{N} \qquad\qquad (13.12)$$

Let us correlate the frequency of participation for the five schools in Table 13.4 using the standard score format for computing the Pearsonian r:

Academic Departments	X	Y	X²	Y²	z_X	z_Y	$z_X z_Y$
Berkeley	26	22	676	484	1.07	.66	.71
Wisconsin	26	18	676	324	1.07	−.66	−.71
Columbia	23	18	529	324	−.27	−.66	.18
Yale	23	25	529	625	−.27	1.65	−.44
Chicago	20	17	400	289	−1.61	−.99	1.59
	Σ=118	Σ=100	Σ=2,810	Σ=2,046	Σ ≈ 0	Σ = 0	Σ=1.33

Since a z score is computed $z = (X_i - \overline{X})/s$, it is necessary to obtain the mean and standard deviation for X.

$$\overline{X} = \frac{\Sigma X}{N} \qquad\qquad s_x = \sqrt{\frac{\Sigma X^2 - (\Sigma X)^2/N}{N}}$$

$$= \frac{118}{5} \qquad\qquad = \sqrt{\frac{2,810 - (118)^2/5}{5}}$$

$$= 23.6 \qquad\qquad = 2.24$$

Next we obtain the mean and standard deviation for Y.

$$\overline{Y} = \frac{100}{5} \qquad\qquad s_y = \sqrt{\frac{2,046 - (100)^2/5}{5}}$$

$$= 20 \qquad\qquad = 3.03$$

Let us express each raw score for X and Y as a z score, respectively:

Berkeley	(26−23.6)/2.24= 1.07
Wisconsin	(26−23.6)/2.24= 1.07
Columbia	(23−23.6)/2.24= −.27
Yale	(23−23.6)/2.24= −.27
Chicago	(20−23.6)/2.24= −1.61

Berkeley	(22−20)/3.03 = .66
Wisconsin	(18−20)/3.03 = −.66
Columbia	(18−20)/3.03 = −.66
Yale	(25−20)/3.03 = 1.65
Chicago	(17−20)/3.03 = −.99

Notice that the *algebraic* sum of z scores for *each* year equals .00. With the z scores for X and Y we obtain the cross products of the respective standard scores ($z_X z_Y$) and sum them. $(1.07)(.66) = .71$, $(1.07)(−.66) = −.71$, $(−.27)(−.66) = .18$, $(−.27)(1.65) = −.44$, $(1.61)(−.99) = 1.59$. Therefore, adding algebraically, the sum equals 1.33. Finally, we divide this sum by N, the number of pairs, in this case 5, according to formula (13.12):

$$\frac{1.33}{5} = .266$$

The Pearsonian r for the five departments in Table 13.4, computed the z score way, is .266. Notice that this value is nearly equal to the one computed using formula (13.11).

Interpretation of Pearsonian r.   What does an r of .266 mean? Frequently after computing a measure of relationship a question arises concerning its exact meaning and interpretation. In other words, *How large (or small) does an association coefficient have to be in order to be considered small, medium, or large?* Unfortunately, there is *no* definitive answer to this query since it depends upon the use to which it will be put, among other things. In any event, the Pearsonian r is a *symmetrical* measure of association between interval/ratio level variables. It varies between +1.00 (perfect positive association) and −1.00 (perfect negative association) and indicates the existence, direction, and strength of the correlation. However, Table 13.5, modified from Guilford (1950: 165), is recommended for use as a *guide* in interpreting coefficients of association.

TABLE 13.5

A Guide for Interpreting Coefficients of Association: Guilford's Table

Magnitude of Raw Coefficient*	Degree of Relationship
Less than or equal to ±.20	Slight, almost negligible
±.21 to ± .40	Low correlation, definite but small
±.41 to ± .70	Moderate correlation, substantial
±.71 to ± .90	High correlation, marked
±.91 to ±1.00	Very high and dependable

*This assumes the coefficient is *statistically significant*!

Using Table 13.5 for interpretative purposes, we may conclude that the correlation between participation at the two ASA meetings is *low*. While this table is provided as a guide for interpreting r, Blalock (1979: 409) cautions us in this interpretation. He writes, ". . . there is no direct and simple interpretation for r itself. In fact, it is possible to be misled by values of r since these values will be numerically larger than those of r^2 unless r is 0 or ±1.0." He provides Table 13.6, modified by this writer, to illustrate the point.

Let us use Table 13.6 to demonstrate (1) some important statistical concepts for interpreting the Pearsonian product-moment correlation coefficient, and (2) the strong interpretative features of r. We have already noted that the *raw coefficient* may be interpreted by consulting Guilford's table (Table 13.5).

TABLE 13.6

Numerical Relationships between r, r^2, and $1-r^2$: The PRE Approach

r (Raw Coefficient) (1)	r^2 (Explained Variation) (2)	$1 - r^2$ (Unexplained Variation) (3)
.90	.81	.19
.85	.72	.28
.80	.64	.36
.75	.56	.44
.70	.49	.51
.65	.42	.58
.60	.36	.64
.55	.30	.70
.50	.25	.75
.45	.20	.80
.40	.16	.84
.35	.12	.88
.30	.09	.91
.25	.06	.94
.20	.04	.96
.15	.02	.98
.10	.01	.99
.05	.0025	.9975
	[coefficients of determination]	[coefficients of nondetermination]

In column 2 of Table 13.6 are listed r^2 values of selected correlation coefficients. When the raw correlation coefficient is *squared* we may say that a certain amount of variation is explained. This is technically known as *explained variation*, denoted by r^2. In the present example, approximately 7 percent ($.266^2 = .071$) of the variation in frequency of participation at the later meeting using the earlier meeting as our base has been explained. In other words, when a cause-effect relationship between variables is construed, the explained variation notion becomes a very useful and sophisticated way of interpreting the correlation coefficient. Since the present example is more concerned with the *relationship* between frequency of participation at the two meetings, per se, this interpretation isn't particularly applicable. Another illustration will make more intuitive sense.

Assume we are interested in the relationship between years of education (independent variable) and annual income (dependent variable). Furthermore, assume that we have computed the coefficient of correlation to be .70. In this case, the predictor variable is years of education and the predicted variable is annual income.[6] When r is squared, that is, r^2, we obtain a measure of *the proportional reduction in error* which may be attributed to the linear relationship between the independent and dependent variables. Since $r^2 = .49$ ($.70^2 = .4900$), we can say that 49 percent of the variation in Y is explained or accounted for by using X as the independent variable. The proportional reduction in error interpretation is simply another way of stating that so much of the variation in Y is explained or accounted for by X. In statistical terminology, r^2 is sometimes referred to as the **coefficient of determination** or as the **proportion of explained variation** (Mueller, Schuessler, and Costner, 1970: 314). Edwards (1963: 163) says, "r^2 represents the proportion of Σy^2 that is associated with variation in X."

In column 3 of Table 13.6 are listed the "$1 - r^2$" values of selected correlation coefficients. When r^2 is subtracted from unity, it gives the researcher information concerning the *linear* variation in Y that is *not* accounted for by X. In other words, another interpretation of r has to do with the *amount of error* involved in predicting one variable from another. Let us illustrate this from the scattergram in Figure 13.6.

FIGURE 13.6

Scattergram and Regression Line for (X) and (Y): Hypothetical Data

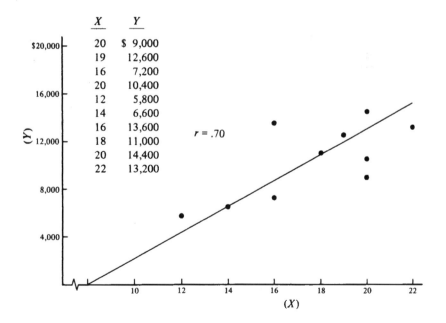

---

[6]Since r is *symmetrical* in nature its interpretation is reversible. That is, it can also be said that 49 percent of the variation in X is explained by Y.

A straight line has been drawn in Figure 13.6 that approximates the relation-ship between income and education. But, a number of points do *not* fall on the straight line. In other words, there's a certain amount of deviation of the points from the straight line. In trying to predict Y from X there is not a perfect relation-ship (+1.00 or −1.00); instead, $r = .70$. When this happens it's conventional to say that there exists a certain amount of error in predicting Y from X. Error, or variation, is measured by $1 - r^2$. In this example, the proportion of the variance in income not predictable from the linear relation between income and education is $1 - r^2$, or $1 - (.70)^2 = 1 - .49 = .51$. In short, 51 percent of the variation in income is unexplained by the linear relation between income and education. This coefficient may be thought of as the proportion of variation in the dependent variable left linearly unexplained by the independent variable. $1 - r^2$ is sometimes called the **coefficient of nondetermination** or $1 -$ (explained variation/total variation). Ed-wards (1963: 163) says, "The value '$1 - r^2$' indicates the proportion of Σy^2 that is independent of the regression of Y on X."

Senter (1969: 429) makes a point well worth reiterating. The concept "error" has a special statistical meaning. In everyday discourse error implies incorrect, not correct, wrong, and so forth. In statistics "error" usually means *variation*. For example, when statisticians talk about sampling error they are suggesting that statis-tical values taken from different samples *vary* from each other. Also, the standard error is really an index of variability. Following Senter's suggestion, it would be well for us to remember that *reduction in error, statistically speaking, means reduc-tion in variability*. "To say that we have reduced 'error' . . . means that we have been able (through some technique such as correlation) to reduce the total amount by which some set of scores 'scatter' around some specified value (values) in that distribution" (Senter, 1969: 429).

Testing the Significance of the Pearsonian r. As we have seen, the matter of measuring *degree* of association between two sets of scores is quite different from that of testing for the *existence* of an association in the population from which the sample was selected. While it's interesting to know that a correlation exists between two sets of sample scores, it may be even more important to be able to say whether or not some observed association in a sample of scores indicates that the variables under study are associated in the *population* from which the sample was drawn. Therefore, it is necessary to test the significance of the corresponding coefficients.

To test r for significance when $n > 50$ we use formula (13.13) for computing the standard error of r:

$$s_r = \frac{1}{\sqrt{n - 1}} \tag{13.13}$$

where: s_r = the standard error of the Pearsonian coefficient

In the full study dealing with the degree of association between frequency of participation at two ASA meetings n was 70 and $r = .83$. Let us test this for significance. We are testing the null hypothesis that H_0: P=0 against the alternative hypothesis that H_1: $|P| > 0$.

To test r when $n > 50$ the z test, formula (13.14) is appropriate:

$$z = \frac{r}{\frac{1}{\sqrt{n-1}}} \qquad (13.14)$$

where: z = z test statistic

r =   Pearsonian correlation coefficient

$1/\sqrt{n-1}$ =   the standard error of error (s_r in formula [13.13])

Substituting our values:

$$z = \frac{.83}{\frac{1}{\sqrt{70-1}}}$$

$$= \frac{.83}{\frac{1}{\sqrt{69}}}$$

$$= \frac{.83}{\frac{1}{8.31}}$$

$$= \frac{.83}{.12}$$

$$= 6.92$$

To determine whether r is significant at the .01 level (any level of significance may be used) the normal curve table for a one-tailed test is consulted. Doing this reveals the critical value for r at the .01 level to be 2.33. Since our value of 6.92 is larger than the table value, that is, 6.92 > 2.33, we conclude there is a statistically significant correlation in the population from which the observations were secured.

To test r for significance when $n < 50$ we use the t test statistic rather than the z test statistic. Formula (13.15) for r's significance when $n < 50$ is:

$$t = \frac{r}{\sqrt{1 - r^2}} \left(\sqrt{n-2} \right) \qquad (13.15)$$

where: t = t test statistic

r =   Pearsonian correlation coefficient

$\sqrt{1-r^2}$ =   standard error of Pearsonian r

$n-2$ =   degrees of freedom (number of *paired* data minus 2 in this case)

Let us test the correlation coefficient of .264 (for the five institutions appearing in Table 13.4) for significance at the .05 level (one-tailed test). Again we are testing H_0: P=0 versus H_1: $|P| > 0$.

Substituting our values into formula (13.15):

$$t = \frac{.264}{\sqrt{1-(.264)^2}} \, (\sqrt{5-2})$$

$$= \frac{.264}{\sqrt{.9303}} \, (1.73)$$

$$= (.274)(1.73)$$

$$= .474$$

What does $t = .474$ mean? Turning to the t table we see that with three degrees of freedom ($n - 2$ or $5 - 2 = 3$) a critical value of 2.353 or larger is sufficient to reject H_0. Since our value is less than the table value, that is, $.474 < 2.353$, we cannot reject the null hypothesis. Consequently, we do not have statistical evidence that an association exists in the population from which the sample was selected.

THE SPECIAL CASE OF DICHOTOMOUS VARIABLES

Throughout this text the importance of the measurement level of the characteristic (or variable) and the appropriate statistical techniques has been stressed. In the case of dichotomies, variables having two subclasses, an interesting and notable exception to the level of measurement—appropriate statistical tools relationship is encountered. Dividing a variable into two subclasses can occur at any measurement level, for example, male/female (nominal), superior/inferior (ordinal), and 175 pounds and above/less than 175 pounds (interval/ratio). As a consequence, a dichotomous variable may be statistically treated as though it were a nominal, ordinal, or interval/ratio measured variable, depending upon the research situation. It can be demonstrated that in a 2 x 2 table $T = V = \phi = \tau_b = r = \eta$. Theoretically and practically this means that higher measurement level statistics can be applied to lower level concepts under certain circumstances.

THE DISTINCTION BETWEEN MEASURES OF ASSOCIATION AND TESTS OF SIGNIFICANCE

Students frequently confuse the conceptual distinction between measures of association and tests of significance. A correlation coefficient tells us the *degree* or *strength* of the relationship between variables. A test of significance, on the other hand, reveals the likelihood that chance factors could have produced the results. After any correlation coefficient has been computed one should adopt the practice of testing it for significance. To do this, we pose the question, *Does the coefficient of correlation represent a real correlation or is it due to chance variation?* We are asking whether the correlation is a chance deviation from a population where $P=0$, that is, H_0: $P=0$ and H_1: $|P| > 0$.

Computing the degree of association between the two data-sets is different from testing for the existence of an association in the universe from which the data were selected. While it is interesting to ascertain the strength of relationship between two sets of *sample* scores, it's more important, theoretically, to determine whether the association in the sample indicates that the variables under investigation are related in the population from which the sample was drawn. Therefore, it is desirable to test the significance of the corresponding coefficients.

LINEAR REGRESSION

In the social sciences increasing use of an extension of correlation has become part of the researcher's repertoire of statistical techniques. This extension is called *regression* and conveys the idea of *predicting* one variable, usually the dependent, from another, usually the independent. Let's briefly develop the logic of regression analysis. Suppose we had the hypothetical data in Table 13.7 for five individuals.

TABLE 13.7

Hypothetical Data for Illustrating Linear Regression

Individual	(X)	(Y)
A	3	$ 3,000
B	5	5,000
C	8	8,000
D	10	10,000
E	15	15,000

Let us construct a scattergram for these data, Figure 13.7. Notice that the dots in the scattergram proceed from the lower left to the upper right and that a straight line, called a *regression line,* accurately describes this relationship. If we were to devise a mathematical formula for predicting (Y) from (X) it would be:

$$Y = \$1,000X \qquad (13.16)$$

FIGURE 13.7

Scattergram for Data in Table 13.7

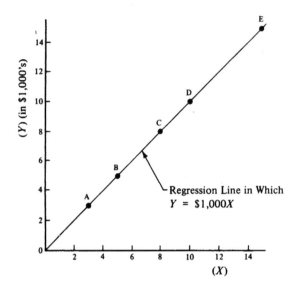

If any X value were substituted into the formula (13.16) the value of Y could easily be obtained. Hence, for the five individuals:

$$Y_A = \$1,000(3) = \$\ 3,000$$
$$Y_B = \$1,000(5) = \$\ 5,000$$
$$Y_C = \$1,000(8) = \$\ 8,000$$
$$Y_D = \$1,000(10) = \$10,000$$
$$Y_E = \$1,000(15) = \$15,000$$

Let an additional factor be added. If each of the five persons were given a $200 bonus the equation would be altered to read:

$$Y = \$200 + \$1,000X \tag{13.17}$$

Therefore, in predicting Y from X the individual values would become:

$$Y_A = \$200 + \$1,000(3) = \$\ 3,200$$
$$Y_B = \$200 + \$1,000(5) = \$\ 5,200$$
$$Y_C = \$200 + \$1,000(8) = \$\ 8,200$$
$$Y_D = \$200 + \$1,000(10) = \$10,200$$
$$Y_E = \$200 + \$1,000(15) = \$15,200$$

Formula (13.17), "$Y = \$200 + \$1,000X$," is but a special case of the formula for a straight line, or:

$$Y' = a_{yx} + b_{yx}(X) \tag{13.18}$$

where: Y' = predicted variable
       X = predictor variable
       a_{yx} = the value of Y when $X=0$, sometimes called the Y-intercept[7]
       b_{yx} = the *slope* of the line relating X and Y, often referred to as the *b*-coefficient[7]

Both X and Y are *variables* which will change from one person to the next and a_{yx} and b_{yx} are *constants* for a given data-set. In our illustration b_{yx} (the slope) is \$1,000 meaning that each unit change in X produces a 1,000 unit change in Y. In statistical vernacular, b_{yx} is referred to as the regression of Y on X. The regression equation is *asymmetrical* (see Figure 13.1) since it is possible to regress X on Y also.

    In most research, perfect correlations are practically never found and rarely will the dots in a scattergram fall *exactly* on the regression line. Consequently, we want to find the straight line which best fits our data. Furthermore, it is from this line that predictions are made. The criterion for discovering the best straight line to fit one's data is the one that makes the squared deviations around it minimal. You will recall that the arithmetic mean is that measure of central tendency around which the sum of squared deviations is minimal ($\Sigma(X_i - \overline{X})^2 =$ minimum). It is from this idea that some statisticians refer to the regression line as a type of floating mean.

    When we predict an outcome on the dependent variable from knowledge of the independent variable, the symbol Y', called Y *prime*, Y *predicted*, or *estimated Y*, is used. Recall that the formula for a straight line is $Y = a_{yx}$ (Y-intercept) + b_{yx} (slope) (X).

    Let us determine and interpret the regression equation for the data in Table 13.7. There are numerous computational formulae that could be used to find the values for the regression formula. For convenience's sake, simplified but correct, raw score formulae will be used. Then, more theoretically oriented formulae will be defined. Two values, b_{yx} (the slope coefficient) and a_{yx} (Y-intercept) must be computed. Formula (13.19) may be used for computing the *b*-coefficient.

$$b_{yx} = \frac{N(\Sigma XY) - (\Sigma X)(\Sigma Y)}{N(\Sigma X^2) - (\Sigma X)^2} \tag{13.19}$$

where: b_{yx} = slope or *b*-coefficient
       N = number of paired observations
     ΣXY = sum of XY cross products
      ΣX = sum of X values
      ΣY = sum of Y values

---

[7] Since the regression equation may be *asymmetrical* it is important to distinguish the independent and dependent variables. As a consequence we adopt the convention of using subscripts, for example, a_{yx} and b_{yx}, in which the first represents the dependent and the latter the independent variable.

$\Sigma X^2 =$ sum of X^2 values

$(\Sigma X)^2 =$ sum of X, quantity squared

Conceptually, formula (13.19) can be thought of as the ratio between the co-variation of X and Y and the variation of X. Table 13.8 provides the format for obtaining the necessary numerical values. Substituting these values into formula (13.19):

$$b_{yx} = \frac{5(4,230) - (41)(410)}{5(423) - (41)^2}$$

$$= \frac{21,150 - 16,810}{2,115 - 1,681}$$

$$= \frac{4,340}{434}$$

$$= 10$$

The b-coefficient is 10, meaning that for each unit change in X, Y changes by 10 units.

To compute a_{yx}, the Y-intercept value, formula (13.20) may be used.

$$a_{yx} = \frac{\Sigma Y - b_{yx}(\Sigma X)}{N} \tag{13.20}$$

where: a_{yx} = Y-intercept
  b_{yx} = b-coefficient
  ΣX = sum of X values
  N = number of paired observations

Substituting our data into formula (13.20):

$$a_{yx} = \frac{410 - 10(41)}{5}$$

$$= \frac{410 - 410}{5}$$

$$= \frac{0}{5}$$

$$= 0$$

The Y-intercept is equal to zero. This means that the regression line crosses the Y axis at zero.

With these two values, b_{yx} and a_{yx}, we may express the regression equation for the data in Tables 13.7 and 13.8 as:

$$Y' = 0 + 10X$$

TABLE 13.8

Format for Computing Regression Equation: Raw Score Formulae

Individual	X	X²	Y (Hundreds)	Y²	XY
A	3	9	30	900	90
B	5	25	50	2,500	250
C	8	64	80	6,400	640
D	10	100	100	10,000	1,000
E	15	225	150	22,500	2,250
N=5	Σ=41	Σ=423	Σ=410	Σ=42,300	Σ=4,230

$$b_{yx} = \frac{N(\Sigma XY) - (\Sigma X)(\Sigma Y)}{N(\Sigma X^2) - (\Sigma X)^2}$$

$$a_{yx} = \frac{\Sigma Y - b_{yx}(\Sigma X)}{N}$$

An Alternative Way of Computing b_{yx} and a_{yx}

It was noted above that formulae (13.19) and (13.20) are technically correct but simplified formulae for determining b_{yx} and a_{yx}, respectively. Let us look at an alternate way of computing the b-coefficient and Y-intercept. As we will see, this approach is more complicated but it is included for the light it may shed on the conceptual understanding of linear regression. Again, equations for b_{yx} and a_{yx} will be presented.

To obtain the slope of the line we may use formula (13.21) which is derived as follows:

$$b_{yx} = \frac{\Sigma xy}{\Sigma x^2}$$

$$\Sigma xy = r\sqrt{(\Sigma x^2)(\Sigma y^2)}$$

where: $\Sigma x^2 = Ns_x^2$
$\Sigma y^2 = Ns_y^2$

Thus:

$$b_{yx} = \frac{r\sqrt{(N^2 s_x^2)(s_y^2)}}{Ns_x^2}$$

$$= r \left[\frac{N s_x s_y}{N s_x^2} \right]$$

$$= r \left[\frac{s_y}{s_x} \right] \qquad\qquad (13.21)$$

Formula (13.21) requires a computation of the Pearsonian product-moment correlation coefficient, the standard deviation of Y, and the standard deviation of X. To obtain r we may substitute the data in Table 13.8 into formula (13.11). Hence,

$$r = \frac{5(4{,}230) - (41)(410)}{\sqrt{[5(423) - (41)^2]\,[5(42{,}300) - (410)^2]}}$$

$$= \frac{21{,}150 - 16{,}810}{\sqrt{(2{,}115 - 1{,}681)(211{,}500 - 168{,}100)}}$$

$$= \frac{4{,}340}{\sqrt{(434)(43{,}400)}}$$

$$= \frac{4{,}340}{\sqrt{18{,}835{,}600}}$$

$$= \frac{4{,}340}{4{,}340}$$

$$= +1.00$$

To obtain the standard deviation of X and Y we may substitute the data in Table 13.8 into formula (5.11). Hence,

$$s_x = \sqrt{\frac{423 - (41)^2/5}{5}} \qquad\qquad s_y = \sqrt{\frac{42{,}300 - (410)^2/5}{5}}$$

$$= 4.17 \qquad\qquad\qquad\qquad = 41.7$$

Substituting this information into formula (13.21):

$$b_{yx} = 1.00\left(\frac{41.7}{4.17}\right)$$

$$= 1.00(10)$$

$$= 10$$

The slope, b_{yx}, in our illustration is 10, meaning that for each unit change in X, Y changes by a factor of 10. Of course, this value is identical to the one previously computed using a simpler formula. Therefore, if $X = 1$, $Y = 10$; if $X = 3$, $Y = 30$, and so forth.

To obtain a_{yx}, formula (13.22) may be employed.

$$a_{yx} = \bar{Y} - b_{yx}(\bar{X}) \tag{13.22}$$

Note that we need two additional quantities, the arithmetic mean of X and the arithmetic mean of Y. Substituting the data in Table 13.8 into formula (4.5):

$$\bar{X} = \frac{41}{5} = 8.2 \quad \text{and} \quad \bar{Y} = \frac{410}{5} = 82$$

To obtain the Y-intercept, a_{yx} in the linear equation, we substitute this information into formula (13.22):

$$a_{yx} = 82 - 10(8.2)$$
$$= 82 - 82$$
$$= 0$$

The y-intercept is equal to zero. This means that when $X = 0$ so, too, does Y. The regression equation may be expressed as: $Y' = 0 + 10X$.

Let us take some different data and compute the regression equation. Suppose we have five different individuals' sales bonuses and years of formal education as shown in Table 13.9. Then:

TABLE 13.9

Format for Computing Regression Equation

Individual	Years of Formal Education (X)	X^2	Sales Bonus (Y)	Y^2	XY
A	12	144	$11,000	121,000,000	132,000
B	13	169	12,500	156,250,000	162,500
C	14	196	15,500	240,250,000	217,000
D	15	225	18,000	324,000,000	270,000
E	16	256	14,000	196,000,000	224,000
$N=5$	70	990	$71,000	1,037,500,000	1,005,500

$$\bar{X} = 14 \qquad\qquad \bar{Y} = \$14,200$$

$$S_x = \sqrt{\frac{990 - (70)^2/5}{5}} \qquad\qquad S_y = \sqrt{\frac{1,037,500,000 - (71,000)^2/5}{5}}$$

$$= 1.41 \qquad\qquad\qquad = \$2,420.74$$

$$r = \frac{5(1,005,500) - (70)(71,000)}{\sqrt{[5(990) - (70)^2]\,[5(1,037,250,000) - (71,000)^2]}}$$

$$= \frac{5,027,500 - 4,970,000}{\sqrt{(4,950 - 4,900)(5,186,250,000 - 5,041,000,000)}}$$

$$= \frac{57,500}{\sqrt{(50)(145,250,000)}}$$

$$= \frac{57,500}{85,220}$$

$$= .675$$

To obtain the slope of the regression line for these data we substitute our values into formula (13.19). Hence,

$$b_{yx} = \frac{5(1,005,500) - (70)(71,000)}{5(990) - (70)^2}$$

$$= 1,150$$

For our data, each unit change in X will produce a $1,150 change in Y.

The Y-intercept is determined by substituting our data into formula (13.20):

$$a_{yx} = \frac{\$71,000 - 1,150(70)}{5}$$

$$= -1,900$$

In other words, when $X=0$, $Y=-1,900$. The regression equation for the data in Table 13.9 is $Y' = -1,900 - 1,150X$.

SUMMARY

This chapter has been devoted to a discussion of ordinal and interval/ratio measures of association. To understand the logic of such ordinal measures of association as tau-a, gamma, Somer's d, and tau-b it was necessary to consider the different types of pairs, for example, concordant, discordant, ties on X, ties on Y, ties on X and Y, and the total number of possible unique pairs that can stem from ordinal level data. Most of the ordinal measures of association presented in this chapter were ratios between the preponderance of concordant-discordant pairs to one of the other pair types. A separate discussion of Spearman's rank order correlation coefficient was also included. Finally, tests of significance and assets and liabilities of each were noted.

The interval/ratio measure of association, Pearson's product-moment correlation coefficient, was preceded by an examination of scattergrams for perfect positive, perfect negative, zero, and curvilinear relationships. In addition to the test of significance for r, several important guides and concepts for interpreting r were discussed.

Finally, an extension of correlation known as linear regression was briefly considered. The predictive character of regression was illustrated with a couple of examples which required the computation of the b-coefficient and Y-intercept.

IMPORTANT CONCEPTS DISCUSSED IN THIS CHAPTER

Ordinal measures of association

Combinations

Permutations

Concordant (same-ordered) pairs (n_s)

Discordant (reverse-ordered) pairs (n_d)

Pairs tied on X (independent variable) (t_x)

Pairs tied on Y (dependent variables) (t_y)

Pairs tied on X and Y (variables) (t_{xy})

Total number of possible unique pairs

Tau-a

Gamma

Somer's d

Tau-b

Spearman's rho

Guilford's table

Interval/ratio measure of association

Scattergram

Pearsonian product-moment correlation coefficient (r)

Homoscedasticity

Tests of significance for association coefficients

Coefficient of determination (proportion of explained variation)

Coefficient of nondetermination (proportion of unexplained variation)

Linear (rectilinear) regression

Y-intercept

b-coefficient

REVIEW QUESTIONS

1. For this exercise we wish to measure the association between education and occupational mobility using the hypothetical data listed below. To do this you must first of all identify the positive and negative diagonals.

| | Education (X) | | | | |
Occupational Mobility (Y)	Some H.S. or Less	H.S. Diploma	Some College	College Diploma	Totals
High	10	25	40	55	130
Medium	20	45	50	35	150
Low	60	30	20	10	120
Totals	90	100	110	100	400

a. Compute the number of concordant pairs (n_s).
b. Compute the number of discordant pairs (n_d).
c. Compute the number of pairs tied on X (t_x).
d. Compute the number of pairs tied on Y (t_y).
e. Compute the number of pairs tied on both X and Y (t_{xy}).
f. Compute the total number of unique pairs.
g. Sum n_s, n_d, t_x, t_y, and t_{xy} to "double check" your calculations. Remember, these five sums must add up to the total number of unique pairs.

2. With the information obtained from question 1, calculate:
   a. Tau-*a* and test it for statistical significance.
   b. Gamma and test it for statistical significance.
   c. Tau-*b* and test it for statistical significance.
   d. Somer's d_{yx} and d_{xy} and test each for statistical significance.

3. Suppose we are interested in the correlation between a worker's interest in his or her job and the effectiveness at that job. Specifically we rank order fourteen computer operators by interest (R_x) and effectiveness (R_y). Calculate Spearman's rho to measure the degree of association between the two variables and then test it for statistical significance.

Computer Operator	R_x	R_y
A	12	9
B	9	11
C	7	7
D	14	12
E	2	3
F	5	6
G	13	14
H	4	4
I	8	10
J	11	13
K	6	5
L	1	1
M	3	2
N	10	8

4. Suppose we are interested in the relationship between graduate and professional school examination scores for persons who have taken the medical school admissions test (MCAT) and the graduate record exam (GRE). Ten students' exam scores are listed below. For these hypothetical data, calculate Pearson's product moment correlation

coefficient to determine the magnitude of the association between the two sets of test scores.

Student	MCAT (X)	GRE (Y)
1	59	86
2	68	95
3	49	76
4	74	97
5	65	80
6	54	83
7	47	70
8	72	96
9	62	90
10	50	77

a.   Interpret your computed r according to Guilford's table.
b.   Test r for statistical significance.

5.   Given the following data:

Individuals	X	Y
1	8	6,000
2	12	9,000
3	14	12,000
4	16	15,000
5	18	18,000

a.   Determine the slope, b_{yx}, of the regression line.
b.   Determine the Y-intercept, a_{yx}, of the regression line.
c.   Write out the regression equation for these data.

*

CHAPTER **14**

A SUMMARY:
LOOKING BACK
AND LOOKING AHEAD

The twentieth century witnessed the inception and growth of the use of quantitative techniques in the social sciences. In sociology, for example, Emile Durkheim (1858–1917) did *not* make use of statistical techniques in his classic work entitled *Suicide* (1897). Although the concept of correlation had been developed by Galton (circa 1886), it was not widely known nor understood during the time Durkheim was conducting his study. However, Durkheim did use the *reasoning* underlying modern social statistics. The point is to underscore the relatively recent use of quantification in sociology. Although there is still some reluctance in certain academic circles to admit the utility of quantification in the study of human behavior, the following passage (Mueller, Schuessler, and Costner, 1970: 8) places statistics in the perspective this writer has tried to unfold:

The aim of social science is to analyze . . . variations in order to make them understandable. Such an analysis presumes that the variation of interest be described by measuring amounts or by classifying objects into subclasses. Measurement and classification are essential to knowledge. They are also essential to statistics.

It must be emphasized, however, that statistical techniques are not panaceas. There are many investigations where their use would be inappropriate and/or impractical. Furthermore, the statistical formulae themselves are straightforward, but the *when, if,* and *why* surrounding their implementation is dependent upon the ingenuity, understanding, and creativity of the researcher.

The future of statistics will be undoubtedly linked with the technology of computers. This "marriage" will open vistas of inquiry previously untapped.

Already, increasing use of multivariate analysis has taken place since computer technology takes the time and drudgery out of the computations. However, those in the computer world caution us about expecting too much from their hardware. The apt expression *GIGO—Garbage In-Garbage Out*—captures their caveat.

In any event, the dual objectives of statistics, description and inference, will be with the social investigator for the foreseeable future. It seems appropriate to briefly review some of the *key themes* of the material presented in the previous thirteen chapters. Figure 14.1 is a completed summary table of the appropriate statistical techniques by levels of measurement for the outline that appeared in Figure 2.5.

In Chapter 1 statistics was defined as the general body of techniques for *assembling, describing,* and *inferring* something from numerical data. The three underscored terms capture the major purposes of statistics. One of the fundamental entities in statistics is a *data-distribution.* In Chapter 3 we saw how the researcher goes about assembling data to produce meaningful distributions, frequency and percentage, which facilitate statistical description.

With some of the guidelines for assembling data clearly spelled out, we moved into separate chapters devoted entirely to the understanding and calculation of such generic **descriptive statistics** as *measures of central tendency* (Chapter 4), *dispersion* (Chapter 5), and *association* (Chapters 12 and 13). The computation of appropriate descriptive statistics enables one to describe succinctly key mathematical properties of a distribution. Furthermore, these statistics provided us with an overall summary of the data.

The foundation for **inferential statistics** lies in descriptive statistics. The discussion of *parameter estimation* (Chapter 7) and *hypothesis testing* (Chapters 8, 9, 10, and 11) gave the two fundamental components of *inductive statistics.* In both cases the concern is with inferring properties/characteristics of a *population* on the basis of a carefully selected *sample.* Chapter 2 provided the background for understanding the relationships among *statistics, social theory,* and *methodology.* The discussion of the *normal curve* was, in some respects, a transition between descriptive and inferential statistics. The normal curve reaches back to descriptive statistics in the sense that many empirical distributions are approximately normally distributed and ahead to inferential statistics in that the sampling distribution of some statistics is known or assumed to be normally distributed.

In this concluding chapter it is worth repeating (see Chapter 2) the stages of social research and the role of statistics in this process.

When the investigator has decided upon a problem to explore, he or she must convert this idea, sometimes called a *research* or *working hypothesis*, into a form that is amenable to testing. To be consistent with the *hypothetico-deductive* approach, testable hypotheses are logically derived from a larger theoretical concern. To test such hypotheses requires the *operationalization* of the relevant concepts.

Having done this, a *data-gathering instrument*, for example, questionnaire, interview schedule, and so forth, is developed or obtained. Any good instrument must demonstrate both *reliable* and *valid* features. The data collection ordinarily entails a specification of the sample and population to be studied.

After the data have been collected, they are analyzed for their bearing on the initial hypothesis. It is in the data-analysis stage that a comprehension of statistical techniques becomes all-important. During this phase of the research process raw data are tabulated, calculated, counted, summarized, rearranged, compared, and contrasted. In a broad sense statistics can be seen as an *information-processing tool*.

Statistical methodology has developed to the point where no *single* technique is always applicable to a given data-set. Instead, there are usually several meaningful statistical tests that *could* be used to process the data. In deciding which technique to use the researcher should ask several questions:

1. *What is the level of measurement of my data?* Answering this query will restrict the range of statistical tests and techniques which can legitimately be used for a particular research problem. The **level of measurement** concept has been the single most important organizing feature of this book. Figure 2.5 provided this general framework.

2. *What assumptions must I meet in order to employ a given statistic?* Virtually all tests make certain assumptions and the researcher is obliged to find the one(s) that best conform(s) to his/her situation. Though we often violate assumptions it is important to be aware of what problems can arise from such infractions.

3. *With what kind of sample or population am I dealing?* Is the sample random or not? Has the universe been adequately defined?

4. *What rules of decision am I going to use?* Level of significance? One- or two-tailed test? and so forth. Decision rules are necessary because of the very nature of social phenomena. In Chapter 2 it was indicated that human behavior is *stochastic* and not *deterministic* in character. Consequently, to come to terms with stochastic behavior we must be content with *probabilistic* understanding since there are few, if any, invariable laws of social behavior.

HOW TO TALK BACK TO A STATISTIC

Occasionally it has been reiterated that in some social circles a distrust of statistics is often found. While it is possible to lie with statistics, such deception is tantamount to anathema to the professional social scientist. In any case, the "critical thinker" to which I referred in Chapter 1 may help to protect himself or herself from being duped by asking and answering the following questions:

1. *Who says so?* Since it is possible to be misled by statistics, one must examine the *source* of the information critically. Given the vested interests of both individuals and groups, one must be attuned to the bias that may enter into the communication of the results of studies, surveys, opinion polls, and the like. This bias may be conscious as when the vague concept of *average* rather than the specific, that is, *mean, median, mode,* average is used. In this text we have seen that different averages may lead to different conclusions. *Bias* may also be due to ignorance or lack of statistical sophistication. While this latter type of bias may not

FIGURE 14.1

Summary Table of Some Appropriate Statistical Techniques by Levels of Measurement

Appropriate Statistical Techniques	Levels of Measurement		
	Nominal	Ordinal	Interval/Ratio
Graphic techniques	Bar graph Pie diagram	Bar graph Pie diagram Boxplot	Frequency and percentage polygons Frequency and percentage histograms Cumulative frequency and cumulative percentage polygons (ogives) Line graph Stemplot
Measures of central tendency	Mode	Median	Arithmetic mean Geometric mean Harmonic mean
Measures of dispersion	Index of qualitative variation Index of dispersion	Interquartile range	Range Average deviation Standard deviation Variance Coefficient of variability
Measures of association	*Non-PRE* C, T, V, ϵ^* *PRE* $Q, \phi, \lambda_y, \lambda^*$	*PRE* $\tau_a, \gamma, \tau_b, \tau_c, d_{xy}^*, d_{yx}^*$	*PRE* r linear regression

Descriptive Statistics

Inferential Statistics

	Confidence interval for a mean	Confidence interval for a proportion† (percentage†)	Confidence interval for a proportion† (percentage†)
Parameter estimation			
Measures of significance: One-sample test	z test (large sample) / t test (small sample)	Kolmogorov-Smirnov test / Runs test	Chi-square goodness-of-fit test
Two-sample test	Independent Samples t test / Related Samples t test	Independent Samples: Wald-Wolfowitz runs test, Mann-Whitney U test / Related Samples: Sign test, Wilcoxon matched pairs—signed ranks test	Independent Samples: Chi-square test of independence, Fisher's exact test, z test for differences between proportions / Related Samples: McNemar test
k-sample test	F test	Kruskal-Wallis H test / Friedman two-way analysis of variance test	Chi-square test for k independent samples / Cochran Q test

* Asymmetric measure.
† Variable must be dichotomized.

carry the same ethical overtones, it may still play havoc with the data analysis and its interpretation.

2. *How does one know?* The educated consumer of statistics is concerned with the *nature* of the sample. Without a probability sample, it's uncertain as to what population the results can be generalized. Moreover, even with a probability sample there is an element of "error," but this sampling error, as we have seen, is patterned. Equally important is considering the sample size. With a small sample we know that there may be a great deal of instability, relatively speaking, and one should be cautious about drawing conclusions.

3. *Does it make sense?* We humans can be quite gullible creatures. Consider a gimmick used by the U.S. Navy to recruit civilians for military duty. Years ago the Navy proudly stated that the death rate among naval personnel during the Spanish-American War was 9/1,000 whereas the death rate in New York City was 16/1,000. This claim conveyed the fallacious impression that it was safer to be in the Navy than in New York City! Does it make sense? Are the groups comparable? The two populations, if you will, are not equivalent. The Navy is mainly made up of young men in good health. The civilian population in New York City includes all age groups, young and old, and people of varying degrees of health.

4. *What's missing?* A propagandist is one who *selectively* uses the facts. Earlier we alluded to the deception that may follow when an average is reported without an indication of variability. Statistical data are easily misconstrued if certain statistical information providing a fuller perspective is missing.

Consumers of statistics will not be infallible if they answer these questions, but they will be more on guard against their naiveté. Maybe H. G. Wells was correct when he said, "Statistical thinking will one day be as necessary for efficient citizenship as the ability to read and write . . . ."

In closing I would like to reiterate two paragraphs I often write on the cover sheet of my course syllabus. It combines the critical thinking of the late C. Wright Mills (1916–62) and several statements of contemporary statisticians.

> "Statistics, when competently cultivated by the social scientist, comprises much more than the manipulation of figures and formulas. Statistical procedures, when applied, consist in relating or fitting social data to the appropriate statistical formulas and equations." (Mueller, Schuessler, and Costner, 1970: 5)

> Since statistical models rarely exactly fit social data it becomes imperative to develop what might be called *the statistical imagination*— an ability to come to terms with the hiatus between the statistical-mathematical world and social reality—this merger we will call **statistical reasoning**.

APPENDICES

TABLES

TABLE A
COMBATTING INNUMERACY

Because numbers can be overwhelming and incomprehensible, mathematicians have attempted to assist us in grasping and understanding their meaning, particularly in dealing with large numbers. *Exponential notation* is used to help us with large numbers. Here's how it works. You write down the number 10, then write a small number to the right and above—called a superscript—which indicates how many zeros appear after the 1. For example, $10^3 = 1000$; $10^5 = 100,000$; $10^{12} = 1,000,000,000,000$, etc. Mathematicians call these little numbers *exponents* or *powers*. In addition to the simplicity and clarity of exponential notation, you can use the addition of the exponents of numbers as equivalent to multiplying the *original* two numbers. For example, suppose we wanted to multiply 10 by 100. In exponential form, 10=1 and 100=2. Hence, $10^3 = 1,000$ as does 10×100; or $1000 \times 1,000,000 = 1,000,000,000$ or equivalent to 10^9 or 1,000,000,000. In the table on the next page we indicate the number name, the number written out, the number in scientific notation form, and, for interest, how long it would take to count to this number.

Name (U.S.)	Number (written out)	Number (scientific notation)	How long it would take to count to this number from 0 (one count per second, night and day)
One	1	10^0	1 second
Thousand	1,000	10^3	17 minutes
Million	1,000,000	10^6	12 days
Billion	1,000,000,000	10^9	32 years
Trillion	1,000,000,000,000	10^{12}	32,000 years (longer than there has been civilization on Earth)
Quadrillion	1,000,000,000,000,000	10^{15}	32 million years (longer than there have been humans on Earth)
Quintillion	1,000,000,000,000,000,000	10^{18}	32 billion years (more than the age of the universe)

• Larger numbers are called a sextillion (10^{21}), septillion (10^{24}), octillion (10^{27}), nonillion (10^{30}) and decillion (10^{33}).

THE USE OF TABLE B

The use of Table B requires that the raw score be transformed into a z score and that the variable be normally distributed (see equations 6.2 and 6.3).

The values in Table B represent the proportion of area in the standard normal curve which has a mean of 0, a standard deviation of 1.00, and a total area also equal to 1.00.

Since the normal curve is symmetrical, it is sufficient to indicate only the areas corresponding to positive z values. Negative z values will have precisely the same proportions of area as their positive counterparts.

Column B represents the proportion of area *between* the mean and a given z.

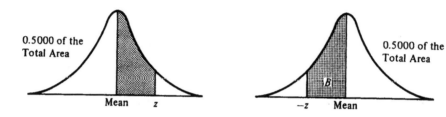

Column C represents the proportion of area *beyond* a given z.

TABLE B Proportions of Area under the Normal Curve

(A) z	(B) area between mean and z	(C) area beyond z	(A) z	(B) area between mean and z	(C) area beyond z	(A) z	(B) area between mean and z	(C) area beyond z
0.00	.0000	.5000	0.55	.2088	.2912	1.10	.3643	.1357
0.01	.0040	.4960	0.56	.2123	.2877	1.11	.3665	.1335
0.02	.0080	.4920	0.57	.2157	.2843	1.12	.3686	.1314
0.03	.0120	.4880	0.58	.2190	.2810	1.13	.3708	.1292
0.04	.0160	.4840	0.59	.2224	.2776	1.14	.3729	.1271
0.05	.0199	.4801	0.60	.2257	.2743	1.15	.3749	.1251
0.06	.0239	.4761	0.61	.2291	.2709	1.16	.3770	.1230
0.07	.0279	.4721	0.62	.2324	.2676	1.17	.3790	.1210
0.08	.0319	.4681	0.63	.2357	.2643	1.18	.3810	.1190
0.09	.0359	.4641	0.64	.2389	.2611	1.19	.3830	.1170
0.10	.0398	.4602	0.65	.2422	.2578	1.20	.3849	.1151
0.11	.0438	.4562	0.66	.2454	.2546	1.21	.3869	.1131
0.12	.0478	.4522	0.67	.2486	.2514	1.22	.3888	.1112
0.13	.0517	.4483	0.68	.2517	.2483	1.23	.3907	.1093
0.14	.0557	.4443	0.69	.2549	.2451	1.24	.3925	.1075
0.15	.0596	.4404	0.70	.2580	.2420	1.25	.3944	.1056
0.16	.0636	.4364	0.71	.2611	.2389	1.26	.3962	.1038
0.17	.0675	.4325	0.72	.2642	.2358	1.27	.3980	.1020
0.18	.0714	.4286	0.73	.2673	.2327	1.28	.3997	.1003
0.19	.0753	.4247	0.74	.2704	.2296	1.29	.4015	.0985
0.20	.0793	.4207	0.75	.2734	.2266	1.30	.4032	.0968
0.21	.0832	.4168	0.76	.2764	.2236	1.31	.4049	.0951
0.22	.0871	.4129	0.77	.2794	.2206	1.32	.4066	.0934
0.23	.0910	.4090	0.78	.2823	.2177	1.33	.4082	.0918
0.24	.0948	.4052	0.79	.2852	.2148	1.34	.4099	.0901
0.25	.0987	.4013	0.80	.2881	.2119	1.35	.4115	.0885
0.26	.1026	.3974	0.81	.2910	.2090	1.36	.4131	.0869
0.27	.1064	.3936	0.82	.2939	.2061	1.37	.4147	.0853
0.28	.1103	.3897	0.83	.2967	.2033	1.38	.4162	.0838
0.29	.1141	.3859	0.84	.2995	.2005	1.39	.4177	.0823
0.30	.1179	.3821	0.85	.3023	.1977	1.40	.4192	.0808
0.31	.1217	.3783	0.86	.3051	.1949	1.41	.4207	.0793
0.32	.1255	.3745	0.87	.3078	.1922	1.42	.4222	.0778
0.33	.1293	.3707	0.88	.3106	.1894	1.43	.4236	.0764
0.34	.1331	.3669	0.89	.3133	.1867	1.44	.4251	.0749
0.35	.1368	.3632	0.90	.3159	.1841	1.45	.4265	.0735
0.36	.1406	.3594	0.91	.3186	.1814	1.46	.4279	.0721
0.37	.1443	.3557	0.92	.3212	.1788	1.47	.4292	.0708
0.38	.1480	.3520	0.93	.3238	.1762	1.48	.4306	.0694
0.39	.1517	.3483	0.94	.3264	.1736	1.49	.4319	.0681
0.40	.1554	.3446	0.95	.3289	.1711	1.50	.4332	.0668
0.41	.1591	.3409	0.96	.3315	.1685	1.51	.4345	.0655
0.42	.1628	.3372	0.97	.3340	.1660	1.52	.4357	.0643
0.43	.1664	.3336	0.98	.3365	.1635	1.53	.4370	.0630
0.44	.1700	.3300	0.99	.3389	.1611	1.54	.4382	.0618
0.45	.1736	.3264	1.00	.3413	.1587	1.55	.4394	.0606
0.46	.1772	.3228	1.01	.3438	.1562	1.56	.4406	.0594
0.47	.1808	.3192	1.02	.3461	.1539	1.57	.4418	.0582
0.48	.1844	.3156	1.03	.3485	.1515	1.58	.4429	.0571
0.49	.1879	.3121	1.04	.3508	.1492	1.59	.4441	.0559
0.50	.1915	.3085	1.05	.3531	.1469	1.60	.4452	.0548
0.51	.1950	.3050	1.06	.3554	.1446	1.61	.4463	.0537
0.52	.1985	.3015	1.07	.3577	.1423	1.62	.4474	.0526
0.53	.2019	.2981	1.08	.3599	.1401	1.63	.4484	.0516
0.54	.2054	.2946	1.09	.3621	.1379	1.64	.4495	.0505

Source: "Table A" (Proportions of Area under the Normal Curve) from Fundamentals of Behavioral Statistics by R. P. Runyon and A. Haber (Addison-Wesley, 1971). Used with the kind permission of the publishers.

TABLE B (continued)

(A) z	(B) area between mean and z	(C) area beyond z	(A) z	(B) area between mean and z	(C) area beyond z	(A) z	(B) area between mean and z	(C) area beyond z
1.65	.4505	.0495	2.22	.4868	.0132	2.79	.4974	.0026
1.66	.4515	.0485	2.23	.4871	.0129	2.80	.4974	.0026
1.67	.4525	.0475	2.24	.4875	.0125	2.81	.4975	.0025
1.68	.4535	.0465	2.25	.4878	.0122	2.82	.4976	.0024
1.69	.4545	.0455	2.26	.4881	.0119	2.83	.4977	.0023
1.70	.4554	.0446	2.27	.4884	.0116	2.84	.4977	.0023
1.71	.4564	.0436	2.28	.4887	.0113	2.85	.4978	.0022
1.72	.4573	.0427	2.29	.4890	.0110	2.86	.4979	.0021
1.73	.4582	.0418	2.30	.4893	.0107	2.87	.4979	.0021
1.74	.4591	.0409	2.31	.4896	.0104	2.88	.4980	.0020
1.75	.4599	.0401	2.32	.4898	.0102	2.89	.4981	.0019
1.76	.4608	.0392	2.33	.4901	.0099	2.90	.4981	.0019
1.77	.4616	.0384	2.34	.4904	.0096	2.91	.4982	.0018
1.78	.4625	.0375	2.35	.4906	.0094	2.92	.4982	.0018
1.79	.4633	.0367	2.36	.4909	.0091	2.93	.4983	.0017
1.80	.4641	.0359	2.37	.4911	.0089	2.94	.4984	.0016
1.81	.4649	.0351	2.38	.4913	.0087	2.95	.4984	.0016
1.82	.4656	.0344	2.39	.4916	.0084	2.96	.4985	.0015
1.83	.4664	.0336	2.40	.4918	.0082	2.97	.4985	.0015
1.84	.4671	.0329	2.41	.4920	.0080	2.98	.4986	.0014
1.85	.4678	.0322	2.42	.4922	.0078	2.99	.4986	.0014
1.86	.4686	.0314	2.43	.4925	.0075	3.00	.4987	.0013
1.87	.4693	.0307	2.44	.4927	.0073	3.01	.4987	.0013
1.88	.4699	.0301	2.45	.4929	.0071	3.02	.4987	.0013
1.89	.4706	.0294	2.46	.4931	.0069	3.03	.4988	.0012
1.90	.4713	.0287	2.47	.4932	.0068	3.04	.4988	.0012
1.91	.4719	.0281	2.48	.4934	.0066	3.05	.4989	.0011
1.92	.4726	.0274	2.49	.4936	.0064	3.06	.4989	.0011
1.93	.4732	.0268	2.50	.4938	.0062	3.07	.4989	.0011
1.94	.4738	.0262	2.51	.4940	.0060	3.08	.4990	.0010
1.95	.4744	.0256	2.52	.4941	.0059	3.09	.4990	.0010
1.96	.4750	.0250	2.53	.4943	.0057	3.10	.4990	.0010
1.97	.4756	.0244	2.54	.4945	.0055	3.11	.4991	.0009
1.98	.4761	.0239	2.55	.4946	.0054	3.12	.4991	.0009
1.99	.4767	.0233	2.56	.4948	.0052	3.13	.4991	.0009
2.00	.4772	.0228	2.57	.4949	.0051	3.14	.4992	.0008
2.01	.4778	.0222	2.58	.4951	.0049	3.15	.4992	.0008
2.02	.4783	.0217	2.59	.4952	.0048	3.16	.4992	.0008
2.03	.4788	.0212	2.60	.4953	.0047	3.17	.4992	.0008
2.04	.4793	.0207	2.61	.4955	.0045	3.18	.4993	.0007
2.05	.4798	.0202	2.62	.4956	.0044	3.19	.4993	.0007
2.06	.4803	.0197	2.63	.4957	.0043	3.20	.4993	.0007
2.07	.4808	.0192	2.64	.4959	.0041	3.21	.4993	.0007
2.08	.4812	.0188	2.65	.4960	.0040	3.22	.4994	.0006
2.09	.4817	.0183	2.66	.4961	.0039	3.23	.4994	.0006
2.10	.4821	.0179	2.67	.4962	.0038	3.24	.4994	.0006
2.11	.4826	.0174	2.68	.4963	.0037	3.25	.4994	.0006
2.12	.4830	.0170	2.69	.4964	.0036	3.30	.4995	.0005
2.13	.4834	.0166	2.70	.4965	.0035	3.35	.4996	.0004
2.14	.4838	.0162	2.71	.4966	.0034	3.40	.4997	.0003
2.15	.4842	.0158	2.72	.4967	.0033	3.45	.4997	.0003
2.16	.4846	.0154	2.73	.4968	.0032	3.50	.4998	.0002
2.17	.4850	.0150	2.74	.4969	.0031	3.60	.4998	.0002
2.18	.4854	.0146	2.75	.4970	.0030	3.70	.4999	.0001
2.19	.4857	.0143	2.76	.4971	.0029	3.80	.4999	.0001
2.20	.4861	.0139	2.77	.4972	.0028	3.90	.49995	.00005
2.21	.4864	.0136	2.78	.4973	.0027	4.00	.49997	.00003

TABLE C   355

TABLE C   Sampling Distribution of χ^2

df						Probability (two-tailed)*								
	.99	.98	.95	.90	.80	.70	.50	.30	.20	.10	.05	.02	.01	.001
1	.0³157	.0³628	.0²393	.0²158	.0²642	.148	.455	1.074	1.642	2.706	3.841	5.412	6.635	10.827
2	.0201	.0404	.103	.211	.446	.713	1.386	2.408	3.219	4.605	5.991	7.824	9.210	13.815
3	.115	.185	.352	.584	1.005	1.424	2.366	3.665	4.642	6.251	7.815	9.837	11.345	16.268
4	.297	.429	.711	1.064	1.649	2.195	3.357	4.878	5.989	7.779	9.488	11.668	13.277	18.465
5	.554	.752	1.145	1.610	2.343	3.000	4.351	6.064	7.289	9.236	11.070	13.388	15.086	20.517
6	.872	1.134	1.635	2.204	3.070	3.828	5.348	7.231	8.558	10.645	12.592	15.033	16.812	22.457
7	1.239	1.564	2.167	2.833	3.822	4.671	6.346	8.383	9.803	12.017	14.067	16.622	18.475	24.322
8	1.646	2.032	2.733	3.490	4.594	5.527	7.344	9.524	11.030	13.362	15.507	18.168	20.090	26.125
9	2.088	2.532	3.325	4.168	5.380	6.393	8.343	10.656	12.242	14.684	16.919	19.679	21.666	27.877
10	2.558	3.059	3.940	4.865	6.179	7.267	9.342	11.781	13.442	15.987	18.307	21.161	23.209	29.588
11	3.053	3.609	4.575	5.578	6.989	8.148	10.341	12.899	14.631	17.275	19.675	22.618	24.725	31.264
12	3.571	4.178	5.226	6.304	7.807	9.034	11.340	14.011	15.812	18.549	21.026	24.054	26.217	32.909
13	4.107	4.765	5.892	7.042	8.634	9.926	12.340	15.119	16.985	19.812	22.362	25.472	27.688	34.528
14	4.660	5.368	6.571	7.790	9.467	10.821	13.339	16.222	18.151	21.064	23.685	26.873	29.141	36.123
15	5.229	5.985	7.261	8.547	10.307	11.721	14.339	17.322	19.311	22.307	24.996	28.259	30.578	37.697
16	5.812	6.614	7.962	9.312	11.152	12.624	15.338	18.418	20.465	23.542	26.296	29.633	32.000	39.252
17	6.408	7.255	8.672	10.085	12.002	13.531	16.338	19.511	21.615	24.769	27.587	30.995	33.409	40.790
18	7.015	7.906	9.390	10.865	12.857	14.440	17.338	20.601	22.760	25.989	28.869	32.346	34.805	42.312
19	7.633	8.567	10.117	11.651	13.716	15.352	18.338	21.689	23.900	27.204	30.144	33.687	36.191	43.820
20	8.260	9.237	10.851	12.443	14.578	16.266	19.337	22.775	25.038	28.412	31.410	35.020	37.566	45.315
21	8.897	9.915	11.591	13.240	15.445	17.182	20.337	23.858	26.171	29.615	32.671	36.343	38.932	46.797
22	9.542	10.600	12.338	14.041	16.314	18.101	21.337	24.939	27.301	30.813	33.924	37.659	40.289	48.268
23	10.196	11.293	13.091	14.848	17.187	19.021	22.337	26.018	28.429	32.007	35.172	38.968	41.638	49.728
24	10.856	11.992	13.848	15.659	18.062	19.943	23.337	27.096	29.553	33.196	36.415	40.270	42.980	51.179
25	11.524	12.697	14.611	16.473	18.940	20.867	24.337	28.172	30.675	34.382	37.652	41.566	44.314	52.620
26	12.198	13.409	15.379	17.292	19.820	21.792	25.336	29.246	31.795	35.563	38.885	42.856	45.642	54.052
27	12.879	14.125	16.151	18.114	20.703	22.719	26.336	30.319	32.912	36.741	40.113	44.140	46.963	55.476
28	13.565	14.847	16.928	18.939	21.588	23.647	27.336	31.391	34.027	37.916	41.337	45.419	48.278	56.893
29	14.256	15.574	17.708	19.768	22.475	24.577	28.336	32.461	35.139	39.087	42.557	46.693	49.588	58.302
30	14.953	16.306	18.493	20.599	23.364	25.508	29.336	33.530	36.250	40.256	43.773	47.962	50.892	59.703

*For one-tailed applications, simply *halve* the probability shown; that is, .10(two-tailed) becomes .10/2, or .05, for a one-tailed probability. The computed chi-square is significant if it is *equal to or larger than* the table chi-square.

Source: Ronald A. Fisher and Frank Yates. *Statistical Tables for Biological, Agricultural and Medical Research*, published by Longman Group Ltd., London (previously published by Oliver & Boyd, Edinburgh), and by permission of the authors and publishers.

TABLE D

How to Read a Table

1. Read the title carefully

2. Read the headnote(s) and any other explanations provided

3. Notice the source

4. Look at the footnote(s)

5. Check the units used

6. Check the column heading(s) and the row stub(s)

7. Look at the overall average(s)

8. Note the variability

TABLE E

Sampling Distribution of t

For any given df, the (absolute) obtained t value is significant if it is *equal to or larger than* the table value at a selected level of significance.

df	Level of significance for one-tailed test					
	.10	.05	.025	.01	.005	.0005
	Level of significance for two-tailed test					
df	.20	.10	.05	.02	.01	.001
1	3.078	6.314	12.706	31.821	63.657	636.619
2	1.886	2.920	4.303	6.965	9.925	31.598
3	1.638	2.353	3.182	4.541	5.841	12.941
4	1.533	2.132	2.776	3.747	4.604	8.610
5	1.476	2.015	2.571	3.365	4.032	6.859
6	1.440	1.943	2.447	3.143	3.707	5.959
7	1.415	1.895	2.365	2.998	3.499	5.405
8	1.397	1.860	2.306	2.896	3.355	5.041
9	1.383	1.833	2.262	2.821	3.250	4.781
10	1.372	1.812	2.228	2.764	3.169	4.587
11	1.363	1.796	2.201	2.718	3.106	4.437
12	1.356	1.782	2.179	2.681	3.055	4.318
13	1.350	1.771	2.160	2.650	3.012	4.221
14	1.345	1.761	2.145	2.624	2.977	4.140
15	1.341	1.753	2.131	2.602	2.947	4.073
16	1.337	1.746	2.120	2.583	2.921	4.015
17	1.333	1.740	2.110	2.567	2.898	3.965
18	1.330	1.734	2.101	2.552	2.878	3.922
19	1.328	1.729	2.093	2.539	2.861	3.883
20	1.325	1.725	2.086	2.528	2.845	3.850
21	1.323	1.721	2.080	2.518	2.831	3.819
22	1.321	1.717	2.074	2.508	2.819	3.792
23	1.319	1.714	2.069	2.500	2.807	3.767
24	1.318	1.711	2.064	2.492	2.797	3.745
25	1.316	1.708	2.060	2.485	2.787	3.725
26	1.315	1.706	2.056	2.479	2.779	3.707
27	1.314	1.703	2.052	2.473	2.771	3.690
28	1.313	1.701	2.048	2.467	2.763	3.674
29	1.311	1.699	2.045	2.462	2.756	3.659
30	1.310	1.697	2.042	2.457	2.750	3.646
40	1.303	1.684	2.021	2.423	2.704	3.551
60	1.296	1.671	2.000	2.390	2.660	3.460
120	1.289	1.658	1.980	2.358	2.617	3.373
∞	1.282	1.645	1.960	2.326	2.576	3.291

Source: Abridged from Ronald A. Fisher and Frank Yates. *Statistical Tables for Biological, Agricultural and Medical Research*, published by Longman Group Ltd., London (previously published by Oliver & Boyd, Edinburgh), and by permission of the authors and publishers.

TABLE F

Critical Values of *D* in the Kolmogorov-Smirnov One-Sample Test*

D, the maximum absolute observed-theoretical cumulative frequency difference, is statistically significant if it is *equal to or larger than* the table value.

Sample size (*n*)	Level of significance for $D = \text{maximum } \lvert F_0(X) - S_n(X) \rvert$				
	.20	.15	.10	.05	.01
1	.900	.925	.950	.975	.995
2	.684	.726	.776	.842	.929
3	.565	.597	.642	.708	.828
4	.494	.525	.564	.624	.733
5	.446	.474	.510	.565	.669
6	.410	.436	.470	.521	.618
7	.381	.405	.438	.486	.577
8	.358	.381	.411	.457	.543
9	.339	.360	.388	.432	.514
10	.322	.342	.368	.410	.490
11	.307	.326	.352	.391	.468
12	.295	.313	.338	.375	.450
13	.284	.302	.325	.361	.433
14	.274	.292	.314	.349	.418
15	.266	.283	.304	.338	.404
16	.258	.274	.295	.328	.392
17	.250	.266	.286	.318	.381
18	.244	.259	.278	.309	.371
19	.237	.252	.272	.301	.363
20	.231	.246	.264	.294	.356
25	.21	.22	.24	.27	.32
30	.19	.20	.22	.24	.29
35	.18	.19	.21	.23	.27
Over 35	$\dfrac{1.07}{\sqrt{n}}$	$\dfrac{1.14}{\sqrt{n}}$	$\dfrac{1.22}{\sqrt{n}}$	$\dfrac{1.36}{\sqrt{n}}$	$\dfrac{1.63}{\sqrt{n}}$

*Two-tailed values.

Source: F. J. Massey, Jr. "The Kolmogorov-Smirnov Test for Goodness of Fit," *Journal of the American Statistical Association*, 46 (1951), p. 70. Used with the kind permission of the publishers.

TABLE G

Table of Critical Values of r in the Runs Test*

Given in the bodies of Table G_I and Table G_{II} are various critical values of r, the number of runs, for various values of n_1 and n_2. For the one-sample runs test, any value of r which is *equal to or smaller than* that shown in Table G_I or *equal to or larger than* that shown in Table G_{II} is significant at the .05 level. For the Wald-Wolfowitz two-sample runs test, any value of r which is *equal to or smaller than* that shown in Table G_I is significant at the .05 level.

TABLE G_I

n_1 \ n_2	2	3	4	5	6	7	8	9	10	11	12	13	14	15	16	17	18	19	20
2											2	2	2	2	2	2	2	2	2
3			2	2	2	2	2	2	2	2	2	2	2	3	3	3	3	3	3
4			2	2	2	3	3	3	3	3	3	3	3	3	4	4	4	4	4
5		2	2	3	3	3	3	3	4	4	4	4	4	4	4	5	5	5	
6	2	2	3	3	3	3	4	4	4	4	5	5	5	5	5	5	6	6	
7	2	2	3	3	3	4	4	5	5	5	5	5	6	6	6	6	6	6	
8	2	3	3	3	4	4	5	5	5	6	6	6	6	6	7	7	7	7	
9	2	3	3	4	4	5	5	5	6	6	6	7	7	7	7	8	8	8	
10	2	3	3	4	5	5	5	6	6	7	7	7	7	8	8	8	8	9	
11	2	3	4	4	5	5	6	6	7	7	7	8	8	8	9	9	9	9	
12	2	2	3	4	4	5	6	6	7	7	7	8	8	8	9	9	9	10	10
13	2	2	3	4	5	5	6	6	7	7	8	8	9	9	9	10	10	10	10
14	2	2	3	4	5	5	6	7	7	8	8	9	9	9	10	10	10	11	11
15	2	3	3	4	5	6	6	7	7	8	8	9	9	10	10	11	11	11	12
16	2	3	4	4	5	6	6	7	8	8	9	9	10	10	11	11	11	12	12
17	2	3	4	4	5	6	7	7	8	9	9	10	10	11	11	11	12	12	13
18	2	3	4	5	5	6	7	8	8	9	9	10	10	11	11	12	12	13	13
19	2	3	4	5	6	6	7	8	8	9	10	10	11	11	12	12	13	13	13
20	2	3	4	5	6	6	7	8	9	9	10	10	11	12	12	13	13	13	14

* Adapted from Frieda S. Swed and C. Eisenhart, 1943. "Tables for testing randomness of grouping in a sequence of alternatives," *Annals of Mathematical Statistics,* 14 (1943), pp. 83–86, with the kind permission of the authors and publisher.

TABLE G$_{II}$

n_1 \ n_2	2	3	4	5	6	7	8	9	10	11	12	13	14	15	16	17	18	19	20
2																			
3																			
4				9	9														
5			9	10	10	11	11												
6			9	10	11	12	12	13	13	13	13								
7				11	12	13	13	14	14	14	14	15	15	15					
8				11	12	13	14	14	15	15	16	16	16	16	17	17	17	17	17
9					13	14	14	15	16	16	16	17	17	18	18	18	18	18	18
10					13	14	15	16	16	17	17	18	18	18	19	19	19	20	20
11					13	14	15	16	17	17	18	19	19	19	20	20	20	21	21
12					13	14	16	16	17	18	19	19	20	20	21	21	21	22	22
13						15	16	17	18	19	19	20	20	21	21	22	22	23	23
14						15	16	17	18	19	20	20	21	22	22	23	23	23	24
15						15	16	18	18	19	20	21	22	22	23	23	24	24	25
16							17	18	19	20	21	21	22	23	23	24	25	25	25
17							17	18	19	20	21	22	23	23	24	25	25	26	26
18							17	18	19	20	21	22	23	24	25	25	26	26	27
19							17	18	20	21	22	23	23	24	25	26	26	27	27
20							17	18	20	21	22	23	24	25	25	26	27	27	28

* Adapted from Frieda S. Swed and C. Eisenhart. "Tables for testing randomness of grouping in a sequence of alternatives," *Annals of Mathematical Statistics*, 14 (1943), pp. 83–86, with the kind permission of the authors and publisher.

TABLE H

Critical Values of U_1 and U_2

Critical Values of U_1 and U_2 for a One-Tailed Test at $\alpha = 0.005$ or a Two-Tailed Test at $\alpha = 0.01$. To be significant for any given n_1 and n_2: Obtained U_1 must be equal to or *less than* the value shown in the table. Obtained U_2 must be equal to or *greater than* the value shown in the table.

Each cell shows U_1 / U_2.

n_2 \ n_1	1	2	3	4	5	6	7	8	9	10	11	12	13	14	15	16	17	18	19	20
1	--	--	--	--	--	--	--	--	--	--	--	--	--	--	--	--	--	--	--	--
2	--	--	--	--	--	--	--	--	--	--	--	--	--	--	--	--	--	--	0/38	0/40
3	--	--	--	--	--	--	--	--	0/27	0/30	0/33	1/35	1/38	1/41	2/43	2/46	2/49	2/52	3/54	3/57
4	--	--	--	--	--	0/24	0/28	1/31	1/35	2/38	2/42	3/45	3/49	4/52	5/55	5/59	6/62	6/66	7/69	8/72
5	--	--	--	--	0/25	1/29	1/34	2/38	3/42	4/46	5/50	6/54	7/58	7/63	8/67	9/71	10/75	11/79	12/83	13/87
6	--	--	--	0/24	1/29	2/34	3/39	4/44	5/49	6/54	7/59	9/63	10/68	11/73	12/78	13/83	15/87	16/92	17/97	18/102
7	--	--	--	0/28	1/34	3/39	4/45	6/50	7/56	9/61	10/67	12/72	13/78	15/83	16/89	18/94	19/100	21/105	22/111	24/116
8	--	--	--	1/31	2/38	4/44	6/50	7/57	9/63	11/69	13/75	15/81	17/87	18/94	20/100	22/106	24/112	26/118	28/124	30/130
9	--	--	0/27	1/35	3/42	5/49	7/56	9/63	11/70	13/77	16/83	18/90	20/97	22/104	24/111	27/117	29/124	31/131	33/138	36/144
10	--	--	0/30	2/38	4/46	6/54	9/61	11/69	13/77	16/84	18/92	21/99	24/106	26/114	29/121	31/129	34/136	37/143	39/151	42/158
11	--	--	0/33	2/42	5/50	7/59	10/67	13/75	16/83	18/92	21/100	24/108	27/116	30/124	33/132	36/140	39/148	42/156	45/164	48/172
12	--	--	1/35	3/45	6/54	9/63	12/72	15/81	18/90	21/99	24/108	27/117	31/125	34/134	37/143	41/151	44/160	47/169	51/177	54/186
13	--	--	1/38	3/49	7/58	10/68	13/78	17/87	20/97	24/106	27/116	31/125	34/125	38/144	42/153	45/163	49/172	53/181	56/191	60/200
14	--	--	1/41	4/52	7/63	11/73	15/83	18/94	22/104	26/114	30/124	34/134	38/144	42/154	46/164	50/174	54/184	58/194	63/203	67/213
15	--	--	2/43	5/55	8/67	12/78	16/89	20/100	24/111	29/121	33/132	37/143	42/153	46/164	51/174	55/185	60/195	64/206	69/216	73/227
16	--	--	2/46	5/59	9/71	13/83	18/94	22/106	27/117	31/129	36/140	41/151	45/163	50/174	55/185	60/196	65/207	70/218	74/230	79/241
17	--	--	2/49	6/62	10/75	15/87	19/100	24/112	29/124	34/136	39/148	44/160	49/172	54/184	60/195	65/207	70/219	75/231	81/242	86/254
18	--	--	2/52	6/66	11/79	16/92	21/105	26/118	31/131	37/143	42/156	47/169	53/181	58/194	64/206	70/218	75/231	81/243	87/255	92/268
19	--	0/38	3/54	7/69	12/83	17/97	22/111	28/124	33/138	39/151	45/164	51/177	56/191	63/203	69/216	74/230	81/242	87/255	93/268	99/281
20	--	0/40	3/57	8/72	13/87	18/102	24/116	30/130	36/144	42/158	48/172	54/186	60/200	67/213	73/227	79/241	86/254	92/268	99/281	105/295

(Dashes in the body of the table indicate that no decision is possible at the stated level of significance.)

Source: D. Auble, Extended Tables for the Mann-Whitney statistic. Bulletin of the Institute of Educational Research at Indiana University, 1, No. 2, 1953. Used with the kind permission of the publishers.

TABLE H (continued)

Critical Values of U_1 and U_2 for a One-Tailed Test at $\alpha = 0.01$ or a Two-Tailed Test at $\alpha = 0.02$. To be significant for any given n_1 and n_2: Obtained U_1 must be equal to or *less than* the value shown in the table. Obtained U_2 must be equal to or *greater than* the value shown in the table.

n_2 \ n_1	1	2	3	4	5	6	7	8	9	10	11	12	13	14	15	16	17	18	19	20
1	--	--	--	--	--	--	--	--	--	--	--	--	--	--	--	--	--	--	--	--
2	--	--	--	--	--	--	--	--	--	--	--	--	0/26	0/28	0/30	0/32	0/34	0/36	1/37	1/39
3	--	--	--	--	--	--	0/21	0/24	1/26	1/29	1/32	2/34	2/37	2/40	3/42	3/45	4/47	4/50	4/52	5/55
4	--	--	--	--	0/20	1/23	1/27	2/30	3/33	3/37	4/40	5/43	5/47	6/50	7/53	7/57	8/60	9/63	9/67	10/70
5	--	--	--	0/20	1/24	2/28	3/32	4/36	5/40	6/44	7/48	8/52	9/56	10/60	11/64	12/68	13/72	14/76	15/80	16/84
6	--	--	--	1/23	2/28	3/33	4/38	6/42	7/47	8/52	9/57	11/61	12/66	13/71	15/75	16/80	18/84	19/89	20/94	22/98
7	--	--	0/21	1/27	3/32	4/38	6/43	7/49	9/54	11/59	12/65	14/70	16/75	17/81	19/86	21/91	23/96	24/102	26/107	28/112
8	--	--	0/24	2/30	4/36	6/42	7/49	9/55	11/61	13/67	15/73	17/79	20/84	22/90	24/96	26/102	28/108	30/114	32/120	34/126
9	--	--	1/26	3/33	5/40	7/47	9/54	11/61	14/67	16/74	18/81	21/87	23/94	26/100	28/107	31/113	33/120	36/126	38/133	40/140
10	--	--	1/29	3/37	6/44	8/52	11/59	13/67	16/74	19/81	22/88	24/96	27/103	30/110	33/117	36/124	38/132	41/139	44/146	47/153
11	--	--	1/32	4/40	7/48	9/57	12/65	15/73	18/81	22/88	25/96	28/104	31/112	34/120	37/128	41/135	44/143	47/151	50/159	53/167
12	--	--	2/34	5/43	8/52	11/61	14/70	17/79	21/87	24/96	28/104	31/113	35/121	38/130	42/138	46/146	49/155	53/163	56/172	60/180
13	--	0/26	2/37	5/47	9/56	12/66	16/75	20/84	23/94	27/103	31/112	35/121	39/130	43/139	47/148	51/157	55/166	59/175	63/184	67/193
14	--	0/28	2/40	6/50	10/60	13/71	17/81	22/90	26/100	30/110	34/120	38/130	43/139	47/149	51/159	56/168	60/178	65/187	69/197	73/207
15	--	0/30	3/42	7/53	11/64	15/75	19/86	24/96	28/107	33/117	37/128	42/138	47/148	51/159	56/169	61/179	66/189	70/200	75/210	80/220
16	--	0/32	3/45	7/57	12/68	16/80	21/91	26/102	31/113	36/124	41/135	46/146	51/157	56/168	61/179	66/190	71/201	76/212	82/222	87/233
17	--	0/34	4/47	8/60	13/72	18/84	23/96	28/108	33/120	38/132	44/143	49/155	55/166	60/178	66/189	71/201	77/212	82/224	88/234	93/247
18	--	0/36	4/50	9/63	14/76	19/89	24/102	30/114	36/126	41/139	47/151	53/163	59/175	65/187	70/200	76/212	82/224	88/236	94/248	100/260
19	--	1/37	4/53	9/67	15/80	20/94	26/107	32/120	38/133	44/146	50/159	56/172	63/184	69/197	75/210	82/222	88/235	94/248	101/260	107/273
20	--	1/39	5/55	10/70	16/84	22/98	28/112	34/126	40/140	47/153	53/167	60/180	67/193	73/207	80/220	87/233	93/247	100/260	107/273	114/286

(Dashes in the body of the table indicate that no decision is possible at the stated level of significance.)

TABLE H (continued)

Critical Values of U_1 and U_2 for a One-Tailed test at $\alpha = 0.025$ or a Two-Tailed Test at $\alpha = 0.05$. To be significant for any given n_1 and n_2: Obtained U_1 must be equal to or *less than* the value shown in the table. Obtained U_2 must be equal to or *greater than* the value shown in the table.

n_2＼n_1	1	2	3	4	5	6	7	8	9	10	11	12	13	14	15	16	17	18	19	20
1	--	--	--	--	--	--	--	--	--	--	--	--	--	--	--	--	--	--	--	--
2	--	--	--	--	--	--	--	0/16	0/18	0/20	0/22	1/23	1/25	1/27	1/29	1/31	2/32	2/34	2/36	2/38
3	--	--	--	--	0/15	1/17	1/20	2/22	2/25	3/27	3/30	4/32	4/35	5/37	5/40	6/42	6/45	7/47	7/50	8/52
4	--	--	--	0/16	1/19	2/22	3/25	4/28	4/32	5/35	6/38	7/41	8/44	9/47	10/50	11/53	11/57	12/60	13/63	13/67
5	--	--	0/15	1/19	2/23	3/27	5/30	6/34	7/38	8/42	9/46	11/49	12/53	13/57	14/61	15/65	17/68	18/72	19/76	20/80
6	--	--	1/17	2/22	3/27	5/31	6/36	8/40	10/44	11/49	13/53	14/58	16/62	17/67	19/71	21/75	22/80	24/84	25/89	27/93
7	--	--	1/20	3/25	5/30	6/36	8/41	10/46	12/51	14/56	16/61	18/66	20/71	22/76	24/81	26/86	28/91	30/96	32/101	34/106
8	--	0/16	2/22	4/28	6/34	8/40	10/46	13/51	15/57	17/63	19/69	22/74	24/80	26/86	29/91	31/97	34/102	36/108	38/111	41/119
9	--	0/18	2/25	4/32	7/38	10/44	12/51	15/57	17/64	20/70	23/76	26/82	28/89	31/95	34/101	37/107	39/114	42/120	45/126	48/132
10	--	0/20	3/27	5/35	8/42	11/49	14/56	17/63	20/70	23/77	26/84	29/91	33/97	36/104	39/111	42/118	45/125	48/132	52/138	55/145
11	--	0/22	3/30	6/38	9/46	13/53	16/61	19/69	23/76	26/84	30/91	33/99	37/106	40/114	44/121	47/129	51/136	55/143	58/151	62/158
12	--	1/23	4/32	7/41	11/49	14/58	18/66	22/74	26/82	29/91	33/99	37/107	41/115	45/123	49/131	53/139	57/147	61/155	65/163	69/171
13	--	1/25	4/35	8/44	12/53	16/62	20/71	24/80	28/89	33/97	37/106	41/115	45/124	50/132	54/141	59/149	63/158	67/167	72/175	76/184
14	--	1/27	5/37	9/47	13/57	17/67	22/76	26/86	31/95	36/104	40/114	45/123	50/132	55/141	59/151	64/160	67/171	74/178	78/188	83/197
15	--	1/29	5/40	10/50	14/61	19/71	24/81	29/91	34/101	39/111	44/121	49/131	54/141	59/151	64/161	70/170	75/180	80/190	85/200	90/210
16	--	1/31	6/42	11/53	15/65	21/75	26/86	31/97	37/107	42/118	47/129	53/139	59/149	64/160	70/170	75/181	81/191	86/202	92/212	98/222
17	--	2/32	6/45	11/57	17/68	22/80	28/91	34/102	39/114	45/125	51/136	57/147	63/158	67/171	75/180	81/191	87/202	93/213	99/224	105/235
18	--	2/34	7/47	12/60	18/72	24/84	30/96	36/108	42/120	48/132	55/143	61/155	67/167	74/178	80/190	86/202	93/213	99/225	106/236	112/248
19	--	2/36	7/50	13/63	19/76	25/89	32/101	38/114	45/126	52/138	58/151	65/163	72/175	78/188	85/200	92/212	99/224	106/236	113/248	119/261
20	--	2/38	8/52	13/67	20/80	27/93	34/106	41/119	48/132	55/145	62/158	69/171	76/184	83/197	90/210	98/222	105/235	112/248	119/261	127/273

(Dashes in the body of the table indicate that no decision is possible at the stated level of significance.)

TABLE H (continued)

Critical Values of U_1 and U_2 for a One-Tailed Test at $\alpha = 0.05$ or a Two-Tailed Test at $\alpha = 0.10$. To be significant for any given n_1 and n_2: Obtained U_1 must be equal to or *less than* the value shown in the table. Obtained U_2 must be equal to or *greater than* the value shown in the table.

n_2 \ n_1	1	2	3	4	5	6	7	8	9	10	11	12	13	14	15	16	17	18	19	20
1	--	--	--	--	--	--	--	--	--	--	--	--	--	--	--	--	--	--	0 19	0 20
2	--	--	--	--	0 10	0 12	0 14	1 15	1 17	1 19	1 21	2 22	2 24	2 26	3 27	3 29	3 31	4 32	4 34	4 36
3	--	--	0 9	0 12	1 14	2 16	2 19	3 21	3 24	4 26	5 28	5 31	6 33	7 35	7 38	8 40	9 42	9 45	10 47	11 49
4	--	--	0 12	1 15	2 18	3 21	4 24	5 27	6 30	7 33	8 36	9 39	10 42	11 45	12 48	14 50	15 53	16 56	17 59	18 62
5	--	0 10	1 14	2 18	4 21	5 25	6 29	8 32	9 36	11 39	12 43	13 47	15 50	16 54	18 57	19 61	20 65	22 68	23 72	25 75
6	--	0 12	2 16	3 21	5 25	7 29	8 34	10 38	12 42	14 46	16 50	17 55	19 59	21 63	23 67	25 71	26 76	28 80	30 84	32 88
7	--	0 14	2 19	4 24	6 29	8 34	11 38	13 43	15 48	17 53	19 58	21 63	24 67	26 72	28 77	30 82	33 86	35 91	37 96	39 101
8	--	1 15	3 21	5 27	8 32	10 38	13 43	15 49	18 54	20 60	23 65	26 70	28 76	31 81	33 87	36 92	39 -97	41 103	44 108	47 113
9	--	1 17	3 24	6 30	9 36	12 42	15 48	18 54	21 60	24 66	27 72	30 78	33 84	36 90	39 96	42 102	45 108	48 114	51 120	54 126
10	--	1 19	4 26	7 33	11 39	14 46	17 53	20 60	24 66	27 73	31 79	34 86	37 93	41 99	44 106	48 112	51 119	55 125	58 132	62 138
11	--	1 21	5 28	8 36	12 43	16 50	19 58	23 65	27 72	31 79	34 87	38 94	42 101	46 108	50 115	54 122	57 130	61 137	65 144	69 151
12	--	2 22	5 31	9 39	13 47	17 55	21 63	26 70	30 78	34 86	38 94	42 102	47 109	51 117	55 125	60 132	64 140	68 148	72 156	77 163
13	--	2 24	6 33	10 42	15 50	19 59	24 67	28 76	33 84	37 93	42 101	47 109	51 118	56 126	61 134	65 143	70 151	75 159	80 167	84 176
14	--	2 26	7 35	11 45	16 54	21 63	26 72	31 81	36 90	41 99	46 108	51 117	56 126	61 135	66 144	71 153	77 161	82 170	87 179	92 188
15	--	3 27	7 38	12 48	18 57	23 67	28 77	33 87	39 96	44 106	50 115	55 125	61 134	66 144	72 153	77 163	83 172	88 182	94 191	100 200
16	--	3 29	8 40	14 50	19 61	25 71	30 82	36 92	42 102	48 112	54 122	60 132	65 143	71 153	77 163	83 173	89 183	95 193	101 203	107 213
17	--	3 31	9 42	15 53	20 65	26 76	33 86	39 97	45 108	51 119	57 130	64 140	70 151	77 161	83 172	89 183	96 193	102 204	109 214	115 225
18	--	4 32	9 45	16 56	22 68	28 80	35 91	41 103	48 114	55 123	61 137	68 148	75 159	82 170	88 182	95 193	102 204	109 215	116 226	123 237
19	0 19	4 34	10 47	17 59	23 72	30 84	37 96	44 108	51 120	58 132	65 144	72 156	80 167	87 179	94 191	101 203	109 214	116 226	123 238	130 250
20	0 20	4 36	11 49	18 62	25 75	32 88	39 101	47 113	54 126	62 138	69 151	77 163	84 176	92 188	100 200	107 213	115 225	123 237	130 250	138 262

(Dashes in the body of the table indicate that no decision is possible at the stated level of significance.)

TABLE I   365

TABLE I

Table of Random Numbers

Row number									
00000	10097	32533	76520	13586	34673	54876	80959	09117	39292	74945
00001	37542	04805	64894	74296	24805	24037	20636	10402	00822	91665
00002	08422	68953	19645	09303	23209	02560	15953	34764	35080	33606
00003	99019	02529	09376	70715	38311	31165	88676	74397	04436	27659
00004	12807	99970	80157	36147	64032	36653	98951	16877	12171	76833
00005	66065	74717	34072	76850	36697	36170	65813	39885	11199	29170
00006	31060	10805	45571	82406	35303	42614	86799	07439	23403	09732
00007	85269	77602	02051	65692	68665	74818	73053	85247	18623	88579
00008	63573	32135	05325	47048	90553	57548	28468	28709	83491	25624
00009	73796	45753	03529	64778	35808	34282	60935	20344	35273	88435
00010	98520	17767	14905	68607	22109	40558	60970	93433	50500	73998
00011	11805	05431	39808	27732	50725	68248	29405	24201	52775	67851
00012	83452	99634	06288	98033	13746	70078	18475	40610	68711	77817
00013	88685	40200	86507	58401	36766	67951	90364	76493	29609	11062
00014	99594	67348	87517	64969	91826	08928	93785	61368	23478	34113
00015	65481	17674	17468	50950	58047	76974	73039	57186	40218	16544
00016	80124	35635	17727	08015	45318	22374	21115	78253	14385	53763
00017	74350	99817	77402	77214	43236	00210	45521	64237	96286	02655
00018	69916	26803	66252	29148	36936	87203	76621	13990	94400	56418
00019	09893	20505	14225	68514	46427	56788	96297	78822	54382	14598
00020	91499	14523	68479	27686	46162	83554	94750	89923	37089	20048
00021	80336	94598	26940	36858	70297	34135	53140	33340	42050	82341
00022	44104	81949	85157	47954	32979	26575	57600	40881	22222	06413
00023	12550	73742	11100	02040	12860	74697	96644	89439	28707	25815
00024	63606	49329	16505	34484	40219	52563	43651	77082	07207	31790
00025	61196	90446	26457	47774	51924	33729	65394	59593	42582	60527
00026	15474	45266	95270	79953	59367	83848	82396	10118	33211	59466
00027	94557	28573	67897	54387	54622	44431	91190	42592	92927	45973
00028	42481	16213	97344	08721	16868	48767	03071	12059	25701	46670
00029	23523	78317	73208	89837	68935	91416	26252	29663	05522	82562
00030	04493	52494	75246	33824	45862	51025	61962	79335	65337	12472
00031	00549	97654	64051	88159	96119	63896	54692	82391	23287	29529
00032	35963	15307	26898	09354	33351	35462	77974	50024	90103	39333
00033	59808	08391	45427	26842	83609	49700	13021	24892	78565	20106
00034	46058	85236	01390	92286	77281	44077	93910	83647	70617	42941
00035	32179	00597	87379	25241	05567	07007	86743	17157	85394	11838
00036	69234	61406	20117	45204	15956	60000	18743	92423	97118	96338
00037	19565	41430	01758	75379	40419	21585	66674	36806	84962	85207
00038	45155	14938	19476	07246	43667	94543	59047	90033	20826	69541
00039	94864	31994	36168	10851	34888	81553	01540	35456	05014	51176
00040	98086	24826	45240	28404	44999	08896	39094	73407	35441	31880
00041	33185	16232	41941	50949	89435	48581	88695	41994	37548	73043
00042	80951	00406	96382	70774	20151	23387	25016	25298	94624	61171
00043	79752	49140	71961	28296	69861	02591	74852	20539	00387	59579
00044	18633	32537	98145	06571	31010	24674	05455	61427	77938	91936
00045	74029	43902	77557	32270	97790	17119	52527	58021	80814	51748
00046	54178	45611	80993	37143	05335	12969	56127	19255	36040	90324
00047	11664	49883	52079	84827	59381	71539	09973	33440	88461	23356
00048	48324	77928	31249	64710	02295	36870	32307	57546	15020	09994
00049	69074	94138	87637	91976	35584	04401	10518	21615	01848	76938
00050	09188	20097	32825	39527	04220	86304	83389	87374	64278	58044
00051	90045	85497	51981	50654	94938	81997	91870	76150	68476	64659
00052	73189	50207	47677	26269	62290	64464	27124	67018	41361	82760
00053	75768	76490	20971	87749	90429	12272	95375	05871	93823	43178
00054	54016	44056	66281	31003	00682	27398	20714	53295	07706	17813
00055	08358	69910	78542	42785	13661	58873	04618	97553	31223	08420
00056	28306	03264	81333	10591	40510	07893	32604	60475	94119	01840
00057	53840	86233	81594	13628	51215	90290	28466	68795	77762	20791
00058	91757	53741	61613	62669	50263	90212	55781	76514	83483	47055
00059	89415	92694	00397	58391	12607	17646	48949	72306	94541	37408

Source: The RAND corporation. *A Million Random Digits*. The Free Press, Glencoe, Illinois, 1955. By the kind permission of the publishers.

TABLE J

Cumulative Binomial Probabilities: $p = .5$

n \ m	0	1	2	3	4	5	6	7	8	9	10	11	12	13	14	15
5	031	188	500	812	969	†										
6	016	109	344	656	891	984	†									
7	008	062	227	500	773	938	992	†								
8	004	035	145	363	637	855	965	996	†							
9	002	020	090	254	500	746	910	980	998	†						
10	001	011	055	172	377	623	828	945	989	999	†					
11		006	033	113	274	500	726	887	967	994	†	†				
12		003	019	073	194	387	613	806	927	981	997	†	†			
13		002	011	046	133	291	500	709	867	954	989	998	†	†		
14		001	006	029	090	212	395	605	788	910	971	994	999	†	†	
15			004	018	059	151	304	500	696	849	941	982	996	†	†	†
16			002	011	038	105	227	402	598	773	895	962	989	998	†	†
17			001	006	025	072	166	315	500	685	834	928	975	994	999	†
18			001	004	015	048	119	240	407	593	760	881	952	985	996	999
19				002	010	032	084	180	324	500	676	820	916	968	990	998
20				001	006	021	058	132	252	412	588	748	868	942	979	994
21				001	004	013	039	095	192	332	500	668	808	905	961	987
22					002	008	026	067	143	262	416	584	738	857	933	974
23					001	005	017	047	105	202	339	500	661	798	895	953
24					001	003	011	032	076	154	271	419	581	729	846	924
25						002	007	022	054	115	212	345	500	655	788	885

†1.0 or approximately 1.0.

Source: Helen M. Walker and Joseph Lev. *Statistical Inference*. New York: Henry Holt and Company, 1953. Copyright 1953 by Holt, Rinehart and Winston, Inc. Used with the kind permission of the publishers and Miss Helen M. Walker.

TABLE K

Critical Values of ΣT in the Wilcoxon Matched Pairs–Signed Ranks Test

T, the sum of the ranks with the less frequent sign, is statistically significant if it is *equal to or less than* the table value.

n	Level of significance for one-tailed test		
	.025	.01	.005
	Level of significance for two-tailed test		
	.05	.02	.01
6	0	—	—
7	2	0	—
8	4	2	0
9	6	3	2
10	8	5	3
11	11	7	5
12	14	10	7
13	17	13	10
14	21	16	13
15	25	20	16
16	30	24	20
17	35	28	23
18	40	33	28
19	46	38	32
20	52	43	38
21	59	49	43
22	66	56	49
23	73	62	55
24	81	69	61
25	89	77	68

Source: Adapted from Table I of F. Wilcoxon. *Some Rapid Approximate Statistical Procedures*, p. 13. New York: American Cyanamid Company, 1949. Used with the kind permission of the author and publisher.

TABLE L

Probabilities Associated with Values as Large as Observed Values of H in the Kruskal-Wallis One-Way Analysis of Variance by Ranks

Sample sizes			H	p	Sample sizes			H	p
n_1	n_2	n_3			n_1	n_2	n_3		
2	1	1	2.7000	.500	4	3	2	6.4444	.008
								6.3000	.011
2	2	1	3.6000	.200				5.4444	.046
								5.4000	.051
2	2	2	4.5714	.067				4.5111	.098
			3.7143	.200				4.4444	.102
3	1	1	3.2000	.300	4	3	3	6.7455	.010
3	2	1	4.2857	.100				6.7091	.013
			3.8571	.133				5.7909	.046
								5.7273	.050
3	2	2	5.3572	.029				4.7091	.092
			4.7143	.048				4.7000	.101
			4.5000	.067					
			4.4643	.105	4	4	1	6.6667	.010
								6.1667	.022
3	3	1	5.1429	.043				4.9667	.048
			4.5714	.100				4.8667	.054
			4.0000	.129				4.1667	.082
3	3	2	6.2500	.011				4.0667	.102
			5.3611	.032					
			5.1389	.061	4	4	2	7.0364	.006
			4.5556	.100				6.8727	.011
			4.2500	.121				5.4545	.046
								5.2364	.052
3	3	3	7.2000	.004				4.5545	.098
			6.4889	.011				4.4455	.103
			5.6889	.029					
			5.6000	.050	4	4	3	7.1439	.010
			5.0667	.086				7.1364	.011
			4.6222	.100				5.5985	.049
								5.5758	.051
4	1	1	3.5714	.200				4.5455	.099
4	2	1	4.8214	.057				4.4773	.102
			4.5000	.076	4	4	4	7.6538	.008
			4.0179	.114				7.5385	.011
4	2	2	6.0000	.014				5.6923	.049
			5.3333	.033				5.6538	.054
			5.1250	.052				4.6539	.097
			4.4583	.100				4.5001	.104
			4.1667	.105	5	1	1	3.8571	.143
4	3	1	5.8333	.021	5	2	1	5.2500	.036
			5.2083	.050				5.0000	.048
			5.0000	.057				4.4500	.071
			4.0556	.093				4.2000	.095
			3.8889	.129				4.0500	.119

Source: W. H. Kruskal and W. A. Wallis. "Use of Ranks in One-Criterion Variance Analysis." *Journal of the American Statistical Association*, 47 (1947), pp. 614–617; adapted and abridged. Used with the kind permission of the publisher.

TABLE L   369

TABLE L (continued)

Sample sizes			H	p	Sample sizes			H	p
n_1	n_2	n_3			n_1	n_2	n_3		
5	2	2	6.5333	.008				5.6308	.050
			6.1333	.013				4.5487	.099
			5.1600	.034				4.5231	.103
			5.0400	.056	5	4	4	7.7604	.009
			4.3733	.090				7.7440	.011
			4.2933	.122				5.6571	.049
5	3	1	6.4000	.012				5.6176	.050
			4.9600	.048				4.6187	.100
			4.8711	.052				4.5527	.102
			4.0178	.095	5	5	1	7.3091	.009
			3.8400	.123				6.8364	.011
5	3	2	6.9091	.009				5.1273	.046
			6.8218	.010				4.9091	.053
			5.2509	.049				4.1091	.086
			5.1055	.052				4.0364	.105
			4.6509	.091	5	5	2	7.3385	.010
			4.4945	.101				7.2692	.010
5	3	3	7.0788	.009				5.3385	.047
			6.9818	.011				5.2462	.051
			5.6485	.049				4.6231	.097
			5.5152	.051				4.5077	.100
			4.5333	.097	5	5	3	7.5780	.010
			4.4121	.109				7.5429	.010
5	4	1	6.9545	.008				5.7055	.046
			6.8400	.011				5.6264	.051
			4.9855	.044				4.5451	.100
			4.8600	.056				4.5363	.102
			3.9873	.098	5	5	4	7.8229	.010
			3.9600	.102				7.7914	.010
5	4	2	7.2045	.009				5.6657	.049
			7.1182	.010				5.6429	.050
			5.2727	.049				4.5229	.099
			5.2682	.050				4.5200	.101
			4.5409	.098	5	5	5	8.0000	.009
			4.5182	.101				7.9800	.010
5	4	3	7.4449	.010				5.7800	.049
			7.3949	.011				5.6600	.051
			5.6564	.049				4.5600	.100
								4.5000	.102

TABLE M Sampling Distribution of F

The obtained F is significant at a given level if it is equal to or *greater than* the value shown in the table. 0.05 (light row) and 0.01 (dark row) points for the distribution of F.

Degrees of freedom for greater mean square (variance)

df	1	2	3	4	5	6	7	8	9	10	11	12	14	16	20	24	30	40	50	75	100	200	500	∞
1	161 / 4052	200 / 4999	216 / 5403	225 / 5625	230 / 5764	234 / 5859	237 / 5928	239 / 5981	241 / 6022	242 / 6056	243 / 6082	244 / 6106	245 / 6142	246 / 6169	248 / 6208	249 / 6234	250 / 6258	251 / 6286	252 / 6302	253 / 6323	253 / 6334	254 / 6352	254 / 6361	254 / 6344
2	18.51 / 98.49	19.00 / 99.01	19.16 / 99.17	19.25 / 99.25	19.30 / 99.30	19.33 / 99.33	19.36 / 99.34	19.37 / 99.36	19.38 / 99.38	19.39 / 99.40	19.40 / 99.41	19.41 / 99.42	19.42 / 99.43	19.43 / 99.44	19.44 / 99.45	19.45 / 99.46	19.46 / 99.47	19.47 / 99.48	19.47 / 99.48	19.48 / 99.49	19.49 / 99.49	19.49 / 99.49	19.50 / 99.50	19.50 / 99.50
3	10.13 / 34.12	9.55 / 30.81	9.28 / 29.46	9.12 / 28.71	9.01 / 28.24	8.94 / 27.91	8.88 / 27.67	8.84 / 27.49	8.81 / 27.34	8.78 / 27.23	8.76 / 27.13	8.74 / 27.05	8.71 / 26.92	8.69 / 26.83	8.66 / 26.69	8.64 / 26.60	8.62 / 26.50	8.60 / 26.41	8.58 / 26.30	8.57 / 26.27	8.56 / 26.23	8.54 / 26.18	8.54 / 26.14	8.53 / 26.12
4	7.71 / 21.20	6.94 / 18.00	6.59 / 16.69	6.39 / 15.98	6.26 / 15.52	6.16 / 15.21	6.09 / 14.98	6.04 / 14.80	6.00 / 14.66	5.96 / 14.54	5.93 / 14.45	5.91 / 14.37	5.87 / 14.24	5.84 / 14.15	5.80 / 14.02	5.77 / 13.93	5.74 / 13.83	5.71 / 13.74	5.70 / 13.69	5.68 / 13.61	5.66 / 13.57	5.65 / 13.52	5.64 / 13.48	5.63 / 13.44
5	6.61 / 16.26	5.79 / 13.27	5.41 / 12.06	5.19 / 11.39	5.05 / 10.97	4.95 / 10.67	4.88 / 10.45	4.82 / 10.27	4.78 / 10.15	4.74 / 10.05	4.70 / 9.96	4.68 / 9.89	4.64 / 9.77	4.60 / 9.68	4.56 / 9.55	4.53 / 9.47	4.50 / 9.38	4.46 / 9.29	4.44 / 9.24	4.42 / 9.17	4.40 / 9.13	4.38 / 9.07	4.37 / 9.04	4.36 / 9.02
6	5.99 / 13.74	5.14 / 10.92	4.76 / 9.78	4.53 / 9.15	4.39 / 8.75	4.28 / 8.47	4.21 / 8.26	4.15 / 8.10	4.10 / 7.98	4.06 / 7.87	4.03 / 7.79	4.00 / 7.72	3.96 / 7.60	3.92 / 7.52	3.87 / 7.39	3.84 / 7.31	3.81 / 7.23	3.77 / 7.14	3.75 / 7.09	3.72 / 7.02	3.71 / 6.99	3.69 / 6.94	3.68 / 6.90	3.67 / 6.88
7	5.59 / 12.25	4.74 / 9.55	4.35 / 8.45	4.12 / 7.85	3.97 / 7.44	3.87 / 7.19	3.79 / 7.00	3.73 / 6.84	3.68 / 6.71	3.63 / 6.62	3.60 / 6.54	3.57 / 6.47	3.52 / 6.35	3.49 / 6.27	3.44 / 6.15	3.41 / 6.07	3.38 / 5.98	3.34 / 5.90	3.32 / 5.85	3.29 / 5.78	3.28 / 5.75	3.25 / 5.70	3.24 / 5.67	3.23 / 5.65
8	5.32 / 11.26	4.46 / 8.65	4.07 / 7.59	3.84 / 7.01	3.69 / 6.63	3.58 / 6.37	3.50 / 6.19	3.44 / 6.03	3.39 / 5.91	3.34 / 5.82	3.31 / 5.74	3.28 / 5.67	3.23 / 5.56	3.20 / 5.48	3.15 / 5.36	3.12 / 5.28	3.08 / 5.20	3.05 / 5.11	3.03 / 5.06	3.00 / 5.00	2.98 / 4.96	2.96 / 4.91	2.94 / 4.88	2.93 / 4.86
9	5.12 / 10.56	4.26 / 8.02	3.86 / 6.99	3.63 / 6.42	3.48 / 6.06	3.37 / 5.80	3.29 / 5.62	3.23 / 5.47	3.18 / 5.35	3.13 / 5.26	3.10 / 5.18	3.07 / 5.11	3.02 / 5.00	2.98 / 4.92	2.93 / 4.80	2.90 / 4.73	2.86 / 4.64	2.82 / 4.56	2.80 / 4.51	2.77 / 4.45	2.76 / 4.41	2.73 / 4.36	2.72 / 4.33	2.71 / 4.31
10	4.96 / 10.04	4.10 / 7.56	3.71 / 6.55	3.48 / 5.99	3.33 / 5.64	3.22 / 5.39	3.14 / 5.21	3.07 / 5.06	3.02 / 4.95	2.97 / 4.85	2.94 / 4.78	2.91 / 4.71	2.86 / 4.60	2.82 / 4.52	2.77 / 4.41	2.74 / 4.33	2.70 / 4.25	2.67 / 4.17	2.64 / 4.12	2.61 / 4.05	2.59 / 4.01	2.56 / 3.96	2.55 / 3.93	2.54 / 3.91
11	4.84 / 9.65	3.98 / 7.20	3.59 / 6.22	3.36 / 5.67	3.20 / 5.32	3.09 / 5.07	3.01 / 4.88	2.95 / 4.74	2.90 / 4.63	2.86 / 4.54	2.82 / 4.46	2.79 / 4.40	2.74 / 4.29	2.70 / 4.21	2.65 / 4.10	2.61 / 4.02	2.57 / 3.94	2.53 / 3.86	2.50 / 3.80	2.47 / 3.74	2.45 / 3.70	2.42 / 3.66	2.41 / 3.62	2.40 / 3.60
12	4.75 / 9.33	3.88 / 6.93	3.49 / 5.95	3.26 / 5.41	3.11 / 5.06	3.00 / 4.82	2.92 / 4.65	2.85 / 4.50	2.80 / 4.39	2.76 / 4.30	2.72 / 4.22	2.69 / 4.16	2.64 / 4.05	2.60 / 3.98	2.54 / 3.86	2.50 / 3.78	2.46 / 3.70	2.42 / 3.61	2.40 / 3.56	2.36 / 3.49	2.35 / 3.46	2.32 / 3.41	2.31 / 3.38	2.30 / 3.34
13	4.67 / 9.07	3.80 / 6.70	3.41 / 5.74	3.18 / 5.20	3.02 / 4.86	2.92 / 4.62	2.84 / 4.44	2.77 / 4.30	2.72 / 4.19	2.67 / 4.10	2.63 / 4.02	2.60 / 3.96	2.55 / 3.85	2.51 / 3.78	2.46 / 3.67	2.42 / 3.59	2.38 / 3.51	2.34 / 3.42	2.32 / 3.37	2.28 / 3.30	2.26 / 3.27	2.24 / 3.21	2.22 / 3.18	2.21 / 3.16
14	4.60 / 8.86	3.74 / 6.51	3.34 / 5.56	3.11 / 5.03	2.96 / 4.69	2.85 / 4.46	2.77 / 4.28	2.70 / 4.14	2.65 / 4.03	2.60 / 3.94	2.56 / 3.86	2.53 / 3.80	2.48 / 3.70	2.44 / 3.62	2.39 / 3.51	2.35 / 3.43	2.31 / 3.34	2.27 / 3.26	2.24 / 3.21	2.21 / 3.14	2.19 / 3.11	2.16 / 3.06	2.14 / 3.02	2.13 / 3.00
15	4.54 / 8.68	3.68 / 6.36	3.29 / 5.42	3.06 / 4.89	2.90 / 4.56	2.79 / 4.32	2.70 / 4.14	2.64 / 4.00	2.59 / 3.89	2.55 / 3.80	2.51 / 3.73	2.48 / 3.67	2.43 / 3.56	2.39 / 3.48	2.33 / 3.36	2.29 / 3.29	2.25 / 3.20	2.21 / 3.12	2.18 / 3.07	2.15 / 3.00	2.12 / 2.97	2.10 / 2.92	2.08 / 2.89	2.07 / 2.87

Degrees of freedom for greater mean square (variance)

Source: Table M is taken from Fisher and Yates, *Statistical Tables for Biological, Agricultural, and Medical Research*, published by Longman Group Ltd., London (previously published by Oliver and Boyd, Edinburgh), and by permission of the authors and publishers.

TABLE M (continued)

df																								
16	2.01 2.75	2.02 2.77	2.04 2.80	2.07 2.86	2.09 2.89	2.13 2.96	2.16 3.01	2.20 3.10	2.24 3.18	2.28 3.25	2.33 3.37	2.37 3.45	2.42 3.55	2.45 3.61	2.49 3.69	2.54 3.78	2.59 3.89	2.66 4.03	2.74 4.20	2.85 4.44	3.01 4.77	3.24 5.29	3.63 6.23	4.49 8.53
17	1.96 2.65	1.97 2.67	1.99 2.70	2.02 2.76	2.04 2.79	2.08 2.86	2.11 2.92	2.15 3.00	2.19 3.08	2.23 3.16	2.29 3.27	2.33 3.35	2.38 3.45	2.41 3.52	2.45 3.59	2.50 3.68	2.55 3.79	2.62 3.93	2.70 4.10	2.81 4.34	2.96 4.67	3.20 5.18	3.59 6.11	4.45 8.40
18	1.92 2.57	1.93 2.59	1.95 2.62	1.98 2.68	2.00 2.71	2.04 2.78	2.07 2.83	2.11 2.91	2.15 3.00	2.19 3.07	2.25 3.19	2.29 3.27	2.34 3.37	2.37 3.44	2.41 3.51	2.46 3.60	2.51 3.71	2.58 3.85	2.66 4.01	2.77 4.25	2.93 4.58	3.16 5.09	3.55 6.01	4.41 8.28
19	1.88 2.49	1.90 2.51	1.91 2.54	1.94 2.60	1.96 2.63	2.00 2.70	2.02 2.76	2.07 2.84	2.11 2.92	2.15 3.00	2.21 3.12	2.26 3.19	2.31 3.30	2.34 3.36	2.38 3.43	2.43 3.52	2.48 3.63	2.55 3.77	2.63 3.94	2.74 4.17	2.90 4.50	3.13 5.01	3.52 5.93	4.38 8.18
20	1.84 2.42	1.85 2.44	1.87 2.47	1.90 2.53	1.92 2.56	1.96 2.63	1.99 2.69	2.04 2.77	2.08 2.86	2.12 2.94	2.18 3.05	2.23 3.13	2.28 3.23	2.31 3.30	2.35 3.37	2.40 3.45	2.45 3.56	2.52 3.71	2.60 3.87	2.71 4.10	2.87 4.43	3.10 4.94	3.49 5.85	4.35 8.10
21	1.81 2.36	1.82 2.38	1.84 2.42	1.87 2.47	1.89 2.51	1.93 2.58	1.96 2.63	2.00 2.72	2.05 2.80	2.09 2.88	2.15 2.99	2.20 3.07	2.25 3.17	2.28 3.24	2.32 3.31	2.37 3.40	2.42 3.51	2.49 3.65	2.57 3.81	2.68 4.04	2.84 4.37	3.07 4.87	3.47 5.78	4.32 8.02
22	1.78 2.31	1.80 2.33	1.81 2.37	1.84 2.42	1.87 2.46	1.91 2.53	1.93 2.58	1.98 2.67	2.03 2.75	2.07 2.83	2.13 2.94	2.18 3.02	2.23 3.12	2.26 3.18	2.30 3.26	2.35 3.35	2.40 3.45	2.47 3.59	2.55 3.76	2.66 3.99	2.82 4.31	3.05 4.82	3.44 5.72	4.30 7.94
23	1.76 2.26	1.77 2.28	1.79 2.32	1.82 2.37	1.84 2.41	1.88 2.48	1.91 2.53	1.96 2.62	2.00 2.70	2.04 2.78	2.10 2.89	2.14 2.97	2.20 3.07	2.24 3.14	2.28 3.21	2.32 3.30	2.38 3.41	2.45 3.54	2.53 3.71	2.64 3.94	2.80 4.26	3.03 4.76	3.42 5.66	4.28 7.88
24	1.73 2.21	1.74 2.23	1.76 2.27	1.80 2.33	1.82 2.36	1.86 2.44	1.89 2.49	1.94 2.58	1.98 2.66	2.02 2.74	2.09 2.85	2.13 2.93	2.18 3.03	2.22 3.09	2.26 3.17	2.30 3.25	2.36 3.36	2.43 3.50	2.51 3.67	2.62 3.90	2.78 4.22	3.01 4.72	3.40 5.61	4.26 7.82
25	1.71 2.17	1.72 2.19	1.74 2.23	1.77 2.29	1.80 2.32	1.84 2.40	1.87 2.45	1.92 2.54	1.96 2.62	2.00 2.70	2.06 2.81	2.11 2.89	2.16 2.99	2.20 3.05	2.24 3.13	2.28 3.21	2.34 3.32	2.41 3.46	2.49 3.63	2.60 3.86	2.76 4.18	2.99 4.68	3.38 5.57	4.24 7.77
26	1.69 2.13	1.70 2.15	1.72 2.19	1.76 2.25	1.78 2.28	1.82 2.36	1.85 2.41	1.90 2.50	1.95 2.58	1.99 2.66	2.05 2.77	2.10 2.86	2.15 2.96	2.18 3.02	2.22 3.09	2.27 3.17	2.32 3.29	2.39 3.42	2.47 3.59	2.59 3.82	2.74 4.14	2.98 4.64	3.37 5.53	4.22 7.72
27	1.67 2.10	1.68 2.12	1.71 2.16	1.74 2.21	1.76 2.25	1.80 2.33	1.84 2.38	1.88 2.47	1.93 2.55	1.97 2.63	2.03 2.74	2.08 2.83	2.13 2.93	2.16 2.98	2.20 3.06	2.25 3.14	2.30 3.26	2.37 3.39	2.46 3.56	2.57 3.79	2.73 4.11	2.96 4.60	3.35 5.49	4.21 7.68
28	1.65 2.06	1.67 2.09	1.69 2.13	1.72 2.18	1.75 2.22	1.78 2.30	1.81 2.35	1.87 2.44	1.91 2.52	1.96 2.60	2.02 2.71	2.06 2.80	2.12 2.90	2.15 2.95	2.19 3.03	2.24 3.11	2.29 3.23	2.36 3.36	2.44 3.53	2.56 3.76	2.71 4.07	2.95 4.57	3.34 5.45	4.20 7.64
29	1.64 2.03	1.65 2.06	1.68 2.10	1.71 2.15	1.73 2.19	1.77 2.27	1.80 2.32	1.85 2.41	1.90 2.49	1.94 2.57	2.00 2.68	2.05 2.77	2.10 2.87	2.14 2.92	2.18 3.00	2.22 3.08	2.28 3.20	2.35 3.32	2.43 3.50	2.54 3.73	2.70 4.04	2.93 4.54	3.33 5.42	4.18 7.60
30	1.62 2.01	1.64 2.03	1.66 2.07	1.69 2.13	1.72 2.16	1.76 2.24	1.79 2.29	1.84 2.38	1.89 2.47	1.93 2.55	1.99 2.66	2.04 2.74	2.09 2.84	2.12 2.90	2.16 2.98	2.21 3.06	2.27 3.17	2.34 3.30	2.42 3.47	2.53 3.70	2.69 4.02	2.92 4.51	3.32 5.39	4.17 7.56

Degrees of freedom for lesser mean square

TABLE M (continued)

0.05 (light row) and 0.01 (dark row) points for the distribution of F

Each cell shows the 0.05 point / 0.01 point. Columns are **Degrees of freedom for greater mean square**; rows are **Degrees of freedom for lesser mean square**.

df	1	2	3	4	5	6	7	8	9	10	11	12	14	16	20	24	30	40	50	75	100	200	500	∞
32	4.15 / 7.50	3.30 / 5.34	2.90 / 4.46	2.67 / 3.97	2.51 / 3.66	2.40 / 3.42	2.32 / 3.25	2.25 / 3.12	2.19 / 3.01	2.14 / 2.94	2.10 / 2.86	2.07 / 2.80	2.02 / 2.70	1.97 / 2.62	1.91 / 2.51	1.86 / 2.42	1.82 / 2.34	1.76 / 2.25	1.74 / 2.20	1.69 / 2.12	1.67 / 2.08	1.64 / 2.02	1.61 / 1.98	1.59 / 1.96
34	4.13 / 7.44	3.28 / 5.29	2.88 / 4.42	2.65 / 3.93	2.49 / 3.61	2.38 / 3.38	2.30 / 3.21	2.23 / 3.08	2.17 / 2.97	2.12 / 2.89	2.08 / 2.82	2.05 / 2.76	2.00 / 2.66	1.95 / 2.58	1.89 / 2.47	1.84 / 2.38	1.80 / 2.30	1.74 / 2.21	1.71 / 2.15	1.67 / 2.08	1.64 / 2.04	1.61 / 1.98	1.59 / 1.94	1.57 / 1.91
36	4.11 / 7.39	3.26 / 5.25	2.86 / 4.38	2.63 / 3.89	2.48 / 3.58	2.36 / 3.35	2.28 / 3.18	2.21 / 3.04	2.15 / 2.94	2.10 / 2.86	2.06 / 2.78	2.03 / 2.72	1.98 / 2.62	1.93 / 2.54	1.87 / 2.43	1.82 / 2.35	1.78 / 2.26	1.72 / 2.17	1.69 / 2.12	1.65 / 2.04	1.62 / 2.00	1.59 / 1.94	1.56 / 1.90	1.55 / 1.87
38	4.10 / 7.35	3.25 / 5.21	2.85 / 4.34	2.62 / 3.86	2.46 / 3.54	2.35 / 3.32	2.26 / 3.15	2.19 / 3.02	2.14 / 2.91	2.09 / 2.82	2.05 / 2.75	2.02 / 2.69	1.96 / 2.59	1.92 / 2.51	1.85 / 2.40	1.80 / 2.32	1.76 / 2.22	1.71 / 2.14	1.67 / 2.08	1.63 / 2.00	1.60 / 1.97	1.57 / 1.90	1.54 / 1.86	1.53 / 1.84
40	4.08 / 7.31	3.23 / 5.18	2.84 / 4.31	2.61 / 3.83	2.45 / 3.51	2.34 / 3.29	2.25 / 3.12	2.18 / 2.99	2.12 / 2.88	2.07 / 2.80	2.04 / 2.73	2.00 / 2.66	1.95 / 2.56	1.90 / 2.49	1.84 / 2.37	1.79 / 2.29	1.74 / 2.20	1.69 / 2.11	1.66 / 2.05	1.61 / 1.97	1.59 / 1.94	1.55 / 1.88	1.53 / 1.84	1.51 / 1.81
42	4.07 / 7.27	3.22 / 5.15	2.83 / 4.29	2.59 / 3.80	2.44 / 3.49	2.32 / 3.26	2.24 / 3.10	2.17 / 2.96	2.11 / 2.86	2.06 / 2.77	2.02 / 2.70	1.99 / 2.64	1.94 / 2.54	1.89 / 2.46	1.82 / 2.35	1.78 / 2.26	1.73 / 2.17	1.68 / 2.08	1.64 / 2.02	1.60 / 1.94	1.57 / 1.91	1.54 / 1.85	1.51 / 1.80	1.49 / 1.78
44	4.06 / 7.24	3.21 / 5.12	2.82 / 4.26	2.58 / 3.78	2.43 / 3.46	2.31 / 3.24	2.23 / 3.07	2.16 / 2.94	2.10 / 2.84	2.05 / 2.75	2.01 / 2.68	1.98 / 2.62	1.92 / 2.52	1.88 / 2.44	1.81 / 2.32	1.76 / 2.24	1.72 / 2.15	1.66 / 2.06	1.63 / 2.00	1.58 / 1.92	1.56 / 1.88	1.52 / 1.82	1.50 / 1.78	1.48 / 1.75
46	4.05 / 7.21	3.20 / 5.10	2.81 / 4.24	2.57 / 3.76	2.42 / 3.44	2.30 / 3.22	2.22 / 3.05	2.14 / 2.92	2.09 / 2.82	2.04 / 2.73	2.00 / 2.66	1.97 / 2.60	1.91 / 2.50	1.87 / 2.42	1.80 / 2.30	1.75 / 2.22	1.71 / 2.13	1.65 / 2.04	1.62 / 1.98	1.57 / 1.90	1.54 / 1.86	1.51 / 1.80	1.48 / 1.76	1.46 / 1.72
48	4.04 / 7.19	3.19 / 5.08	2.80 / 4.22	2.56 / 3.74	2.41 / 3.42	2.30 / 3.20	2.21 / 3.04	2.14 / 2.90	2.08 / 2.80	2.03 / 2.71	1.99 / 2.64	1.96 / 2.58	1.90 / 2.48	1.86 / 2.40	1.79 / 2.28	1.74 / 2.20	1.70 / 2.11	1.64 / 2.02	1.61 / 1.96	1.56 / 1.88	1.53 / 1.84	1.50 / 1.78	1.47 / 1.73	1.45 / 1.70
50	4.03 / 7.17	3.18 / 5.06	2.79 / 4.20	2.56 / 3.72	2.40 / 3.41	2.29 / 3.18	2.20 / 3.02	2.13 / 2.88	2.07 / 2.78	2.02 / 2.70	1.98 / 2.62	1.95 / 2.56	1.90 / 2.46	1.85 / 2.39	1.78 / 2.26	1.74 / 2.18	1.69 / 2.10	1.63 / 2.00	1.60 / 1.94	1.55 / 1.86	1.52 / 1.82	1.48 / 1.76	1.46 / 1.71	1.44 / 1.68
55	4.02 / 7.12	3.17 / 5.01	2.78 / 4.16	2.54 / 3.68	2.38 / 3.37	2.27 / 3.15	2.18 / 2.98	2.11 / 2.85	2.05 / 2.75	2.00 / 2.66	1.97 / 2.59	1.93 / 2.53	1.88 / 2.43	1.83 / 2.35	1.76 / 2.23	1.72 / 2.15	1.67 / 2.06	1.61 / 1.96	1.58 / 1.90	1.52 / 1.82	1.50 / 1.78	1.46 / 1.71	1.43 / 1.66	1.41 / 1.64
60	4.00 / 7.08	3.15 / 4.98	2.76 / 4.13	2.52 / 3.65	2.37 / 3.34	2.25 / 3.12	2.17 / 2.95	2.10 / 2.82	2.04 / 2.72	1.99 / 2.63	1.95 / 2.56	1.92 / 2.50	1.86 / 2.40	1.81 / 2.32	1.75 / 2.20	1.70 / 2.12	1.65 / 2.03	1.59 / 1.93	1.56 / 1.87	1.50 / 1.79	1.48 / 1.74	1.44 / 1.68	1.41 / 1.63	1.39 / 1.60
65	3.99 / 7.04	3.14 / 4.95	2.75 / 4.10	2.51 / 3.62	2.36 / 3.31	2.24 / 3.09	2.15 / 2.93	2.08 / 2.79	2.02 / 2.70	1.98 / 2.61	1.94 / 2.54	1.90 / 2.47	1.85 / 2.37	1.80 / 2.30	1.73 / 2.18	1.68 / 2.09	1.63 / 2.00	1.57 / 1.90	1.54 / 1.84	1.49 / 1.76	1.46 / 1.71	1.42 / 1.64	1.39 / 1.60	1.37 / 1.56
70	3.98 / 7.01	3.13 / 4.92	2.74 / 4.08	2.50 / 3.60	2.35 / 3.29	2.23 / 3.07	2.14 / 2.91	2.07 / 2.77	2.01 / 2.67	1.97 / 2.59	1.93 / 2.51	1.89 / 2.45	1.84 / 2.35	1.79 / 2.28	1.72 / 2.15	1.67 / 2.07	1.62 / 1.98	1.56 / 1.88	1.53 / 1.82	1.47 / 1.74	1.45 / 1.69	1.40 / 1.62	1.37 / 1.56	1.35 / 1.53
80	3.96 / 6.96	3.11 / 4.88	2.72 / 4.04	2.48 / 3.56	2.33 / 3.25	2.21 / 3.04	2.12 / 2.87	2.05 / 2.74	1.99 / 2.64	1.95 / 2.55	1.91 / 2.48	1.88 / 2.41	1.82 / 2.32	1.77 / 2.24	1.70 / 2.11	1.65 / 2.03	1.60 / 1.94	1.54 / 1.84	1.51 / 1.78	1.45 / 1.70	1.42 / 1.65	1.38 / 1.57	1.35 / 1.52	1.32 / 1.49

TABLE M (continued)

Degrees of freedom for lesser mean square																								
100	1.28 / 1.43	1.30 / 1.44	1.34 / 1.51	1.39 / 1.59	1.42 / 1.64	1.48 / 1.73	1.51 / 1.79	1.57 / 1.89	1.63 / 1.98	1.68 / 2.06	1.75 / 2.19	1.79 / 2.26	1.85 / 2.36	1.88 / 2.43	1.92 / 2.51	1.97 / 2.59	2.03 / 2.69	2.10 / 2.82	2.19 / 2.99	2.30 / 3.20	2.46 / 3.51	2.70 / 3.98	3.09 / 4.82	3.94 / 6.90
125	1.25 / 1.37	1.27 / 1.40	1.31 / 1.46	1.36 / 1.54	1.39 / 1.59	1.45 / 1.68	1.49 / 1.75	1.55 / 1.85	1.60 / 1.94	1.65 / 2.03	1.72 / 2.15	1.77 / 2.23	1.83 / 2.33	1.86 / 2.40	1.90 / 2.47	1.95 / 2.56	2.01 / 2.65	2.08 / 2.79	2.17 / 2.95	2.29 / 3.17	2.44 / 3.47	2.68 / 3.94	3.07 / 4.78	3.92 / 6.84
150	1.22 / 1.33	1.25 / 1.37	1.29 / 1.43	1.34 / 1.51	1.37 / 1.56	1.44 / 1.66	1.47 / 1.72	1.54 / 1.83	1.59 / 1.91	1.64 / 2.00	1.71 / 2.12	1.76 / 2.20	1.82 / 2.30	1.85 / 2.37	1.89 / 2.44	1.94 / 2.53	2.00 / 2.62	2.07 / 2.76	2.16 / 2.92	2.27 / 3.13	2.43 / 3.44	2.67 / 3.91	3.06 / 4.75	3.91 / 6.81
200	1.19 / 1.28	1.22 / 1.33	1.26 / 1.39	1.32 / 1.48	1.35 / 1.53	1.42 / 1.62	1.45 / 1.69	1.52 / 1.79	1.57 / 1.88	1.62 / 1.97	1.69 / 2.09	1.74 / 1.17	1.80 / 2.28	1.83 / 2.34	1.87 / 2.41	1.92 / 2.50	1.98 / 2.60	2.05 / 2.73	2.14 / 2.90	2.26 / 3.11	2.41 / 3.41	2.65 / 3.88	3.04 / 4.71	3.89 / 6.76
400	1.13 / 1.19	1.16 / 1.24	1.22 / 1.32	1.28 / 1.42	1.32 / 1.47	1.38 / 1.57	1.42 / 1.64	1.49 / 1.74	1.54 / 1.84	1.60 / 1.92	1.67 / 2.04	1.72 / 2.12	1.78 / 2.23	1.81 / 2.29	1.85 / 2.37	1.90 / 2.46	1.96 / 2.55	2.03 / 2.69	2.12 / 2.85	2.23 / 3.06	2.39 / 3.36	2.62 / 3.83	3.02 / 4.66	3.86 / 6.70
1000	1.08 / 1.11	1.13 / 1.19	1.19 / 1.28	1.26 / 1.38	1.30 / 1.44	1.36 / 1.54	1.41 / 1.61	1.47 / 1.71	1.53 / 1.81	1.58 / 1.89	1.65 / 2.01	1.70 / 2.09	1.76 / 2.20	1.80 / 2.26	1.84 / 2.34	1.89 / 2.43	1.95 / 2.53	2.02 / 2.66	2.10 / 2.82	2.22 / 3.04	2.38 / 3.34	2.61 / 3.80	3.00 / 4.62	3.85 / 6.66
∞	1.00 / 1.00	1.11 / 1.15	1.17 / 1.25	1.24 / 1.36	1.28 / 1.41	1.35 / 1.52	1.40 / 1.59	1.46 / 1.69	1.52 / 1.79	1.57 / 1.87	1.64 / 1.99	1.69 / 2.07	1.75 / 2.18	1.79 / 2.24	1.83 / 2.32	1.88 / 2.41	1.94 / 2.51	2.01 / 2.64	2.09 / 2.80	2.21 / 3.02	2.37 / 3.32	2.60 / 3.78	2.99 / 4.60	3.84 / 6.64

TABLE N

Critical Values of r_s, the Spearman Rank Correlation Coefficient

n	Significance level (one-tailed test)	
	.05	.01
4	1.000	
5	.900	1.000
6	.829	.943
7	.714	.893
8	.643	.833
9	.600	.783
10	.564	.746
12	.506	.712
14	.456	.645
16	.425	.601
18	.399	.564
20	.377	.534
22	359	.508
24	.343	.485
26	.329	.465
28	.317	.448
30	.306	.432

Sources: E. G. Olds. "Distributions of Sums of Rank Differences for Small Numbers of Individuals." *Annals of Mathematical Statistics*, 9 (1943), pp. 133–148. "The 5% Significance Levels for Sums of Squares of Rank Differences and a Correction." *Annals of Mathematical Statistics*, 20 (1949), pp. 117–118. Used with the kind permission of the editor.

*

A REVIEW OF SOME MATH BASICS

The purpose of this Appendix is to review a miscellany of basic mathematical operations that you have probably already been exposed to but may have forgotten. Students often approach statistics with an unrealistic fear of not being able to grasp the mathematics that it entails. In fact, the math involved in any of the computations in this and many basic statistics courses is *not* complex. While they do require a certain degree of meticulousness, the operations are not complicated. A mastery of this review will be sufficient to perform any of the statistical computations in this book. To provide you with the necessary background, the following topics will be briefly discussed: (1) calculations involving decimals, (2) calculations involving fractions, (3) calculations involving negative numbers, (4) operations involving zero, (5) exponents, (6) simplifying quantities, (7) calculating proportions and percentages, (8) rounding numbers and determining significant digits, and (9) the grammar of statistical notation. The mastery of the contents of this appendix is essential for understanding and doing well in basic social statistics.

CALCULATIONS INVOLVING DECIMALS

Addition and Subtraction

The addition and subtraction of decimals is a simple procedure. The most important thing to remember is that the numbers and the decimals must be *aligned* correctly. For example, suppose you wish to add the following numbers: 56.017, 1.0872, 101.1, and

5,000.82. These numbers must be aligned with due regard to position, for example, tenths (.1), hundredths (.82), thousandths (.017), ten thousandths (.0872), hundred thousandths (.11111), millionths (.828282), and so forth. Thus,

$$
\begin{array}{ll}
\textbf{(1)} & \left.\begin{array}{r} 56.017 \\ 1.0872 \\ 101.1 \\ 5,000.82 \end{array}\right\} \text{ addends} \\
& \overline{5,159.0242} \text{ (sum)}
\end{array}
$$

After the numbers (sometimes called *addends*) and their decimal points have been arranged vertically, proceed as in ordinary addition. Similarly, suppose you wished to subtract 87.294 from 100.16. Again, align the numbers with due regard to position and subtract the *subtrahend* from the *minuend* to determine the difference.

$$
\begin{array}{llr}
\textbf{(2)} & & 100.16 \quad \text{(minuend)} \\
& - & 87.294 \quad \text{(subtrahend)} \\
& & \overline{12.866} \quad \text{(difference or remainder)}
\end{array}
$$

Multiplication and Division

The most important point to remember here is that the *product* has as many decimal places as there are in both the *multiplicand* and the *multiplier*, for example,

(3) 1.0975	(multiplicand)	**(4)** .87	**(5)** .212	**(6)** .17
.112	(multiplier)	.9	.13	.1134
.1229200	(product)	.783	.02756	.019278

In division remember that the number of decimal places in the *quotient* is equal to the number of decimal places in the *dividend* minus the number of decimal places in the *divisor* (when there is no remainder), for example,

$$
\textbf{(7)} \quad \frac{\text{(dividend)} \;.120}{\text{(divisor)} \;.24} = .5 \text{ (quotient)} \qquad \textbf{(8)} \quad \frac{.1848}{.231} = .8 \qquad \textbf{(9)} \quad \frac{.02}{.2} = .1
$$

Note that if your division is correct, the product of the quotient multiplied by the divisor equals the dividend. For example,

(10) .5(.24) = .120   **(11)** .8(.231) = .1848   **(12)** .1(.2) = .02

CALCULATIONS INVOLVING FRACTIONS

Addition and Subtraction

When adding and subtracting, you must remember to find a *common denominator* first, for example,

(13) $1/6 + 1/9 = 9/54 + 6/54 = 15/54 = .28 \ (.2777)$

common denominator

(14) $1/5 - 1/8 = 8/40 - 5/40 = 3/40 = .075$

common denominator

It is customary to reduce fractions to decimals, as we have done in examples 13 and 14.

Multiplication and Division

Remember to multiply all the *numerators* (the top number of the fraction) and place this quantity over the product of all *denominators* (the bottom number of the fraction), for example,

(15) $3/4 \times 6/8 \times 5/7 = 90/224 = .40 \ (.4017)$

(16) $2/3 \times 3/4 \times 4/5 \times 5/6 = 120/360 = .3\overline{3} \ (.3333)$

When dividing fractions, *invert* the divisor and proceed as in multiplication, for example,

(17) $5/9 \div 8/16 \text{ (divisor)} = 5/9 \times 16/8 = 80/72 = 1.1\overline{1} \ (1.1111)$

(18) $2/10 \div 15/31 = 2/10 \times 31/15 = 62/150 = .41 \ (.4133)$

Again, notice the custom of converting fractions into decimals. Note, too, that repeating decimals are often indicated by $.3\overline{3}$ and $1.1\overline{1}$ as in examples (16) and (17).

CALCULATIONS INVOLVING NEGATIVE NUMBERS

Addition

When all the signs are negative, sum the values and place a *negative* sign in front of the sum, for example,

(19) $(-10) + (-12) + (-15) = -37$

(20) $(-5) + (-2) + (-8) + (-22) = -37$

When the signs are *mixed*, subtract the smaller quantity from the larger quantity and attach the sign of the larger quantity to the remainder, for example,

(21) $\begin{array}{r} -32 \\ 12 \\ \hline -20 \end{array}$ **(22)** $\begin{array}{r} -95 \\ 78 \\ \hline -17 \end{array}$ **(23)** $\begin{array}{r} -54 \\ 27 \\ \hline -27 \end{array}$

Subtraction

To subtract negative numbers, change the sign of the subtrahend and proceed as in addition, for example,

(24) $\begin{array}{r} 54 = 54 \\ -(-18) = 18 \\ \hline 72 \end{array}$ **(25)** $\begin{array}{r} -32 = -32 \\ -(-30) = 30 \\ \hline -2 \end{array}$ **(26)** $\begin{array}{r} -5.23 = -5.23 \\ -(-7.08) = 7.08 \\ \hline 1.85 \end{array}$

Multiplication

There are two basic rules to remember when multiplying numbers: (1) *when quantities of the same sign are multiplied, the product is always positive*, and (2) *when quantities of unlike signs are multiplied, the product is always negative*, for example,

(27) $\begin{array}{r} -68 \\ -22 \\ \hline 1,496 \end{array}$ **(28)** $\begin{array}{r} 79 \\ -8 \\ \hline -632 \end{array}$ **(29)** $\begin{array}{r} -43 \\ 8 \\ \hline -344 \end{array}$

Division

The same *sign* rules apply in the division of negative numbers as in multiplying numbers, for example,

(30) $8/4 = 2$ **(31)** $-76/-38 = 2$ **(32)** $90/-45 = -2$ **(33)** $-100/50 = -2$

OPERATIONS INVOLVING ZERO

Often students find operations involving zero somewhat troublesome. Adopting a few basic rules should ease any of these problems.

Addition and Subtraction

When zero is added to numbers, as in illustrations 34 and 35 below, no change in the final outcome is produced. Similarly, zero subtracted from numbers does not change their values, as in examples 36 and 37.

(34) $17 + 0 = 17$ **(35)** $342 + 0 = 342$

(36) $117 - 0 = 117$ **(37)** $102 - 0 = 102$

Multiplication and Division

The product of any number multiplied by zero is always zero, for example,

(38) $175 \times 0 = 0$ **(39)** $27 \times 0 = 0$ **(40)** $(175)(27)(0)(15) = 0$

When zero is divided by a number the quotient is always zero, for example,

(41) $0/8 = 0$ **(42)** $0/15782 = 0$

However, numbers can*not* be divided by zero for the quotient is infinity (∞), for example,

(43) $25/0 = \infty$

Any base with zero as an exponent equals unity (one). For example,

(44) $500^0 = 1$ **(45)** $2^0 = 1$ **(46)** $1^0 = 1$

SQUARE ROOTS AND SQUARE ROOT EXTRACTION

There are several different methods for obtaining a square root. With the increasing availability of desk calculators and tables (e.g., Barlow) the long method of square root extraction has become less useful and practical. Should you wish to use the long method, consult Walker (1951: 200–215). The extraction of square roots is a very important operation to be able to perform since some statistical techniques, for example, standard deviation and Pearsonian r, require you to extract such roots. The *radical sign* ($\sqrt{}$) indicates that a root of the number beneath it, the *radicand,* is to be extracted. For example, the expression $\sqrt[2]{5^2}$ means that the radicand, 5, is to be squared and the square root of 25 is to be extracted. The square root of a number is the value which, if multiplied by itself, produces the value of the radicand. In math, extraction of roots other than square ones is dealt with; however, only square root extraction is necessary in basic statistics.[1] Instead of the radical sign, the number whose root is to be extracted may be expressed by an exponent, for example:

(47) $\sqrt{6} = 6^{1/2} = 2.4495$ **(48)** $\sqrt{80} = 80^{1/2} = 8.9443$

The following are illustrations of the extraction of square roots:

(49) $\sqrt{36} = 6$ **(50)** $\sqrt{81} = 9$ **(51)** $\sqrt{100} = 10$ **(52)** $\sqrt{18} \approx 4.24$
since   since   since   since
$6 \times 6 = 36$ $9 \times 9 = 81$ $10 \times 10 = 100$ $4.24 \times 4.24 \approx 18(17.9776)$

    To multiply square roots, multiply the quantities under the radicals and take the square root of their product, for example,

(53) $(\sqrt{8})(\sqrt{10}) = 8.94 \, (= \sqrt{80})$ **(54)** $(\sqrt{4})(\sqrt{5}) = 4.47 \, (= \sqrt{20})$

EXPONENTS

When a number (technically called the *base*) is raised to another power (technically called the *exponent*) we perform successive multiplication, for example,

(55) $5^2 = 25$ (5 is the base and 2 is the exponent) $= 5 \times 5 = 25$

(56) $9^3 = 729$ (9 is the base and 3 is the exponent) $= 9 \times 9 \times 9 = 729$

SIMPLIFYING QUANTITIES

There are occasions when it will be necessary to simplify a quantity. When quantities are to be simplified, *signs of grouping,* that is, parentheses ( ), brackets [ ], and braces { }, are used to indicate that the enclosed expressions are to be considered single numbers in algebraic operations. To illustrate, $\frac{1}{2}(15 + 5) = 10$ whereas $\frac{1}{2} \times 15 + 5 = 12.5$. *An algebraic convention is to perform multiplication and division first, then addition and subtraction unless signs of grouping indicate otherwise.* Note in the expression $\frac{1}{2} \times 15 + 5$ that if addition takes place first the final value is 10, not 12.5, since $20 \times \frac{1}{2} = 10$. The general rule is to perform the operations *within* parentheses, brackets, or braces first, moving from the innermost grouping signs outward. For example,

$$[(5 + 2)8] - [(15 + 4) + (2 \times -12)] = [(7)8] - [(19) + (-24)]$$
$$= 56 - (-5)$$
$$= 56 + 5$$
$$= 61$$

---

[1] One exception to this is a measure of central tendency known as the geometric mean. However, this statistic is not frequently used in basic statistics.

CALCULATING PROPORTIONS AND PERCENTAGES

A *proportion* is by definition a part of a whole, whereas a *percent* is a proportion multiplied by 100. Suppose in a class of twenty students there are fourteen working-class students, four middle-class students, and two upper-class students. What proportion and percentage of the students are from the different social class positions?

A proportion may be calculated using the following formula:

$$p = \frac{n_i}{N} \quad \text{or} \quad \frac{fi}{N}$$

where:
    p = proportion of the total
    (fi) or n_i = the number of observations in a specific category
    N = the total number of observations in all categories

The proportion of working-class, middle-class, and upper-class students is, respectively:

$$\frac{14}{20} = .70 \qquad \frac{4}{20} = .20 \qquad \frac{2}{20} = .10$$

A *percentage* is a proportion multiplied by 100. Thus, the percentages of working-class, middle-class, and upper-class students are, respectively, 70 percent, 20 percent, and 10 percent. Percentages are easier to comprehend and, consequently, their use is highly recommended.

$$P = \frac{n_i}{N} (100) \quad \text{or} \quad \frac{fi}{N} (100)$$

where:
    P = percentage of the total
    (fi) or n_i = the number of observations in a specific category
    N = the total number of observations in all categories

$$P = \left[\frac{14}{20}\right] (100) = 70 \text{ percent}$$

$$P = \left[\frac{4}{20}\right] (100) = 20 \text{ percent}$$

$$P = \left[\frac{2}{20}\right] (100) = 10 \text{ percent}$$

In summary form, a frequency distribution for *discrete data* is:

	f	Proportion	Percent
Working class	14	$\frac{14}{20} = .70$	70
Middle class	4	$\frac{4}{20} = .20$	20
Upper class	2	$\frac{2}{20} = \frac{.10}{1.00}$	$\frac{10}{100}$
	$N = 20$		

Notice that, if no rounding errors occur, the sum of the proportions equals 1.00 and the sum of the percents equals 100.

ROUNDING NUMBERS AND DETERMINING SIGNIFICANT DIGITS

There are several conventions that statisticians have adopted to standardize procedures for rounding numbers and retaining significant digits. *As a general rule of thumb, if the last digit is more than 5*, for example, 15.66, *then the preceding digit is increased by unity*, that is, 15.66 becomes 15.7. On the other hand, *if the last digit is less than 5*, for example, 2.84, *then the last digit is simply dropped*, that is, 2.84 becomes 2.8. The major complication that may arise occurs when the last digit is exactly 5, for example, 5.55. In these instances the *engineer's rule* is adopted. That is, when the preceding digit is odd, as in 5.55, we round up; for example, 5.55 rounded to the nearest tenth becomes 5.6. When the preceding digit is even, as in 5.65, we round down; for example, 5.65 becomes 5.6. The logic underlying this convention is that in the long run odd and even numbers should occur about equally and this rule of thumb is not likely to introduce any systematic biases.

These general rules apply to rounding both *whole numbers* (*integers*) and *decimals*, as in the following illustrations:

17.2 rounded to the nearest whole number = 17
528.6 rounded to the nearest whole number = 529

85.74 rounded to the nearest tenth = 85.7
28.66 rounded to the nearest tenth = 28.7

526.877 rounded to the nearest hundredth = 526.88
14.563 rounded to the nearest hundredth =   14.56

8.55 rounded to the nearest tenth =   8.6
22.45 rounded to the nearest tenth = 22.4

8.585 rounded to the nearest hundredth =   8.58
205.615 rounded to the nearest hundredth = 205.62

22.5 rounded to the nearest whole number = 22
21.5 rounded to the nearest whole number = 22

The precision with which one rounds is determined by the precision of the initial measuring process coupled with practical considerations. For example, to say that the average classroom size at a large state university is 25.86473 is impractical, if not absurd.

While there exist few clearly agreed upon guidelines for retaining significant digits, as a rule one should have at least one more digit in the answer than existed in the original data. If an operation involves several steps, each requiring rounding, then one must be particularly careful in these operations since *small individual errors may accumulate into a large composite one*.

THE GRAMMAR OF STATISTICAL NOTATION

In statistics, like mathematics, the use of symbols is standard procedure. *Symbolic nota-tion* is, in some respects, like a language with its own grammar. While the various symbols adopted by statisticians are often confusing to the beginning student, they do have an underlying rationale that eases statistical computations and sometimes facilitates con-ceptual understanding. As such, mathematical notation (or symbols) can be thought of in terms of nouns, adjectives, verbs, and adverbs. In this text we ordinarily define and discuss a symbol upon its first appearance but, for the present, a general overview of the use of symbols in statistics is worthwhile. Let us look at some selected symbols that function as nouns, adjectives, verbs, and adverbs, respectively.

Three commonly used statistical symbols will illustrate the nature of a *mathe-matical noun*. These symbols, N, X, and Y, represent quantities. N is the total number of observations under consideration; X is generically used for the quantity represented by any score; and Y is occasionally used to designate the same as X, as can be seen in the discussion of measures of association.

Sometimes we may want to distinguish the specific scores under examination and this can be done with a *mathematical adjective*. If we have data comprised of five scores they may be referred to as X_1, X_2, X_3, X_4, and X_5. Sometimes X_i will be designated and the subscript i indicates that any value may be taken.

Statistical notations that direct the person to do something or perform some opera-tion are called *mathematical verbs*. One of the most important verbs is Σ, the capital Greek letter sigma. This symbol is termed the *summation operator* or *summation index* and instructs us to sum (add up) all quantities following it. Thus,

$$\Sigma\ X_1,\ X_2,\ X_3,\ X_4,\ X_5,\ \ldots,\ X_{10}$$

directs us to add together all quantities X_1 through X_{10}. Sometimes *subscripts* and *superscripts* are used to specify the quantity to begin with and the quantity where the summation is to be terminated. For example,

$$\sum_{i=2}^{6}$$

instructs us to begin adding with the second quantity (X_2) and stop adding after the sixth quantity (X_6). In basic statistics such specifications are rarely used.

Sometimes the symbol

$$\sum_{i=1}^{N}$$

is used. It is more elaborate than Σ but directs us to do the exact same thing. The subscript $i = 1$ tells us to begin adding with the first observation and the superscript N directs us to stop adding with the last score. In other words, the limits of the summation operator are sometimes made explicit by numbers and/or symbols above and below it. Let us look at some additional illustrations.

Suppose we administered a prestige index to five students and find their scores to be $X_1 = 50$, $X_2 = 80$, $X_3 = 40$, $X_4 = 60$, $X_5 = 55$. Then, if we were to add all scores the notation would be:

$$\Sigma X_i \text{ or } \sum_{i=1}^{5} X_i = X_1 + X_2 + X_3 + X_4 + X_5$$

$$= 50 + 80 + 40 + 60 + 55$$

$$= 285$$

If we only wanted to add scores three through five this would be indicated as follows:

$$\sum_{i=3}^{5} X_i = X_3 + X_4 + X_5$$

$$= 40 + 60 + 55$$

$$= 155$$

In general, with N terms,

$$\sum_{i=1}^{N} X_i = X_1 + X_2 + X_3 + \ldots + X_N$$

Three other mathematical verbs often encountered are $\sqrt{}$, X^a, and $N!$. The first indicates that the root, usually square if unqualified, of the radicand is to be extracted and the second tells us to raise a quantity to a certain power. $N!$ is called *N factorial* and directs us to multiply N by all integers less than it but greater than zero. For example, $5!$ equals $5 \times 4 \times 3 \times 2 \times 1 = 120$. Factorials are used in statistics to obtain binomial probabilities but $0! = 1$ and any value other than zero raised to the zero power equals 1, for example, $5^0 = 1$. In general, a factorial can be expressed: $(N)(N-1)(N-2) \ldots$ and so forth.

In English grammar adverbs are employed for the purpose of modifying a verb. The above discussion of the use of subscripts and superscripts with the summation operator illustrates the modification of the mathematical verb. That is, it modified the adding procedure by specifying a beginning and an ending point. Instead of summing all quantities we were instructed to add only selected ones. Such an instance exemplifies a *mathematical adverb*.

The Greek Alphabet

Because of the extensive use of Greek symbols in statistical analysis, we will present the Greek alphabet along with its English equivalent in the following figure:

The Greek Alphabet

Greek Letter		Name	English Equivalent	Greek Letter		Name	English Equivalent
A	α	alpha	A	N	ν	nu	N
B	β	beta	B	Ξ	ξ	xi	X
Γ	γ	gamma	G	O	o	omicron	short O
Δ	δ	delta	D	Π	π	pi	P
E	ϵ	epsilon	short E	P	ρ	rho	R
Z	ζ	zeta	Z, DZ	Σ	σ	sigma	S
H	η	eta	long E	T	τ	tau	T
Θ	θ	theta	TH	Υ	υ	upsilon	U
I	ι	iota	I	Φ	ϕ	phi	PH
K	κ	kappa	K	X	χ	chi	CH
Λ	λ	lambda	L	Ψ	ψ	psi	PS
M	μ	mu	M	Ω	ω	omega	long O

GLOSSARY OF TERMS

Abscissa See horizontal axis.

Adequacy (of sample) Due to the instability of small samples, a sample must be sufficiently large, that is, adequate, in order to permit broader generalizations.

Alpha (type I) error A statistical decision error that occurs when we reject the null hypothesis when it should have been accepted. When the researcher claims a significant difference when, in fact, there is none, an alpha error (type I error) is made. Symbolized α. The potential probability of an alpha error is equal to the level of significance selected.

Alternative hypothesis The hypothesis or statement that is accepted or retained when the null hypothesis is rejected. Usually reflects the operationalization of the research hypothesis. Symbolized H_1. See null and research hypothesis.

Arithmetic mean An interval/ratio level measure of central tendency defined as the sum of all scores in a distribution divided by the number of scores. Symbolized $\overline{X}_u = \Sigma X_i/N$ or $\frac{1}{N}\Sigma X_i$.

Array See rank order distribution.

Asymmetric association coefficient One that makes a computational and conceptual distinction between independent and dependent variables. For example, lambda and Somer's d.

Asymptotic A property of the normal curve whereby the tails almost, but not quite, touch the horizontal axis of the graph.

Attribute Frequently a distinction is made in statistics between *quantitative phenomena* (in which case the term *variable* applies) and *qualitative phenomena* (in which case the term *attribute* applies). Examples of attributes include sex, for example, male, female; ethnicity, for example, White, Asian-American, African-American, Hispanic; and religion, for example, Protestant, Catholic, Jew. With attributes, unlike variables, there is usually a distinction of kind rather than true numerical differences. Also referred to as *frequency, enumerative,* or *categorical data.*

Averages See measures of central tendency.

Average deviation *(mean deviation)* An interval/ratio measure of dispersion, not used much in recent years, obtained by subtracting the mean from each raw score, disregarding the sign of the difference, summing the absolute deviations, and dividing by the number of observations. Symbolized AD_u (or MD_u) $= \Sigma| X_i - \overline{X} |/N$.

Bar graph A type of graph used with nominal level data depicting the absolute number or percentage of times each category of the variable is represented.

Bayesian statistical inference In the social sciences a relatively unused form of statistical inference developed by the Rev. Thomas Bayes and based upon the notion of "subjective probabilities." Bayesian analysis, sometimes called prior-posterior inference, permits changing the original probabilities on the basis of new evidence.

Beta coefficient In regression analysis the b-coefficient indicates the slope of the regression line and tells us how much the Y values change for each unit change in X.

Beta (type II) error A statistical decision error that occurs when we accept the null hypothesis when it should have been rejected. When the researcher claims there is no significant difference when, in fact, there is, a beta error (type II error) is committed. Symbolized β.

Between sum of squares (BSS) A value used in the F test and obtained by subtracting each group mean from the grand mean, squaring the differences, and summing these squared differences. When divided by the appropriate df, $(k - 1)$, it becomes the between groups variance estimate.

Bias A predisposition to favor or oppose a given outcome irrespective of the "objective" information.

Biased estimate A parameter estimate which tends to be under- or over-represented by a sample statistic. For example, $s < \sigma$ or $\sigma_{\overline{x}} < \sigma$.

Binomial sampling distribution The appropriate sampling distribution for dichotomized nominal level data.

Bivariate distribution Data in which two characteristics or phenomena are of interest. A correlation coefficient is often computed for a bivariate distribution.

Bivariate frequency distribution A contingency table containing the frequency of the respective row and column categories.

Bivariate percentage distribution A contingency table containing the percentages of the respective row and column categories.

Boxplot A graphic technique that combines indices of central tendency, variability, and form.

C_{max} The contingency coefficient (C) does not have unity as its upper limit; instead, the maximum is a function of the r by c composition. Consequently, for any table, with varying rows and columns, there is a maximum value that C can attain. This maximum value is called C_{max}.

Causality This notion is implicit in most hypothesis testing. In order to demonstrate causality, that is, a cause-effect relationship between variables, four criteria must be established: (1) concomitant variation, (2) ruling out spurious relationships, (3) cause must precede effect (temporal sequence), and (4) a theoretical rationale.

Cell frequency The number of observations (frequency) at the intersection of a particular row and a particular column in a contingency table.

Cells The entries, usually for frequencies or percentages, in a contingency table are called cells. When frequency counts are entered at the intersection of a given column and row variable, the entries are known as cell frequencies.

Census A term used when every element in the population has been considered or counted, in contrast to a sample.

Central limit theorem (CLT) A proven mathematical theorem that states if random samples of size n are selected from any population with mean $= \mu$ and standard deviation $= \sigma$, the means of the samples will be normally distributed with mean $= \mu$ and standard error $= \sigma/\sqrt{n}$ as n becomes larger.

Central tendency See measures of central tendency.

Chebyshev's Theorem (Tchebycheff's inequality) A mathematical theorem that says that even in the most skewed distribution, about 75 percent of the cases will fall between $\pm 2\sigma$ from the mean and approximately 90 percent of the cases between $\pm 3\sigma$. It is important both in interpreting the standard deviation and in inferential statistics.

Chi-square test (χ^2) A nominal level test of significance in which obtained frequencies are compared with expected (theoretical) frequencies. One of the most versatile statistical techniques available.

Chi-square test of independence This is the name applied to the chi-square two-variable test. In effect, the researcher is testing whether or not the variables under examination are independent or related. The expected frequencies are generated by using the marginal and grand totals in a contingency table.

Chi-square test of k independent samples This is the name applied to the chi-square test where larger than 2×2 tables are under examination. The expected frequencies are generated by using the marginal and grand totals.

Class interval When scores are collapsed into meaningful categories the class interval, frequently symbolized i, refers to the width or range of the observations. For example, the class interval 25–29 has a width of 5 (25, 26, 27, 28, 29) units. Obtained by subtracting the lower exact limit from the upper exact limit, for example, 29.5 – 24.5 = 5.

Classical statistical inference The traditional method whereby hypotheses deduced from theory are put into a form that facilitates their empirical testing. It is based upon a relative frequency conception of probability. See Bayesian statistical inference.

Cochran Q test A nominal level test of significance appropriate for use with k related samples.

Coding This concept is used in two generic ways in statistics to denote: (1) the substitution of simpler symbols for more complex values, and (2) the transformation of scores so that they become easier to handle. Used in this text in computing the mean and standard deviation.

Coefficient of determination (r^2) A value expressing the amount of variation in the dependent variable explained or accounted for by the independent variable. Used in interpreting the Pearsonian correlation coefficient.

Coefficient of nondetermination $(1 - r^2)$ A value expressing the amount of variation in the dependent variable left unexplained by the independent variable. Used in interpreting the Pearsonian correlation coefficient.

Coefficient of variability (coefficient of variation) An interval/ratio measure of dispersion obtained by dividing the standard deviation of the distribution by the mean of the distribution. Symbolized $V = s/\overline{X}$ or σ/μ.

Combinations An arrangement of observations without regard to order. For example, two objects labeled A and B can have only one arrangement. $A - B$ and $B - A$ are considered to be a single combination. The order is not important. See permutations.

Comparing table percentages rule After correctly percentaging the table in the direction of the independent variable, compare across.

Computational formulae Statistical formulae that facilitate the computations of mathematical quantities. See theoretical formulae.

Concordant pairs (n_s) One of the pair types for ordinal level variables in which the order of scores on two variables is the same.

Conditional distribution Individual cell frequencies in a contingency table represent the simultaneous occurrence of the category of one variable within the category of another variable. Also referred to as a joint frequency distribution.

Confidence intervals A range of values constructed around the point estimate, for example, $\overline{X} \pm z(\sigma_{\overline{X}})$. One aspect of inferential statistics. Common confidence intervals are 90 percent, 95 percent, and 99 percent. Using the 99 percent interval we would ultimately make a statement to the effect that about 99 percent of the intervals constructed should contain the parameter being estimated.

Confidence (credibility) limits The extreme end values (plus and minus from the point estimate) of an interval estimate. For example, 10 and 20 would be the credibility limits of the confidence interval extending from 10 to 20.

Constant Refers to a value that never changes, for example, pi = 3.1417. Some statistical formulae, such as Spearman's rho and Friedman's test, employ a constant.

Contingency (principle of) The occurrence of events is dependent or contingent upon other events. Our understanding of social phenomena is the result of numerous factors, some known and some unknown.

Contingency coefficient (C) A nominal measure of association used in conjunction with the chi-square test of significance. Symbolized $C = \sqrt{\chi^2/\chi^2 + n}$.

Contingency table Represents a cross-classification of variables (or attributes) containing rows (r) and columns (c). The simplest type is a 2 X 2 or fourfold table. The 2 X 2 means there are two variables, each of which has been dichotomized or has two subdivisions. Fourfold means the body of the table contains four cells.

Continuous data Observations that, theoretically, may take on all possible values assuming the availability of a precise measuring instrument. For example, height, weight, income, and age are considered to be continous in nature. See discrete data.

Correction factor for C Enables the researcher to appraise more systematically the computed C because of its limitations. Symbolized $\bar{C} = C/C_{max}$.

Correlation coefficient A numerical value expressing the existence, degree, and/or direction of the association between variables. See measures of association.

Covariation (principle of) The basis for determining the existence of an association for interval/ratio level data. If family size increases as does annual income, the conclusion is that the two variables are associated. Applicable to quantitative data. See principle of joint occurrence of attributes.

Cramer's V A chi-square based nominal level measure of association.

Critical region (region of rejection) When the test statistic falls in the critical region of the sampling distribution, the researcher is obliged to reject the null hypothesis and accept the alternative one. See critical value.

Critical value The minimum value which is sufficient to reject the null hypothesis and accept the alternative hypothesis. The critical region includes all values at and beyond the critical value which are sufficient to reject the null.

Cumulative frequency distribution A frequency distribution obtained by the successive addition of individual frequencies. It is a prerequisite for constructing certain graphs, for example, ogive, and for computing several positional statistical measures such as the median, percentiles, and quartiles.

Cumulative frequency polygon (ogive) A type of graph in which the cumulative frequencies of the class intervals are depicted. It permits one to determine visually the frequency (or percent) of observations less than or greater than certain specified values.

Cumulative percentage distribution When interest is in the percentage of cases above and below certain score categories, the cumulative frequencies may be converted into cumulative percents by dividing the cumulative frequency in each class interval by N and multiplying each result by 100.

Cumulative percentage polygon (ogive) A type of graph in which dots above the upper exact limit of the class intervals are located corresponding to cumulative percents in the respective class intervals.

Data Numbers or measurements or scores collected from the unit(s) of analysis. One purpose of statistics is to process data.

Degree of association The magnitude or amount of association between variables.

Degrees of freedom (df) The number of values free to vary given certain restrictions on our data. Used in a number of different situations, for example, chi-square test, F test, t test.

Delta The difference between an observed and expected frequency. Symbolized "Δ".

Dependent (effect) variable Variables can be defined in a number of ways but one important distinction is between *independent* (*causal*) and *dependent* (*effect*) variables. If one were interested in differences in cognitive dissonance scores by sex (male and female), dissonance would be the *dependent* or *effect variable*. That is, it's something attributed or due to something else, in this case gender. Sex would be the *independent* or *causal variable*.

Descriptive statistics Reducing data to manageable portions by computing such descriptive measures as percentages, means, standard deviations, and correlation coefficients (descriptive in that they describe or tell us something about the observations). Statistics is often thought of as having two functions, description and inference. See inferential statistics.

Deterministic A relationship in which a change in one variable always occurs because of a change in another variable. See stochastic.

Direct difference method A two-sample interval level test of significance for related samples.

Direction of an association An association coefficient's direction is either *positive* (high scores on one variable coincide with high scores on another variable and the converse) or *negative* (high scores on one variable coincide with low scores on another variable and the converse) and is indicated by the sign, plus ($+$) or minus ($-$). The direction of association only applies to associations at the ordinal and interval/ratio levels of measurement. See positive and negative association.

Discordant pairs (n_d) One of the pair types for ordinal level variables in which the order of scores on two variables is the opposite or different.

Discrete data Observations which may come only in whole number (integer) form. For example, family size. See continuous data.

Dispersion (Variation) See measures of dispersion.

Efficiency When the sampling distribution of a statistic tends to cluster around the parameter (μ) being estimated, it is considered an efficient estimate. Efficiency is an important criterion in establishing estimates of population parameters.

Epsilon The percentage difference between the categories in a contingency table. Used for determining if an association exists.

Exact limits With continuous data we imagine the number as representing a value falling within certain limits, for example, a score of 65 may be thought of as having the exact limits, upper and lower respectively, of 65.5 and 64.5. This distinction applies only to continuous data.

Expected (theoretical) frequencies The frequencies generated in the chi-square test of significance either by the researcher as in the goodness-of-fit case or by the use of the marginal and grand totals as in the test of independence. Such frequencies permit us to establish a model of no association.

F test The analysis of variance test in which the means of k independent samples are tested for significance. Symbolically, the F test is a strategy for testing the null hypothesis: $H_0: \mu_1 = \mu_2 = \mu_k$. Used with interval/ratio level data.

Factorial A mathematical verb directing one to multiply the indicated value by all integers less than it but greater than zero. For example, $3! = 3 \times 2 \times 1 = 6$.

Fisher exact test A nominal level test of significance used in 2×2 tables where the expected frequencies are less than 5. As such, it is an effective substitute for chi-square under these conditions.

Fractiles A general concept implying a point on a measuring scale that divides a total set of scores into known proportions. Common fractiles include percentiles, deciles, and quartiles.

Frequency (*f*) The number of times that a particular score or observation occurs.

Frequency distribution An arrangement of data showing the frequency of occurrence of different categories of the variables.

Frequency polygon A type of graph in which the midpoints of the various class intervals are represented by dots according to the class intervals' frequencies and are connected by straight lines. It provides a visual perspective of a frequency distribution.

Friedman two-way analysis of variance test An ordinal level test of significance appropriate for use with *k* related samples.

Gamma (γ) An ordinal level measure of association.

Geometric mean An interval/ratio measure of central tendency defined as the *N*th root of the product of the *N* values, for example, the *GM* for 2 and 8 $= \sqrt{2 \times 8} = 4$; the *GM* for 3, 3, & 3 $= \sqrt[3]{3 \times 3 \times 3}$ or 3; in general, $GM = \sqrt[N]{X_1 \times X_2 \times X_3 \times X_N}$. Infrequently used in basic social statistics.

Goodness-of-fit (*chi-square*) **test** This is the name applied to the chi-square one-variable case. The expected (theoretical) frequencies are generated by the researcher on the basis of some theoretical scheme. The test enables the researcher to judge how well empirical data approximate some theoretical model.

Graph A geometric picture of a data-set enabling one to conceptualize a problem in visual terms.

Grouped frequency distribution An arrangement of data whereby the scores have been collapsed into a smaller number of meaningful categories.

Grouping error When constructing grouped frequency distributions the midpoint is often used to represent all scores in the class interval. This loss of accuracy, exactness, and precision is termed grouping error.

Guilford's table A useful guide for interpreting the meaning of a measure of correlation. Developed by J. P. Guilford.

Harmonic mean An interval/ratio measure of central tendency defined as the reciprocal of the arithmetic mean of the reciprocals of the measures, that is,

$$HM = \frac{1}{\dfrac{1}{N}\left(\dfrac{1}{X_1} + \dfrac{1}{X_2} + \dfrac{1}{X_N}\right)} = \frac{N}{\Sigma\left(\dfrac{1}{X_i}\right)}$$

Infrequently used in basic social statistics.

Heading The horizontal axis or top of the table on which it is conventional to locate the independent variable.

Histogram A type of graph in which bars extend from the exact limits of the class intervals corresponding to the frequency or percentage in each interval.

Homoscedasticity A condition in which the variances of two or more distributions are considered equal. An assumption underlying the computation of a number of statistics. Symbolically, $\sigma_1^2 = \sigma_2^2 = \sigma_k^2$.

Horizontal axis In graph construction, e.g., scattergram, it is conventional to locate the independent variable (X) and its values along the horizontal axis. Sometimes called the abscissa. See vertical axis.

Hypergeometric distribution A probability distribution generated by the use of factorials as in the Fisher exact test.

Hypothesis testing The branch of inferential statistics whereby hypotheses (ideally derived from a theoretical scheme) are tested to see if the obtained data could have occurred by chance.

Hypothetico-deductive method The dominant analytical mode in the social sciences whereby hypotheses are logically deduced (derived) from theory and then put to an empirical test. This process constitutes a merger of inductive and deductive reasoning.

Inclusiveness A property of a good classification system in which the researcher is able to categorize each and every case. See nominal or classificatory level of measurement.

Independent samples Opposite of matched samples, that is, when the inclusion of certain elements in one sample has no bearing on the inclusion of elements in another sample. See matching.

Independent (causal) variable See dependent variable.

Index of dispersion (D) A nominal measure of dispersion defined as the ratio of the variation that does exist to the maximum variation that could exist. Symbolized, $D = k(N^2 - \Sigma f^2)/N^2(k-1)$.

Index of qualitative variation (IQV) A nominal measure of dispersion defined as 100 times the ratio between the total observed differences and the maximum possible differences. Symbolized,

$$IQV = \frac{\Sigma n_i n_j}{\left[\dfrac{k(k-1)}{2}\right]\left[\dfrac{N}{k}\right]^2} \times 100$$

Inferential (inductive, sampling, probability) statistics The branch of statistics concerned with generalizing or inferring characteristics of the population from a subset of elements (sample) selected from that larger entity. See descriptive statistics. Inferential statistics is divided into two subtopics: parameter estimation and hypothesis testing.

Interpolate A process for ascertaining the equivalency of some unstated term inserted between two succeeding terms. Used in computing the median and fractiles.

Interquartile range (Q) A measure of dispersion indicating the spread in the middle 50 percent of scores. Symbolized, $Q = Q_3 - Q_1$.

Interval estimate A range of values, constructed around the point estimate, to which a certain amount of confidence is attached. See parameter estimation, point estimate, and confidence intervals (limits).

Interval level The level of measurement having an arbitrary zero point and permitting the classification of objects in terms of their known distances from each other.

Interval level measures of association A general term referring to correlation coefficients, most useful for interval level variables. For example, Pearson's product-moment correlation coefficient.

Joint frequency distribution See conditional distribution.

Joint occurrence of attributes (principle of) The basis for determining the existence of an association for nominal level data. For example, if homosexuality is more often found among males than females, the conclusion is that the two attributes are associated. Applicable to qualitative data. See principle of covariation.

Kolmogorov-Smirnov one-sample test An ordinal test of significance.

Kruskal-Wallis one-way analysis of variance test An ordinal level test of significance appropriate for use with k independent samples.

Kurtosis An important mathematical property of a frequency distribution that refers to the flatness or peakedness of one distribution in relation to the normal curve. See mesokurtic, leptokurtic, and platykurtic.

Lambda A nominal level measure of association with both a symmetrical and asymmetrical computational and conceptual formula. Symbolized, λ.

Law of large numbers A proven mathematical proposition that says, in effect, that no matter what the nature of the population from which we've sampled, if the sample size is sufficiently large, then the sampling distribution will approximate normality. See central limit theorem.

Least squares See sum of squared deviations from the mean, that is, $\Sigma(X_i - \bar{X})^2 =$ minimum.

Leptokurtic A curve that is judged to be more peaked than the normal curve.

Level of significance When we test an hypothesis with alpha = .05 level, we test our data at the .05 level of significance. This means that we would be willing to reject the null hypothesis and accept the alternative hypothesis if our data could have been due to chance 5 or less times in 100. The level of significance is the probability of making a type I or alpha error. See type II (beta) error.

Line graph A type of graph, sometimes called a trend line, showing the value of some dependent variable for each of a number of categories of another variable, usually but not always an independent variable.

Linear (rectilinear) regression A condition in which a straight line is the best fit for a series of points in a scattergram. In general, the relationship between variables is linear rather than nonlinear. An extension of correlation is called regression. The regression equation is expressed as $Y' = a_{yx} + b_{yx}(X)$.

Linear transformation A generic term whereby a score is transformed into another mathematically useful form. See z transformation.

Mann-Whitney U test An ordinal level test of significance appropriate for use with two independent samples.

Marginal total The summation of row or column cell frequencies in a contingency table is known as a marginal total or frequency, row marginal frequency, and column marginal frequency, respectively.

Matching (matched samples) When individuals in the study under examination are correlated or related in some fashion. Two research designs, the before-after and the matched group, use matching procedures. See independent sample.

Matrix A rectangular arrangement of data.

McNemar test A nominal level test of significance used with related samples, particularly a pre-post test design, that enables the researcher to test whether or not significant changes have taken place over time.

Mean See arithmetic mean.

Mean of combined groups When interest is focused upon averaging means from different groups, particularly when the number of observations in each group are unequal, the mean of combined groups is obtained by: $\bar{X}_w = n_i \bar{X}_i / N$.

Mean of sampling distribution ($\mu_{\bar{X}}$) The mean of the sampling distribution of means.

Mean square Another name for the variance estimates in the F (analysis of variance) test.

Measurement Assigning numerals (or numbers) to objects and events according to rules (S. S. Stevens). See nominal, ordinal, interval, and ratio levels of measurement.

Measures of association A generic term referring to various statistical techniques whereby the existence, degree, and/or direction of the relationship between variables can be calculated.

Measures of central tendency (central location, typicality) A generic term used to designate the average or typical score in a distribution. There are different types of averages, for example, mean, median, mode, harmonic mean, geometric mean.

Measures of dispersion (variation, spread, variability) A generic term (used in conjunction with central tendency) designating the spread or variability of scores in a distribution.

Measures (tests) of significance A generic term indicating statistical techniques used by a researcher to determine the probability of chance producing obtained outcomes.

Median An ordinal measure of central tendency defined as the score that divides the distribution into two equal parts. Being a positional measure it may be thought of as the 50th percentile, the 5th decile, or the 2nd quartile. Symbolized,

$$\text{median}_G = L + \left[\frac{\frac{N}{2} - F}{f} \right] i$$

Mesokurtic The normal curve, the reference point for determing kurtosis, is said to be mesokurtic.

Methodology Originally, a branch of logic concerned with the principles involved in scientific inquiry; now, it is also used to denote specific techniques involved in scientific research. Considered to consist of basic research designs (case study, sample survey, lab experiment), data collection instruments, and statistical tools.

Midpoint The exact center of a class interval obtained by summing the upper and lower exact limits and dividing by two. For example, the class interval 25–29 has a mid-point of 27 or $(24.5 + 29.5)/2 = 54.0/2 = 27$.

Mode A nominal measure of central tendency defined as the score, category, or value which occurs most frequently.

Moment system Moments, or deviations of scores from the mean, are useful for understanding certain mathematical properties of interval/ratio level data. Statisticians are generally concerned with the first four moments, for example, $m_1 = \Sigma(X_i - \bar{X})/N = \Sigma x = 0$; $m_2 = \Sigma(X_i - \bar{X})^2/N = \Sigma x^2/N = s^2$; $m_3 = \Sigma(X_i - \bar{X})^3/N = \Sigma x^3/N$ (incorporated into a measure of skewness); and $m_4 = \Sigma(X_i - \bar{X})^4/N = \Sigma x^4/N$ (incorporated into a measure of kurtosis).

Multivariate distribution Data in which three or more characteristics or phenomena are of interest.

Mutually exclusive A property of a good classification system in which observations or cases can be unambiguously classified into non-overlapping categories.

Nature of an association Refers to the linearity or nonlinearity (for example, curvilinearity) of an association. With contingency table data the nature of an association is indicated by the cell frequency patterning and with interval/ratio level data by the patterning of points in a scattergram.

Negative (inverse) relationship When the values of one variable are in one direction and the values of the other in the opposite direction, a negative correlation exists. For example, if high scores on an IQ test are related to low scores on college GPAs, or if low scores on an IQ test are related to high scores on college GPAs. Variables must be at least ordinally defined for direction to be meaningful. See positive relationship.

Negative skew Refers to an asymmetrical frequency distribution whereby, when graphically portrayed, the larger frequencies tend to concentrate at the positive end of the graph and the smaller frequencies toward the negative end. See positive skew and skewness.

Nominal (classificatory) level The level of measurement in which numbers or other symbols are used to classify an object, event, or characteristic. See attributes.

Nominal level measures of association A general term referring to those association coefficients most useful for nominally defined variables. For example, C, ϕ, Yule's Q.

Nonparametric tests A generic term that refers to a broad category of tests which do not require the normality assumption or weak assumptions about the exact form of the population. Sometimes the term is used synonymously, though technically incorrectly, with distribution-free tests. See parametric tests.

Nonprobability sampling A generic term indicating that the elements selected from the population do not necessarily have an equal or known chance of being selected. Examples of nonprobability samples include accidental, purposive, and snowball samples. See probability sampling.

Normal curve (N.C.) A curve that describes, approximately, the distribution of many empirical variables, for example, height, weight, and also used as a model (sampling distribution) in inferential statistics. Sometimes referred to as the curve of error. Discussed as a sampling distribution in Chapter 8. Sometimes called a density curve.

Null hypothesis (H_0) A statistical hypothesis that generally is a statement of no difference or equality between the variables/groups in the larger population from which they've been selected. Most often, the researcher's interest is in rejecting the null hypothesis and accepting the alternative hypothesis. See alternative hypothesis.

Numbers The use of numerical symbols to classify and/or order events and legitimating the application of arithmetical manipulations. Used to distinguish the different meaning numbers have when applied to data. See numerals.

Numerals The use of symbols to classify and/or order events implying no arithmetical manipulations. Used to distinguish the different meaning numbers have when applied to data. See numbers.

Objectivity One of the norms governing research whereby one is expected to avoid, as much as humanly possible, letting personal wishes, prejudices, and so forth, influence the collection, analysis and interpretation of one's findings.

Observed frequencies The frequencies actually obtained in the data collection stage of research. This concept is most often used in conjunction with the chi-square test. See expected frequencies.

Observed and theoretical cumulative frequencies Two values necessary to compute the Kolmogorov-Smirnov one-sample test.

One, two, k samples Refers to the number of samples that have been selected. For example, one-sample tests call for the selection of a single, usually random, sample; two-sample tests require the selection of two samples; and k-sample tests call for selecting more than two samples.

One-tailed test When the alternative hypothesis is stated in directional terms, for example, $H_1: \mu_1 < \mu_2$ or $\mu_1 > \mu_2$, only one tail of the sampling distribution is used in assessing the probability of occurrence.

Operational definition A precise statement in which the measurement process for a concept is made explicit.

Ordinal (ranking) level The level of measurement in which objects are ordered in terms of the relative degree to which they possess certain characteristics. While the phenomena can be classified in a more-or-less fashion, no assumptions are made about the exact *degree* to which the phenomena possess the characteristic used as the basis of categorization.

Ordinal level measures of association A general term referring to those association coefficients most useful for ordinally defined variables. For example, tau-a, gamma, Somer's d, Spearman's rho.

Ordinate A vertically drawn straight line constructed from the baseline of a curve to a certain height or point along the contour of the curve. In graph construction, the ordinate is the vertical dimension and usually contains values of the dependent variable.

Ordinate values See vertical axis.

Origin (graph) The origin is the point at which the X (abscissa) and Y (ordinate) axes intersect in graph construction. See horizontal and vertical axes.

Pairs tied on X (t_x) One of the pair types for ordinal level variables in which the concern is with pairs tied on the X variable (usually independent).

Pairs tied on X and Y (t_{xy}) One of the pair types for ordinal level variables in which the concern is with pairs tied on both X (independent variable) and Y (dependent variable).

Pairs tied on Y (t_y) One of the pair types for ordinal level variables in which the concern is with pairs tied on the Y variable (usually dependent).

Parameter A numerical characteristic of a population designated by Greek letters. For example, μ and σ. See statistic.

Parametric tests A generic term that refers to a large category of tests assuming the normality of the underlying population from which the sample(s) was/were selected. See nonparametric tests.

Partial correlation A technique that permits the researcher to determine the degree of association between two variables when the influence of another variable(s) is controlled or held constant.

Pearsonian product-moment correlation coefficient (r) An interval/ratio measure of association indicating the existence, degree, and/or direction of the relationship between variables.

Percentage distribution To aid comprehension, a frequency distribution is often converted into a percentage distribution by dividing the frequency in each class interval by N and multiplying each result by 100.

Percentage histogram A type of graph in which bars extend from the exact limits of the class intervals corresponding to the percentage of cases in each interval.

Percentage polygon A type of graph in which a dot for each class interval's midpoint is located according to the percentage of cases in that class interval and the dots are connected by a straight line.

Percentaging table rule Compute percentages using the independent variables totals as the base.

Permutations The number of different arrangements observations can take. For example, two objects labeled A and B can take on two arrangements, $A - B$ and $B - A$. The order is important. See combinations.

Phi coefficient (ϕ) A nominal level measure of association.

Pictograph Using pictures such as stick figures to represent a standard quantity.

Pie diagram A type of graph in which a "pie" or circle is equal to unity or 100 percent and is "sliced up" to portray where the different "pieces" go.

Platykurtic A curve that is judged to be flatter than the normal curve. See kurtosis.

Point estimate A single value that is used to estimate a population parameter. See statistical estimation and interval estimation.

Point of inflection The point of maximum steepness of a curve.

Population (universe, parent population) A complete set of individuals, objects, or events that have a common observable characteristic. See sample.

Positive (direct) relationship When the values of one variable are in the same direction as the values of the other variable, a positive correlation exists. For example, if high scores on an IQ test are related to high scores on college GPAs, or if low scores on an IQ test are related to low scores on college GPAs. See negative relationship.

Positive skew Refers to an asymmetrical frequency distribution whereby, when graphically portrayed, the larger frequencies tend to concentrate toward the negative end of the graph and the smaller frequencies toward the positive end. See negative skew and skewness.

Power The probability of rejecting the null hypothesis when, in fact, it is false and should be rejected. Symbolically, power = $1 -$ beta.

Power efficiency A statistical concept that allows one to compare the power effectiveness of one statistical test with other statistical tests.

Practical (theoretical) significance A distinction should be made between practical and statistical significance. While data may be statistically significant, they may not be practically significant, and vice versa.

Primitive concepts Concepts that are undefined, for example, in Euclidean geometry the concepts of point and line are undefined; then, the notions of angle, triangle, and rectangle are defined in terms of these undefined terms. Also known as axioms.

Probability sampling A generic term indicating that the elements selected from the population have an equal or known chance of being selected. Examples of probability samples include simple random, systematic, stratified, and cluster samples. See nonprobability samples.

Proportional reduction in error (PRE) interpretation An interpretation feature of some measures of association whereby the prediction error can be reduced by knowing the empirical relationship between the variables under examination. The amount of reduction in prediction error is a ratio between error by rule #1 and error by rule #2, for example,

$$\frac{\text{error by rule \# 1} - \text{error by rule \#2}}{\text{error by rule \#1}}$$

Proposition The term has several specific meanings, but, in general, it connotes statements or hypothesis specifying the relationship between concepts which one puts to an empirical test.

Qualitative measurement A broad term for identifying nominal and ordinal level measurement.

Quantitative measurement A broad term for identifying interval and ratio level measurement.

Range A measure of dispersion obtained by subtracting the lower exact limit of the lowest score from the upper exact limit of the highest score. Symbolically, range$_u$ = UEL (highest score) $- LEL$ (lowest score).

Rank order distribution (array) An arrangement of data, that is, a frequency distribution, in which the scores are listed from smallest to largest (or vice versa).

Ratio level The level of measurement having an absolute zero point and permitting all mathematical operations. Not frequently found in the social sciences.

Raw score A score that appears in the original form as obtained from a set of data. Raw scores are sometimes transformed into different units, for example, standard scores.

Relationship (concept of) A fundamental axiom of an empirical science in which it is understood that events don't just happen but, instead, are related or cloaked in a cause-effect framework. Understanding relationships is a vehicle for understanding causality.

Representativeness (of sample) The extent to which a sample reflects or provides a good microcosm of the universe. All things being equal, a probability vis-à-vis a nonprobability sample is more likely to be representative of the universe. See probability and nonprobability sampling.

Research hypothesis The general question(s) the researcher wishes to put to an empirical test. Before an actual test can be made, this hypothesis must be operationalized and transformed into a statistical hypothesis. Sometimes called a working hypothesis.

Run (r) A series of identical elements which are followed or preceded by different elements or no elements at all.

Runs test (one sample) An ordinal level test of significance.

Sample A subset of elements selected from the population. How the sample is chosen is of major importance. See probability and nonprobability sampling.

Sample size The number of cases or observations actually studied.

Sampling distribution Results when random samples of a fixed size are drawn from a population and when the probabilities of the various outcomes are enumerated. Whenever we associate probabilities with all possible outcomes of an experiment, the resulting distribution is referred to as a sampling distribution. A pivotal concept in inferential statistics.

Sampling fraction The ratio of the number of cases in the sample to the number of cases in the population. Symbolized n/N where n = the number of elements in the sample and N = the number of elements in the population.

Sampling frame An exhaustive list from which a sample (usually random) is selected.

Scattergram A graph in which a pair of scores (one on the ordinate, the other on the abscissa) is represented by a dot and conveys a picture of the existence, degree, direction, and nature of the association between variables.

Semi-interquartile range One-half the interquartile range.

$$Q_{1/2} = \frac{Q_3 - Q_1}{2}$$

Sign test An ordinal level test of significance appropriate for use with two related samples.

Significance See measures of significance or tests of significance.

Simple random sample (SRS) A probability sample in which each element selected has an equal or known chance of being chosen.

Skewness An important mathematical property of a frequency distribution that refers to the asymmetry of a frequency distribution. See positive and negative skew.

Somer's d (d) An ordinal level measure of association with an asymmetric computational format.

Spearman's rho (r_s) A popular ordinal measure of association. Symbolically, $r_s = 1 - 6\Sigma D^2/N(N^2 - 1)$.

Spurious relationship When the presumed relationship between variables is actually due to a third variable.

Standard deviation An interval/ratio level measure of dispersion frequently used to describe the areas under the normal curve and defined as the square root of the arithmetic mean of the squared deviations from the mean.

Standard error of mean The standard deviation of a sampling distribution of means. Symbolized, $\sigma_{\bar{X}} = \sigma/\sqrt{N}$.

Standard error of a proportion The standard deviation of the sampling distribution of proportions.

Standard scores (z scores) When raw scores are converted into standard deviation units that may be interpreted in terms of the properties of the normal curve. The transformed scores are called standard scores. In equation form, $z = (X_i - \bar{X})/s$.

Standardized or normed measures of association In interpreting measures of association we attempt to devise coefficients that have clearly defined upper and lower limits.

Stated limits The score, value, or interval, as reported, for example, a class interval of 65–69 has 65 and 69 as its stated limits in contrast to the exact limits of 64.5 and 69.5.

Statistic A numerical value characteristic of a sample designated by Roman (Latin) letters, for example, $\bar{X}$ and s.

Statistical estimation Another (in addition to hypothesis testing) important branch of inferential statistics in which the researcher estimates a population parameter. Also called parameter estimation. See point and interval estimations.

Statistical independence A condition of no association between variables. In the case of contingency tables, if all epsilons and/or deltas are zero, a state of statistical independence has been achieved.

Statistical inference See inferential statistics.

Statistical significance When the null hypothesis is rejected at a particular level, for example, .001, .01, .05, of significance, the data are said to be significant at such-and-such a level. Statistical significance indicates the probability that chance could have produced the findings.

Statistics The general body of methods by which the researcher assembles, describes, and infers something from collected numerical data. See descriptive and inferential statistics.

Stemplot A graphic technique that records the actual values of the data and is fairly easy and quick to construct.

Stochastic A relationship that occurs frequently or on the average but not always, for example, the relationship between annual salary and formal schooling. See deterministic.

Stub The vertical axis, or side of the table, on which it is conventional to locate the dependent variable.

Sum of deviations from the mean A very important mathematical property of the mean where the algebraic sum of the deviations of the mean from each score is equal to zero. Symbolically, $\Sigma(X_i - \bar{X}) = 0$.

Sum of squared deviations from the mean A very important mathematical property of the mean in which the sum of the squared deviations of the mean from each score is less than the sum of the squared deviations about any other number. Symbolically, $\Sigma(X_i - \bar{X})^2 = $ minimum. Known as the *least squares* property.

Symmetric association coefficient One that makes no computational and conceptual distinction between independent and dependent variables. For example, Pearsonian r or Spearman's rho.

Symmetry When a curve, for example, normal curve, demonstrates no skewness. If the curve is divided into two parts, the one side will be identical with the other. The N.C. is symmetrical.

***t* test** An interval/ratio level test of significance most appropriate when $n \leq 30$ and the parameters are unknown.

Tau-*a* (τ_a) An ordinal level measure of association.

Tau-*b* (τ_b) An ordinal level measure of association.

Tests of significance A generic term referring to those statistical techniques that permit one to determine whether or not there are statistically significant differences between the objects under comparison.

Tests of significance for association coefficients A generic term referring to statistical techniques whereby the researcher tests to see if the obtained correlation is "real" or due to chance factors.

Theoretical definitions A concept defined in terms of other concepts, the latter often termed primitive or undefined concepts. See operational definitions and primitive concepts.

Theoretical formulae Statistical formulae that facilitate conceptualizing or thinking about mathematical relations. See computational formulae.

Theory A system of logically interrelated propositions which purport to explain social behavior.

Three-quarter high rule To avoid distortions in graphing it is useful to make the ordinate (Y axis) three-quarters the length of the abscissa (X axis).

Total number of possible unique pairs One of the pair types for ordinal level variables in which the concern is with the total number of pairs and computed $N(N-1)/2$.

Total sum of squares (TSS) A value used in the F test obtained by subtracting each score from the grand mean, squaring, and summing these squared differences. When divided by the appropriate df, $(N-1)$, it becomes a total variance estimate.

Tschruprow's *t* A chi-square based nominal level measure of association.

Two-tailed test When the alternative hypothesis is stated in nondirectional terms, for example, $H_1: \mu_1 \neq \mu_2$, both tails of the sampling distribution are used in assessing whether the null is rejected or not.

Type I error See alpha error.

Type II error See beta error.

Unbiased estimate When a sample estimate tends to equal the parameter value. Technically, when the mean of the sampling distribution of a statistic ($\mu_{\bar{X}}$) tends to equal the parameter being estimated. For example, $E(\bar{X}) = \mu$.

Ungrouped frequency distribution An arrangement of data in which scores may be rank ordered but not collapsed into a smaller number of categories. See grouped frequency distribution.

Unit normal distribution A term used to describe the normal curve in which the total area equals one (unity) or 100 percent.

Univariate distribution Data in which only a single characteristic or phenomenon is of concern.

Variable (variate) A characteristic or phenomenon which may take on different values, for example, weight, height, attitude scores. Often, however, even nonmetric phenomena, for example, sex and race, are termed variables. See attribute.

Variance The standard deviation squared. A statistic used frequently in interval/ratio tests of significance.

Vertical axis In graph construction, e.g., scattergram, it is conventional to locate the dependent variable (Y) and its values along the vertical axis. Sometimes called the ordinate. See horizontal axis.

Wald-Wolfowitz runs test An ordinal level test of significance appropriate for use with two independent samples.

Wilcoxon matched pairs–signed ranks test An ordinal level test of significance appropriate for use with two related samples.

Within sum of squares (WSS) A value used in the F test obtained by subtracting the group mean from each score within the group, squaring, and summing these squared differences. When divided by the appropriate df, $k(N-1)$, it becomes a within groups variance estimate.

Yates' correction for continuity Because the chi-square sampling distribution is continuous whereas the chi-square test statistic is discrete, a correction must be made in 2 × 2 tables and in larger tables (where 80 percent of the cells have expected frequencies of less than five). This correction is Yates' correction for continuity.

Y-intercept In regression analysis the Y-intercept is the point at which the regression line crosses the Y axis.

Yule's Q A nominal measure of association used exclusively with 2 × 2 tables with a proportional reduction in error interpretation. A special case of gamma.

z test An interval level test of significance in which the mean sample differences are divided by the standard error of the difference between means. Discussed extensively in Chapter 8.

z test for differences between proportions A nominal level test of significance in which the data have been converted into proportions for statistical analysis.

z transformation The process by which raw scores are converted and expressed in standard deviation units as in the equation: $z = (X_i - \bar{X})/s$.

ANSWERS TO REVIEW QUESTIONS

CHAPTER 3

1. a.

Class Intervals (i)	Frequency (f)	Cumulative Frequencies (F)	Midpoints (m)	Percent (%)	Cumulative Percentages (cum %)
150–154	2	100	152	2	100
145–149	3	98	147	3	98
140–144	3	95	142	3	95
135–139	4	92	137	4	92
130–134	6	88	132	7	88
125–129	9	82	127	9	82
120–124	13	73	122	13	73
115–119	14	60	117	14	60
110–114	12	46	112	12	46
105–109	10	34	107	10	34
100–104	9	24	102	9	24
95–99	5	15	97	5	15
90–94	4	10	92	4	10
85–89	3	6	87	3	6
80–84	3	3	82	3	3
	$N = 100$				

5. a.

Class Intervals (i)	Frequency (f)	(b) Cumulative Frequency (F)	(c) Percentage Distribution	(d) Cumulative Percentage (cum %)	(e) Upper and Lower Exact Limits	(f) Midpoints (m)
76–80	2	85	2.35	100.00%	75.5–80.5	78
71–75	2	83	2.35	97.64	70.5–75.5	73
66–70	4	81	4.71	95.29	65.5–70.5	68
61–65	5	77	5.88	90.58	60.5–65.5	63
56–60	8	72	9.41	84.70	55.5–60.5	58
51–55	10	64	11.76	75.29	50.5–55.5	53
46–50	10	54	11.76	63.53	45.5–50.5	48
41–45	11	44	12.94	51.77	40.5–45.5	43
36–40	9	33	10.59	38.83	35.5–40.5	38
31–35	6	24	7.06	28.24	30.5–35.5	33
26–30	7	18	8.24	21.18	25.5–30.5	28
21–25	4	11	4.71	12.94	20.5–25.5	23
16–20	5	7	5.88	8.23	15.5–20.5	18
11–15	2	2	2.35	2.35	10.5–15.5	13
	$N = 85$		99.99			

b. STEMPLOT—SLIGHTLY EXPANDED

0–4	08	0 1 3
5–9	08	5 8 9
0–4	09	0 2 4 4
5–9	09	5 7 8 8 9
0–4	10	0 1 1 1 2 3 3 4 4
5–9	10	5 6 6 7 7 8 9 9 9 9
0–4	11	0 0 1 2 2 2 2 3 3 4 4 4
5–9	11	5 5 5 5 6 6 7 8 8 8 9 9 9 9
0–4	12	0 0 0 0 1 1 2 2 3 3 4 4 4
5–9	12	5 5 6 6 7 7 7 8 9
0–4	13	0 0 1 2 3 4
5–9	13	5 6 8 8
0–4	14	0 1 2
5–9	14	5 6 8
0–4	15	0 4

2a: Frequency Polygon

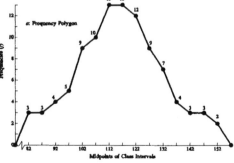

2b: Frequency Histogram

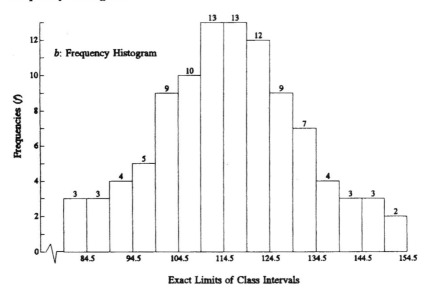

Exact Limits of Class Intervals

3a: Cumulative Frequency Polygon

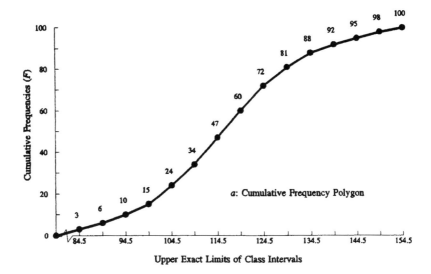

Upper Exact Limits of Class Intervals

4a: Percentage Polygon

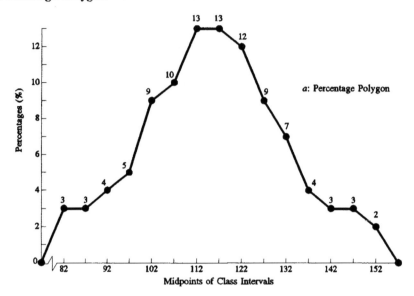

a: Percentage Polygon

4b: Percentage Histogram

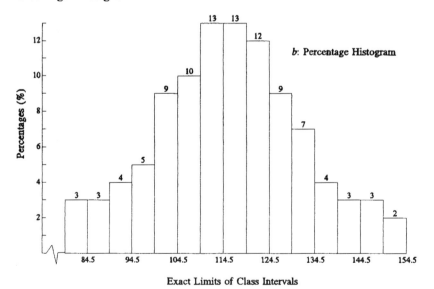

b: Percentage Histogram

4c: Cumulative Percentage Polygon

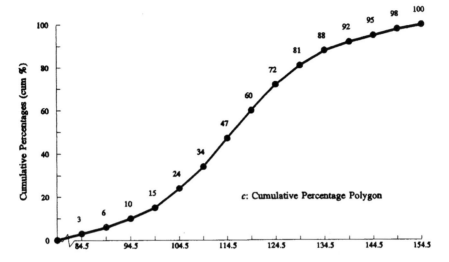

c: Cumulative Percentage Polygon

6a: Frequency Polygon

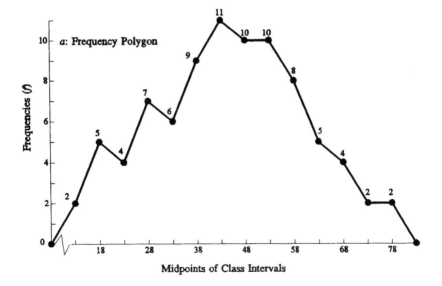

a: Frequency Polygon

Midpoints of Class Intervals

6b: Percentage Polygon

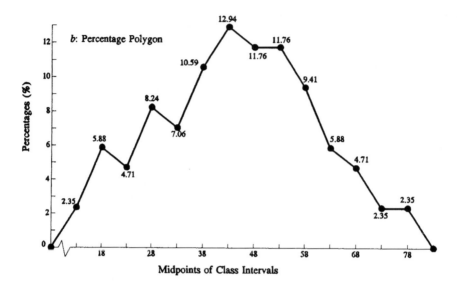

6c: Cumulative Frequency Polygon

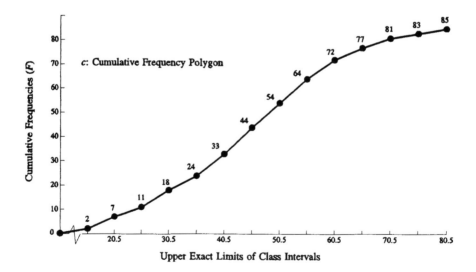

6d: Cumulative Percentage Polygon

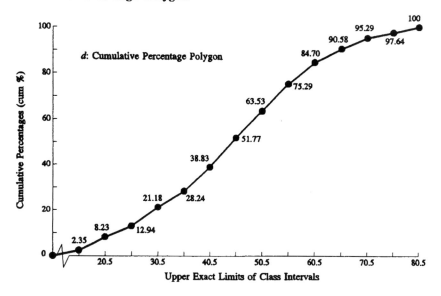

6e: Frequency Histogram

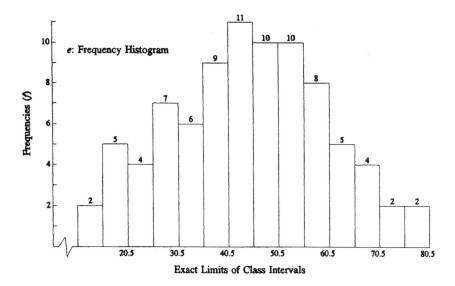

6f: Percentage Histogram

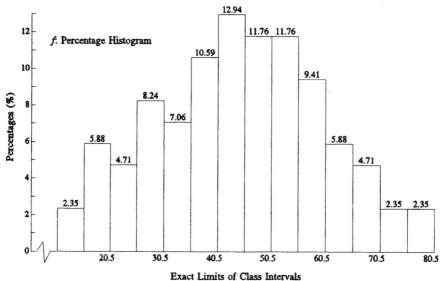

f. Percentage Histogram

y-axis: Percentages (%)

x-axis: Exact Limits of Class Intervals

CHAPTER 4

1. a. $\overline{X}_u = \dfrac{\Sigma X}{N} = \dfrac{224}{20} = 11.2$

    b. median = 10.5
    c. mode = 10

2. $\overline{X}_w = \left[\dfrac{4,537}{98} \right]$

3.
    a. (1) $\overline{X}_G = \dfrac{\Sigma f(m)}{N} = \dfrac{224}{20} = 11.2$

    (2) $\overline{X}_s = $ midpoint $+ \left[\dfrac{\Sigma_f x'}{N} \right] i = 10 + \left[\dfrac{8}{20} \right] 3 = 11.2$

    b. median$_G = L + \left[\dfrac{(N)(P) - F}{f} \right] i = 8.5 + \left[\dfrac{10-6}{5} \right] 3 = 8.5 + (.8)(3) = 10.9$

    c. mode: crude = 10; refined = 10.51

4. $\overline{X}_u = \dfrac{\Sigma X_i}{N} = \dfrac{11,750}{100} = (115.70)$

5.

a. $\overline{X}_G = \dfrac{\Sigma f(m)}{N} = \dfrac{11,575}{100} = 115.75$

b. $\text{median}_G = L + \left[\dfrac{(N)(P) - F}{f}\right] i = 114.5 + \left[\dfrac{50 - 47}{13}\right] 5 = 115.65$

c. mode = bimodal = 112 and 117

6. $HM = 3.43$ $GM = 22.36$

CHAPTER 5

1. a. $\Sigma x^2 = 556$
    b. $s_u^2 = 37.07$
    c. $s_u = 6.09$
    d. $AD_u = 5.33$

2. a. Σx^2 (male) $= 248$; Σx^2 (female) $= 200.86$
    b. s_u^2 (male) $= 31$; s_u^2 (female) $= 28.69$
    c. s_u (male) $= 5.57$; s_u (female) $= 5.36$
    d. AD (male) $= 5.00$; AD (female) $= 4.44$

3. a. Campus 1: $IQV = 85.42$ percent. Campus 2: $IQV = 81.79$ percent.

4. a. s_G (long method) $= \sqrt{\dfrac{24,830}{20} - (34.9)^2} = 4.85$

    s_G (short method) $= \sqrt{\dfrac{469.8}{20}} = 4.85$

    b. $s^2 = 23.52$

    c. range $= 44.5 - 23.5 = 21.0$

    d. $Q = 6.99$
        $Q_1 = 31.51$
        $Q_3 = 38.50$

    e. $\dfrac{Q_3 - Q_1}{2} = 3.495$

    f. $AD = 3.99$

5. a. Range $= 10$ b. (1) minimum $= 1$
                                                 (2) maximum $= 10$
                                                 (3) median $= 6$
       (4) first quartile $= 2$
                                                 (5) third quartile $= 8$

CHAPTER 6

1. a. $z = \dfrac{X_i - \overline{X}}{s} = \dfrac{550 - 500}{100} = .50$

   b. (1) $.5000 + .1915 = .6915$ (69th percentile)
      (2) $1.00 - .6915 = .3085$ (31 percent)

2. raw score $= \overline{X} + z(s) = 500 + -.37(100) = 500 - 37 = 463$
   a. $.3557$ (36th percentile)
   b. 36 percent

3. a. $.2291 - .3830 = .1539$
   b. $.2291 + .2291 = .4582$
   c. $.2291 + .3830 = .6121$
   d. $.2157 - .4979 = .2822$
   e. $.4726 + .4997 = .9723$

5. $S_1: z = -.53; S_2: z = 0; S_3: z = 1.73; S_4: z = 3.33$

6. $S_1 = 27.975; S_2 = 46.725$
   a. $S_1 = 3; S_2 = 74$

CHAPTER 7

5. 90 percent confidence interval $= 90.68 - 95.32$; 95 percent confidence interval $= 90.24 - 95.76$; 99 percent confidence interval $= 89.36 - 96.64$

6. 95 percent confidence interval $= 74.82 - 77.18$; 99 percent confidence interval $= 74.45 - 77.55$

7. 90 percent confidence interval $= 80.47 - 83.53$; 95 percent confidence interval $= 80.18 - 83.82$; 99 percent confidence interval $= 79.60 - 84.40$

8. 90 percent confidence interval $= 163.125 - 166.875$; 95 percent confidence interval $= 162.76 - 167.24$; 99 percent confidence interval $= 162.05 - 167.95$

9. $\overline{X} = 8.7; s = 1.62$; 90 percent confidence interval $= 7.81 - 9.59$; 95 percent confidence interval $= 7.64 - 9.76$; 99 percent confidence interval $= 7.31 - 10.09$

10. $C (.530 \leq \pi \leq .610) = .99$
    $C (.539 \leq \pi \leq .601) = .95$
    $C (.544 \leq \pi \leq .596) = .90$

CHAPTER 9

1. $\chi^2 = \dfrac{(O_f - E_f)^2}{E_f}$

	O_f	E_f	$O_f - E_f$	$(O_f - E_f)^2$	$\dfrac{(O_f - E_f)^2}{E_f}$
Could have been avoided	426	250	176	30,976	123.90
Unavoidable	74	250	−176	30,976	123.90

$\chi^2 = 247.80$: reject H_0

2. $P_1 = \dfrac{2!\,9!\,6!\,5!}{11!\,2!\,0!\,4!\,5!}$

$= \dfrac{(2)(362,880)(720)(120)}{(39,916,800)(2)(1)(24)(120)}$

$= \dfrac{62,705,664,000}{229,920,768,000}$

$= .27$ N.S.

$P_2 = .54$ N.S.

3. $\chi_m^2 = \dfrac{(|55 - 200| - 1)^2}{255}$

$= \dfrac{20,736}{255}$

$= 81.32$ ($p < .05$ reject H_0)

4. $Q = \dfrac{(3-1)[3(2^2 + 3^2 + 4^2)] - 9^2}{3(9) - 19}$

$= \dfrac{2(87 - 81)}{8}$

$= \dfrac{12}{8}$

$= 1.5$ H_0 must be retained

5. $z = \dfrac{.790 - .415}{\sqrt{\dfrac{(.790)(.210)}{50} + \dfrac{(.415)(.585)}{50}}}$

$$= \frac{.375}{\sqrt{.0033 + .0049}}$$

$$= \frac{.375}{\sqrt{.0082}}$$

$$= \frac{.375}{.09}$$

$= 4.17 \ p < .01 \ (\text{reject } H_0)$

6.

Cell	O_f	E_f	$O_f - E_f$	$(O_f - E_f)^2$	$\dfrac{(O_f - E_f)^2}{E_f}$
A	7	4	3	9	2.25
B	5	4	1	1	.25
C	3	4	−1	1	.25
D	1	4	−3	9	2.25
E	10	6.5	3.5	12.25	1.88
F	7	6.5	.5	.25	.04
G	5	6.5	−1.5	2.25	.35
H	4	6.5	−2.5	6.25	.96
I	2	5	−3	9	1.80
J	5	5	0	0	0
K	5	5	0	0	0
L	8	5	3	9	1.80
M	3	4.5	−1.5	2.25	.50
N	4	4.5	− .5	.25	.06
O	6	4.5	1.5	2.25	.50
P	5	4.5	.5	.25	.06
Q	3	5	−2	4	.80
R	4	5	−1	1	.20
S	6	5	1	1	.20
T	7	5	2	4	.80

$\chi^2 = 14.95$

$p < .001$ reject H_0

CHAPTER 10

1. a. two-tailed

   b. $p > .05$ (N.S.)

   c. $p > .01$ (N.S.)

2. a. two-tailed

   b. 7

   c. no, $p > .05$

3. a. $\Sigma R_c = 26; \Sigma R_m = 52$

   b. $U_1 = 31; U_2 = 5$

   c. yes

   d. both samples are drawn from populations with same distribution

   e. reject

4. a. 4
   b. 4
   c. yes

5. $m = 3; p < .05$

6. $\Sigma T = 8; p < .01$

7. $H = 1.438$ (N.S.)

8. $\chi_r^2 = 1.48$ (N.S.)

CHAPTER 11

1. $z = 2.08; p < .05; p > .01$ (N.S.)

2. $t = -1.5$ (N.S.)

3. a. $F = 2.25; p < .05$ (unequal variances)

   b. $t = 2.05$

   c. $p < .05$ (two-tailed)

4. a. $F = 2.25; p > .01$ (equal variances)

   b. $t = 2.11$

   c. $p > .01$ (N.S.)

5. $t = 4.24; p < .05$

6. a. $\Sigma X_I = 70; \Sigma X_{II} = 80; \Sigma X_{III} = 60$

    b. $\Sigma X_I^2 = 502; \Sigma X_{II}^2 = 652; \Sigma X_{III}^2 = 388$

    c. $TSS = 72$

    d. $WSS = 52$

    e. $BSS = 20$

    f. $df(TSS) = 29; df(BSS) = 2; df(WSS) = 27$

    g. $BSS = 20/2 = 10; WSS = 52/27 = 1.92$

    h. $F = 5.21$

    i. $p > .01$ (N.S.)

    j. $p < .05$

CHAPTER 12

1. a. and b.

Sexual Permissiveness	Sex Male N	Female N	
Nonpermissive	37(46%)	48(80%)	85
Permissive	43(54%)	12(20%)	55
	80(100%)	60(100%)	140

    c: determine the E_f for each cell.

    Cell $A, E_f = (85)(80)/140 = 48.57$
    Cell $B, E_f = (85)(60)/140 = 36.43$
    Cell $C, E_f = (55)(80)/140 = 31.43$
    Cell $D, E_f = (55)(60)/140 = 23.57$

    d. $C = .324; T = .342; V = .342; \phi = .342$

    e. $C_{max} = \sqrt{\dfrac{2-1}{2}} = .707; \overline{C} = \dfrac{.324}{.707} = .458$

    f. C is significant at the .001 level

2. $\phi = .523$

    a. $\phi_{max} = .90$

3. $Q = .647$

    a. $z = 3.34$; significant at the .001 level

4. $\lambda_r = .253$; $\lambda_c = .224$; λ_{row} is a better predictor

5. $\lambda = .239$

CHAPTER 13

1. a. $n_s = 31,625$

    b. $n_d = 9,625$

    c. $t_x = 11,850$

    d. $t_y = 18,650$

    e. $t_{xy} = 8,050$

    f. total number = 79,800

    g. $31,625 + 9,625 + 11,850 + 18,650 + 8,050 = 79,800$

2. a. tau-a = .276; $z = 8.36$ ($p < .001$)

    b. gamma = .533; $z = 6.38$ ($p < .001$)

    c. tau-b = .390; $z = 7.92$ ($p < .001$)

    d. $d_{yx} = .367$; $z = 4.01$ ($p < .001$)
        $d_{xy} = .414$; $z = 4.62$ ($p < .001$)

3. $r_s = .925$; $t = 8.44$ ($p < .001$)

4. $r = .91$

    a. very high and dependable

    b. $t = 6.28$ ($p < .001$)

5. a. $b_{yx} = 1,216.22$

    b. $a_{yx} = -4,540.59$

    c. $Y' = -4,540.59 + 1,216.22X$

*

BIBLIOGRAPHY

Adorno, T. W., Frenkel-Brunswik, Else, Levinson, Daniel J., and Sanford, R.N. *The Authoritarian Personality*, New York: Harper, 1950.

Anderson, Theodore R., and Zelditch, Jr., Morris. *A Basic Course in Statistics*. 3d ed. New York: Holt, Rinehart & Winston, Inc. 1975.

Babbie, Earl R. *The Practice of Social Research*. Belmont, Calif.: Wadsworth Publishing Co., Inc., 1992.

Baker, Bela O.; Hardyck, Curtis D.; and Petrinovich, Lewis F. "Weak Measurements vs. Strong Statistics: An Empirical Critique of S. S. Stevens' Proscriptions on Statistics." *Educational and Psychological Measurement*, vol. 26 (1966), pp. 291–309.

Bartlett, M. S. "Some Examples of Statistical Research in Agriculture and Applied Biology." *Journal of the Royal Statistical Society*, vol. 4 (1937), pp. 137–70.

Bierstedt, Robert. "Nominal and Real Definitions in Sociological Theory." *Symposium in Sociological Theory*, chap. 4. Edited by Llewellyn Gross. New York: Harper & Row Publishers, 1959.

Blalock, Hubert M., Jr. *Social Statistics*. Revised 2d ed. New York: McGraw-Hill Book Co., Inc., 1979.

———, and Anne S. *Methodology in Social Research*. New York: McGraw-Hill Book Co., Inc., 1968.

Boneau, C. Alan. "A Note on Measurement Scales and Statistical Text." *American Psychologist*, vol. 16 (1961), pp. 160–61.

Bonjean, Charles M.; Hill, Richard J.; and McLemore, S. Dale. "Continuities in Measurement." *Social Forces,* March 1965, pp. 532–36.

Bradley, J. V. *Distribution-Free Statistical Tests*. Englewood Cliffs, N.J.: Prentice-Hall, Inc., 1968.

Bridgman, Percy W. *The Logic of Modern Physics*. New York: The Macmillan Co., 1938.

Burke, C. J. "Additive Scales and Statistics." *Psychological Review*, vol. 60 (1953), pp. 73–75.

Byrkit, Donald R. *Elements of Statistics*. 2d ed. New York: D. Van Norstrand Co., 1975.

Camic, Charles and Xie, Yu. "The History of Statistics in the Social Sciences," *American Sociological Review*, vol. 59, no. 5 (October, 1994), pp. 773–805.

Caplow, Theodore. *Elementary Sociology*. Englewood Cliffs, N.J.: Prentice-Hall, Inc., 1975.

Champion, Dean J. *Basic Statistics for Social Research*. Scranton, Penn.: Chandler Publishing Co., 1970.

———. "Some Observations on Measurement and Statistics: Comment." *Social Forces*, vol. 46 (1968) p. 541.

Cochran, William G. "Some Consequences When the Assumptions Underlying the Analysis of Variance Have Not Been Met." *Biometrics*, vol. 3 (1947), pp. 22–28.

Cole, Stephen. *The Sociological Method*. Chicago: Markham Publishing Co., 1972.

Conover, W. J. "Some Reasons for Not Using the Yates Continuity Correction on 2 × 2 Contingency Tables." *Journal of the American Statistical Association*, 69: 374–376, 1974.

Coombs, Clyde H. "Theory and Methods of Social Measurement." *Research Methods in the Behavioral Sciences*, chap. 11. Edited by Leon Festinger and Daniel Katz. New York: Holt, Rinehart & Winston, Inc., 1953.

Costner, Herbert L. "Criteria for Measures of Association." *American Sociological Review*, vol. 30 (1965), pp. 341–53.

Crowley, Francis J., and Cohen, Martin. *Statistics for Examination Review*. New York: The Crowell-Collier Publishing Co., 1963.

Dictionary of Modern Sociology. Totowa, N.J.: Littlefield, Adams & Co., 1969.

Dixon, Wilfrid J., and Massey, Frank J. *Introduction to Statistical Analysis*. New York: McGraw-Hill Book Co., 1957.

Downie, Norville M., and Heath, R.W. *Basic Statistical Methods*. 4th ed. New York: Harper & Row Publishers, 1974.

Dudycha, Arthur L., and Dudycha, Linda W. "Behavioral Statistics: An Historical Perspective." *Statistical Issues. A Reader for the Behavioral Sciences*. Edited by Roger E. Kirk. Monterey, Calif.: Brooks/Cole Publishing Co., 1972.

Dumont, R. and Wilson, W. "Aspects of Concept Formation, Explication and Theory Construction in Sociology." *American Sociological Review*, vol. 32 (1967), pp. 985–95.

Edwards, Allen L. *Experimental Design in Psychological Research*. 2d ed. New York: Holt, Rinehart & Winston, Inc., 1960.

Encyclopedia of Sociology. Guilford, Conn.: The Dushkin Publishing Group, Inc., 1991.

Ferguson, George A. *Statistical Analysis in Psychology and Education.* 3d ed. New York: McGraw-Hill Book Co., Inc., 1971.

Fisher, Ronald A. *The Design of Experiments.* Edinburgh: Oliver and Boyd, Ltd., 1935.

Forcese, Dennis P., and Richer, Stephen. *Social Research Methods.* Englewood Cliffs, N.J.: Prentice-Hall, Inc., 1973.

Freeman, Linton C. *Elementary Applied Statistics.* New York: John Wiley & Sons, Inc., 1965.

Freund, J. E. *Modern Elementary Statistics.* Englewood Cliffs, N.J.: Prentice-Hall, Inc., 1952.

Goodman, Leo A., and Kruskal, William H. "Measures of Association for Cross Classifications." *Journal of American Statistical Association,* vol. 49 (1954), pp. 732-64. Also, vol. 54 (1959), pp. 123-63 and vol. 58 (1963), pp. 310-64.

Green, Marcus H., and Radajczak, Frank X. *Mathematical Terms and Simple Operations.* Reading, Pa.: Albright College, 1961.

Haber, Audrey; Runyon, Richard P.; and Badia, Pietro. *Readings in Statistics.* Reading, Mass.: Addison-Wesley Publishing Co., Inc., 1970.

Hagood, Margaret J., and Price, Daniel O. *Statistics for Sociologists.* 2d ed. New York: Holt, Rinehart & Winston, Inc., 1952.

Hankins, F. H. "Adolphe Quetelet as Statistician." *Statistical Reasoning in Sociology,* p. 2. John F. Mueller, Karl F. Schuessler, and Herbert L. Costner. New York: Houghton Mifflin Co., 1970.

Hinkle, Roscoe C., Jr., and Hinkle, Gisela J. *The Development of Modern Sociology.* New York: Random House, Inc., 1954.

Hoel, Paul G. *Elementary Statistics.* New York: John Wiley & Sons, Inc., 1960.

Huff, Darrell. *How to Lie with Statistics.* New York: W. W. Norton & Co., Inc., 1954.

Iverson, Gudmund R. *Statistics and Sociology.* Indianapolis: Bobbs-Merrill Co., Inc., 1972.

Jahoda, Marie; Selltiz, Claire; Deutsch, Morton; and Cook, Stuart W. *Research Methods in Social Relations.* New York: Holt, Rinehart & Winston, Inc., 1965.

Kaplan, Abraham. *The Conduct of Inquiry.* San Francisco: Chandler Publishing Co., 1964.

Kendall, Maurice G. *Rank Correlation Methods.* New York: Hafner Publishing Co., 1955.

Kerlinger, Fred N. *Foundations of Behavioral Research.* 2d ed. New York: Holt, Rinehart & Winston, Inc., 1973.

Kirk, Roger E. *Statistical Issues.* Belmont, Calif.: Wadsworth Publishing Co., Inc., 1972.

Labovitz, Sanford. "Criteria for Selecting a Significance Level: A Note on the Sacredness of .05." *American Sociologist,* vol. 3 (1968), pp. 220-22.

———. "Reply to Champion and Morris." *Social Forces,* vol. 46 (1968), pp. 543-44.

———. "Some Observations on Measurement and Statistics." *Social Forces,* vol. 40 (1967), pp. 152-60.

Labovitz, Sanford, and Hagedorn, Robert. *Introduction to Social Research.* New York: McGraw-Hill Book Co., 1971.

Leonard, Wilbert M. II, and Schmitt, Raymond L. "Institutional Representation at the 1970, 1971, and 1972 American Sociological Association Annual Meetings." *Sociology and Social Research*, vol. 1 (October 1973), pp. 6–12.

Levin, Jack. *Elementary Statistics in Social Research.* New York: Harper & Row, Publishers, 1973.

Loether, Herman J., and McTavish, Donald G. *Descriptive and Inferential Statistics.* Boston: Allyn & Bacon, Inc., 1993.

Lord, Frederick. "On the Statistical Treatment of Football Numbers." *American Psychologist*, vol. 8 (1953), pp. 750–51.

Lundberg, George A. *Foundations of Sociology.* New York: The Macmillan Co., 1939.

Malec, Michael A. *Essential Statistics for Social Research.* Boulder, CO: Westview Press, 1993.

Mantel, N. "Comment and a Suggestion on the Yates Continuity Correction." *Journal of the American Statistical Association*, 69: 378–380, 1974.

Moore, David S. *The Basic Practice of Statistics.* New York: W. H. Freeman, 1995.

Moses, E. L. "Non-Parametric Statistics of Psychological Research." *Psychological Bulletin,* vol. 49 (1952), pp. 122–43.

Mueller, John F.; Schuessler, Karl F.; and Costner, Herbert L. *Statistical Reasoning in Sociology.* New York: Houghton Mifflin Co., 1970.

Nimkoff, Meyer F. *Comparative Family Systems.* Boston: Houghton Mifflin Co., 1965.

Northrop, F. S. C. *The Logic of the Sciences and the Humanities.* New York: The Macmillan Co., 1947.

Norusis, Marija J. *SPSS Guide to Data Analysis.* Englewood Cliffs, NJ: Prentice-Hall, 1995.

Palumbo, Dennis J. *Statistics in Political and Behavioral Science.* New York: Appleton-Century-Crofts, 1969.

Paulos, John A. *Beyond Numeracy.* New York: Alfred Knopf, 1991.

Pierce, Albert. *Fundamentals of Non-Parametric Statistics: A Sample Space Approach.* Encino, Calif.: Dickenson Publishing Co., Inc., 1969.

Pirie, W. R., and Hamden, M. A. "Some Revised Continuity Corrections for Discrete Data." *Biometrics,* vol. 28 (1972), pp. 693–701.

Plackett, R. L. "The Continuity Correction on 2 × 2 Tables." *Biometrika,* vol. 51 (1964), pp. 327–37.

Rosenburg, Milton. *The Logic of Survey Analysis.* New York: Basic Books, 1968.

Runyon, Richard P., and Haber, Audrey. *Fundamentals of Behavioral Statistics.* Reading, Mass.: Addison-Wesley Publishing Co., Inc., 1976.

Sarle, Warren S. "Measurement Theory: Frequently Asked Questions," Disseminations of the International Statistical Applications Institute. Dallas, TX, 1995, pp. 61–66.

Schmidt, Marty J. *Understanding and Using Statistics.* Lexington, Mass.: D. C. Heath & Co., 1975.

Schuessler, Karl. *Analyzing Social Data: A Statistical Orientation.* Boston: Houghton Mifflin Co., 1971.

Selvin, Hanan. "A Critique of Tests of Significance in Survey Research." *Americnan Sociological Review,* October 1957, pp. 519-27.

Senders, V. L. *Measurement and Statistics.* New York: Oxford University Press, 1958.

Senter, R. J. *Analysis of Data.* Glenview, Ill.: Scott, Foresman & Co., 1969.

Siegal, Sidney. *Nonparametric Statistics.* New York: McGraw-Hill Book Co., Inc., 1956.

Skipper, J. K., Jr., et al. "The Sacredness of .05: A Note Concerning Uses of Significance in Social Sciences." *American Sociologist,* February 1967, pp. 16-19.

Snedecor, George W., and Cochran, William G. *Statistical Methods.* 6th ed. Ames, Iowa: The Iowa State University Press, 1967.

Somers, Robert H. "A New Asymmetric Measure of Association for Ordinal Variables." *American Sociological Review,* December 1962, pp. 799-811.

Stevens, S. S. "Mathematics, Measurement and Psychophysics." *Handbook of Experimental Psychology.* Edited by S. S. Stevens. New York: John Wiley & Sons, Inc., 1951.

———. "Measurement, Statistics and the Schemapiric View." *Science,* vol. 161 (1968), pp. 849-56.

———. "On the Theory of Scales of Measurement." *Science,* vol. 103 (1946), pp. 677-80.

Taylor, Peter A. *An Introduction to Statistical Methods.* Itasca, Ill.: F. E. Peacock Publishers, Inc., 1972.

Walker, Helen M. *Mathematics Essential for Elementary Statistics.* Rev. ed. New York: Holt, Rinehart & Winston, Inc., 1951.

Walker, Helen Mary, and Lev, Joseph. *Statistical Inference.* New York: Henry Holt & Co., Inc., 1953.

Wallace, Walter L., ed. *Sociological Theory.* Chicago: Aldine Publishing Co., 1969.

Wilcoxon, Frank, and Wilcox, Roberta A. *Some Rapid Approximate Statistical Procedures.* Pearl River, N.Y.: Lederle Laboratories, 1964.

Winer, B. J. *Statistical Principles in Experimental Design.* New York: McGraw-Hill Book Co., 1962.

Zeisel, Hans. *Say It with Figures.* 4th ed. New York: Harper & Row, Publishers, 1957.

Zetterberg, Hans L. *On Theory and Verification in Sociology.* Totowa, N.J.: The Bedminster Press, 1965.

INDEX
